D1029137

NATIONAL NUCLEAR ENERGY SERIES

Manhattan Project Technical Section

Division I - Volume 1

VACUUM EQUIPMENT AND TECHNIQUES

VACUUM EQUIPMENT AND TECHNIQUES

Edited by

A. GUTHRIE, Ph.D.

Radiation Laboratory, Department of Physics
University of California

and

R. K. WAKERLING, Ph.D.

Radiation Laboratory, Department of Physics
University of California

New York · Toronto · London

McGRAW-HILL BOOK COMPANY, INC.

1949

VACUUM EQUIPMENT AND TECHNIQUES

Printed in the United States of America

VII

74001

Lithoprinted
by
Edwards Brothers, Incorporated
Ann Arbor, Michigan

FOREWORD

The United States program of development of atomic energy has been described by Major General L. R. Groves, who, as Commanding General of the War Department's Manhattan Project, directed the program from mid-1942 until December 31, 1946, as "a generation of scientific development compressed into three years." The tremendous scope of the Manhattan Project Technical Section of the National Nuclear Energy Series, which has been in preparation since 1944, is a tribute to the unprecedented accomplishments of science, industry, government, labor, and the Army and Navy, working together as a team. These volumes can be a firm foundation for the United States atomic energy program which, in the words of the Atomic Energy Act of 1946, is ". . . directed toward improving the public welfare, increasing the standard of living, strengthening free competition in private enterprise, and promoting world peace."

David E. Lilienthal, Chairman
U. S. Atomic Energy Commission

ACKNOWLEDGMENT

The Manhattan Project Technical Section of the National Nuclear Energy Series embodies results of work done in the nation's wartime atomic energy program by numerous contractors, including Columbia University. The arrangements for publication of the series volumes were effected by Columbia University, under a contract with the United States Atomic Energy Commission. The Commission, for itself and for the other contractors who contributed to this series, wishes to record here its appreciation of this service of Columbia University in support of the national nuclear energy program.

PREFACE

This volume is one of a series which has been prepared as a record of the research work done under the Manhattan Project and the Atomic Energy Commission. The name Manhattan Project was assigned by the Corps of Engineers, War Department, to the far-flung scientific and engineering activities which had as their objective the utilization of atomic energy for military purposes. In the attainment of this objective, there were many developments in scientific and technical fields which are of general interest. The National Nuclear Energy Series (Manhattan Project Technical Section) is a record of these scientific and technical contributions, as well as of the developments in these fields which are being sponsored by the Atomic Energy Commission.

The declassified portion of the National Nuclear Energy Series, when completed, is expected to consist of some 60 volumes. These will be grouped into eight divisions, as follows:

Division I — Electromagnetic Separation Project
Division II — Gaseous Diffusion Project
Division III — Special Separations Project
Division IV — Plutonium Project
Division V — Los Alamos Project
Division VI — University of Rochester Project
Division VII — Materials Procurement Project
Division VIII — Manhattan Project

Soon after the close of the war the Manhattan Project was able to give its attention to the preparation of a complete record of the research work accomplished under Project contracts. Writing programs were authorized at all laboratories, with the object of obtaining complete coverage of Project results. Each major installation was requested to designate one or more representatives to make up a committee, which was first called the Manhattan Project Editorial Advisory Board, and later, after the sponsorship of the Series was assumed by the Atomic Energy Commission, the Project Editorial Advisory Board. This group made plans to coordinate the writing programs at all the installations, and acted as an advisory group in all matters affecting the Project-wide writing program. Its last meeting was held on Feb. 9, 1948, when it recommended the publisher for the Series.

The names of the Board members and of the installations which they represented are given below.

Atomic Energy Commission	
Public and Technical Information Service	Alberto F. Thompson
Technical Information Branch, Oak Ridge Extension	Brewer F. Boardman
Office of New York Operations	Charles Slesser, J. H. Hayner, W. M. Hearon *
Brookhaven National Laboratory	Richard W. Dodson
Carbide & Carbon Chemicals Corporation (K-25)	R. B. Korsmeyer, W. L. Harwell, D. E. Hull, Ezra Staple
Carbide & Carbon Chemicals Corporation (Y-12) †	Russell Baldock
Clinton Laboratories ‡	J. R. Coe
General Electric Company, Hanford	T. W. Hauff
General Electric Company, Knolls Atomic Power Laboratory	John P. Howe
Kellex Corporation	John F. Hogerton, Jerome Simson, M. Benedict
Los Alamos	R. R. Davis, Ralph Carlisle Smith
National Bureau of Standards	C. J. Rodden
Plutonium Project	
Argonne National Laboratory	R. S. Mulliken, H. D. Young
Iowa State College	F. H. Spedding
Medical Group	R. E. Zirkle
SAM Laboratories §	G. M. Murphy
Stone & Webster Engineering Corporation	B. W. Whitehurst
University of California	R. K. Wakerling, A. Guthrie
University of Rochester	D. R. Charles, M. J. Wantman

* Represented Madison Square Area of the Manhattan District.

† The Y-12 plant at Oak Ridge was operated by Tennessee Eastman Corporation until May 4, 1947, at which time operations were taken over by Carbide & Carbon Chemicals Corporation.

‡ Clinton Laboratories was the former name of the Oak Ridge National Laboratory.

§ SAM (Substitute Alloy Materials) was the code name for the laboratories operated by Columbia University in New York under the direction of Dr. H. C. Urey, where much of the experimental work on isotope separation was done. On Feb. 1, 1945, the administration of these laboratories became the responsibility of Carbide & Carbon Chemicals Corporation. Research in progress there was transferred to the K-25 plant at Oak Ridge in June, 1946, and the New York laboratories were then closed.

Many difficulties were encountered in preparing a unified account of Atomic Energy Project work. For example, the Project Editorial Advisory Board was the first committee ever organized with representatives from every major installation of the Atomic Energy Project. Compartmentation for security was so rigorous during the war that it had been considered necessary to allow a certain amount of duplication of effort rather than to permit unrestricted circulation of research information between certain installations. As a result, the writing programs of different installations inevitably overlap markedly in many scientific fields. The Editorial Advisory Board has exerted itself to reduce duplication in so far as possible and to eliminate discrepancies in factual data included in the volumes of the NNES. In particular, unified Project-wide volumes have been prepared on Uranium Chemistry and on the Analysis of Project Materials. Nevertheless, the reader will find many instances of differences in results or conclusions on similar subject matter prepared by different authors. This has not seemed wholly undesirable for several reasons. First of all, such divergencies are not unnatural and stimulate investigation. Second, promptness of publication has seemed more important than the removal of all discrepancies. Finally, many Project scientists completed their contributions some time ago and have become engrossed in other activities so that their time has not been available for a detailed review of their work in relation to similar work done at other installations.

The completion of the various individual volumes of the Series has also been beset with difficulties. Many of the key authors and editors have had important responsibilities in planning the future of atomic energy research. Under these circumstances, the completion of this technical series has been delayed longer than its editors wished. The volumes are being released in their present form in the interest of presenting the material as promptly as possible to those who can make use of it.

The Editorial Advisory Board

The Manhattan Project Technical Section of the National Nuclear Energy Series is intended to be a comprehensive account of the scientific and technical achievements of the United States program for the development of atomic energy. It is not intended to be a detailed documentary record of the making of any inventions that happen to be mentioned in it. Therefore, the dates used in the Series should be regarded as a general temporal frame of reference, rather than as establishing dates of conception of inventions, of their reduction to practice, or of occasions of first use. While a reasonable effort has been made to assign credit fairly in the NNES volumes, this may, in many cases, be given to a group identified by the name of its leader rather than to an individual who was an actual inventor.

UNIVERSITY OF CALIFORNIA PROJECT FOREWORD

The existence of adequate experimental equipment, in particular the two operating cyclotrons of the Radiation Laboratory and the large 184-inch unit under construction, together with a nucleus of trained personnel, made it inevitable that work in connection with the war effort would be prosecuted vigorously at the University of California. Prior to the fall of 1941, studies of the properties of the transuranic elements were carried out and artificial radioactive materials were produced in the cyclotrons for use in various laboratories. This work was done informally and primarily on university funds. The importance of the studies of transuranic elements cannot be overestimated since the results formed a basis for the Plutonium Project.

Although the mass spectrographic method of separating uranium isotopes had been under consideration prior to the fall of 1941, there was no unanimity of opinion among physicists regarding the ultimate success of the method, owing to the space-charge effects. The feeling prevailed in the Radiation Laboratory of the University of California that in spite of this uncertainty the method should be pushed vigorously. The first concrete step in this direction was taken in November 1941, when a group was assigned to convert the 37-inch cyclotron to study this method of separating uranium isotopes. At about the same time two other groups started work on other electromagnetic separation schemes, namely, the ionic centrifuge and the radial magnetic separator. All this work was undertaken with the full support of the Uranium Committee but under no formal contract. The first formal contract designed to further work along these lines was entered into between the university and the Office of Scientific Research and Development in late December 1941, with the Laboratory Director as Project Leader.

The work on the mass spectrographic method, now called the "calutron process," proceeded so satisfactorily that by the early fall of 1942 plans were being formulated for a production plant. Also, owing to the very gratifying results obtained with this method, it was decided to discontinue work on the other methods. From the fall of 1942 to the end of hostilities in 1945 the Berkeley project was concerned primarily with the design and testing of prototype units for the plant, in addition to the necessary training of personnel. For a good portion of the time Radiation Laboratory personnel was stationed at Oak Ridge to assist directly in putting the plant into operation. It was on May 1, 1943, that the Berkeley project came directly under the jurisdiction of the Manhattan District. This move, however, did not affect the organizational setup of the Radiation Laboratory in any way, and the development work proceeded without any break.

Perhaps the outstanding factor with regard to the entire electromagnetic separation project lies in the general smoothness with which the work proceeded. It was necessary to build a large development laboratory from a relatively small university research laboratory in a matter of months. This involved greatly multiplying the personnel and increasing the physical facilities and necessary experimental equipment appropriately. In spite of the rapid expansion, personnel and organizational difficulties were inconsequential. The entire laboratory organization was characterized by a minimum of formal procedure consistent with the nature of the work. It is indeed remarkable that the scientific and technical personnel of the Radiation Laboratory, many of whom had been accustomed to the academic freedom of educational institutions, could adjust themselves so readily to the necessary security, governmental regulations, and group action of the project. It must also be kept in mind that the work was predominately of a developmental rather than research nature. The form of laboratory organization was such as to allow a maximum of individual expression with regard to the various problems encountered, which undoubtedly contributed considerably to a maximum of cooperation. The fact that the first unit of the Oak Ridge plant was built and put into operation successfully within a matter of two years from the time that the first mass spectrographic unit was built attests to the close cooperation maintained among all people concerned—the Office of Scientific Research and Development, Manhattan District officials, Radiation Laboratory personnel, and the manufacturing and operating companies. It would not be fair to say that the organization used would have been adopted if the project had been built up on a long-range basis. However, in view of the haste with which the project had to be carried through, it worked extremely well.

In preparing the report on the work done at the Radiation Laboratory, the major emphasis has been placed on those subjects of most interest to people working in related fields. The engineering aspects have been minimized in view of the fact that this phase of the project will be treated elsewhere in this series. A number of papers dealing with the chemical problems of the project have been prepared and will be incorporated in other volumes of the series.

It is impossible to pay proper tribute to the many individuals—scientific, technical, and nontechnical—who participated in the Berkeley project. A cross section of scientific and technical personnel is contained in these volumes, as authors of the various chapters and in the lists of references at the ends of the chapters. Others are referred to in the text. However, the names of many persons who contributed substantially to the progress of the project do not appear in these volumes.

The Office of the Director takes pleasure in expressing its deep appreciation to the project personnel for their unfailing loyalty and confidence; to the university as a whole for its support and cooperation; to the Area Engineer's Office for its very effective expediting of all matters pertaining to the rapid development of the Project; to the plant construction contractor, Stone and Webster Engineering Corporation; to the operating company, Tennessee Eastman Corporation; and to the major manufacturing contractors, Allis-Chalmers Company, Westinghouse Electric and Manufacturing Company, and many others for their close cooperation and effective handling of the engineering and operations problems.

E. O. Lawrence
Professor of Physics
Director, Radiation Laboratory
University of California

June, 1949

VOLUME EDITORS' PREFACE

The studies and developments of high-vacuum equipment and practice made by the personnel of the University of California Radiation Laboratory under contract with the Manhattan District form the basis of this volume.

Wherever possible the material has been contributed by those scientists who were originally connected with the actual work. This, however, was not possible in all cases; for example, Chapter 5 on leak-detection techniques and procedures was prepared by the authors listed herein from existing reports.

Because of the lack of adequate published material concerning the behavior and operation of large-scale vacuum installations, it was decided to expand the volume to make it as useful a reference work as possible. For this reason Chapter 1 on fundamental considerations in vacuum practice and the appendices at the end of the volume have been included. In addition, throughout the volume liberal reference has been made to the available published literature.

As a result of the highly accelerated tempo of the Manhattan Project, most of the high-vacuum studies made at the Radiation Laboratory are of an incomplete nature and do not represent a carefully planned approach to the problems involved. This volume should be considered primarily as a compilation of observations made in the course of developing high-vacuum equipment suitable for use in the electromagnetic separation plants. Relatively little attention has been devoted to the operational difficulties experienced with the large-scale vacuum installations in the Oak Ridge plant since this phase is covered elsewhere in the series.

It is not possible to extend credit to all those who have contributed significantly to the success of the high-vacuum program at the University of California Radiation Laboratory. Reference is made to a number of persons throughout the text and in the reports listed at the end of each chapter. Close collaboration was maintained with others outside the Laboratory, in both operations and manufacturing.

A. Guthrie
R. K. Wakerling

October, 1949

CONTENTS

CONTENTS

Page

Chapter 1

FUNDAMENTAL CONSIDERATIONS IN VACUUM PRACTICE

By Robert Loevinger

1.1 Introduction. In this chapter will be presented those parts of the kinetic theory of gases that are needed in modern industrial and laboratory vacuum practice. For the most part these are presented without proof. It is assumed that the reader is already familiar with the elements of the kinetic theory but not necessarily with vacuum practice. The special equations of vacuum practice are developed here and discussed fully whenever possible. References are not given for the standard results of kinetic theory since these are found in any good book on kinetic theory. Sources are given for all material of special interest in vacuum practice.

In the body of the chapter all equations are given in units of either the cgs system or the metric laboratory system. In both these systems pressure is measured in microns and volume in liters. At the present time other systems are not appropriate in a scientific publication. In Appendix B at the end of the volume the important formulas are grouped together, and, for the convenience of those doing design work, are also given there in the English laboratory system.

The entire chapter employs a consistent notation, and the symbols are listed and defined in Appendix A at the end of the volume.

1.2 The Equation of State. The pressure of a gas at a certain point in a given direction is defined as the time rate of transfer of momentum in the assigned direction across a unit area normal to that direction. For the special case of a gas against a solid wall, this is obviously equivalent to the definition of pressure as the force per unit area. But in the kinetic theory a gas must be considered as a collection of moving particles in a region that is largely empty. Hence the first definition is directly applicable, while the second is not, when concepts such as the pressure of one gas upon another, or pressure gradients, are considered.

Starting with the definition of pressure given above, it is easy to show that the pressure of a homogeneous gas in equilibrium is given by

$$P = \tfrac{1}{3} v_s^2 \rho \tag{1}$$

where $v_s = \sqrt{\overline{v^2}}$ is the root-mean-square velocity of the molecules and ρ is the density of the gas. Then

$$\rho = \frac{\gamma}{V}$$

where V is the volume of the container and γ is the mass of gas in the container. Hence

$$PV = \tfrac{1}{3} \gamma v_s^2$$

This is Boyle's law, since in equilibrium the two terms on the right must be constant. But the principle of equipartition of energy gives

$$v_s^2 = \frac{3kT}{m} \tag{2}$$

where T is the absolute temperature, m is the mass of the molecule, and k, 1.38×10^{-16} dyne-cm/deg, is the Boltzmann constant. Then $PV = kT\gamma/m$. But, if N is the total number of molecules in the container,

$$N = \frac{\gamma}{m}$$

and

$$PV = NkT \quad \text{cgs units} \tag{3}$$

This is the desired equation of state of a homogeneous gas in equilibrium. In scientific work it is customary to set $R = k/m$ so that

$$PV = RmNT$$

But, since $\rho = mN/V$, the equation of state can be written

$$P = \frac{k}{m}\rho T = R\rho T \quad \text{cgs units} \tag{4}$$

But in most vacuum work V is held constant and P and N are varied; therefore Eq. 3 is the one most used.

Sometimes it is desired to know the mass of the gas in a system. From the equation above,

$$\gamma = \frac{m}{kT} PV \quad \text{cgs units} \tag{5}$$

For use in laboratory practice this is converted to convenient units by use of the conversion factors from Appendix C.

$$\gamma = 5.44 \times 10^{-8}\ MPV \quad \text{grams at } 20°C \tag{6}$$

where M is the molecular weight of the gas, P is the pressure in microns of mercury, and V is the volume in liters. It is clear that for a given type of gas the mass is proportional to the product PV, and it is customary to designate amounts of gas in PV units, usually micron-liters (μ Hg is the symbol for microns of mercury pressure). For air M = 28.7; hence the mass of air is

$$\begin{aligned} \gamma &= 1.56 \times 10^{-6}\ PV \quad \text{grams} \\ &= 1.56 \times 10^{-6}\ \text{grams}/\mu\text{-liter} \end{aligned} \tag{7}$$

There are two assumptions implicit in the derivation of Eq. 3. These are: (1) the molecules are of negligible size, and (2) no forces exist between molecules except at the instant of collision.

Consider now a mixture of several kinds of gases inside the volume V. If N_i is the total number of molecules of the ith kind of gas, then the total number of molecules of all kinds is $N = \Sigma N_i$. Moreover, considering again the definition of pressure, it is reasonable to suppose that if P_i is the partial pressure due to the ith kind of gas, then the total pressure is $P = \Sigma P_i$. Likewise, because of the two assumptions mentioned, it is reasonable to suppose that each gas separately obeys an equation of the form $P_i V = kN_i T$. Then it follows at once that Eq. 3 can be interpreted either as the individual equation of each component in the mixture or as the total equation for the sum of the components in the mixture.

Both assumptions contained in the derivation of the perfect-gas law are in fact false for any real gas. But, fortunately for our purposes, they become increasingly accurate as the pressure is decreased, so that gases in even a moderate vacuum obey the perfect-gas law with considerable accuracy.

1.3 Molecular Velocities. If any one molecule in a gas were to be tagged and watched, it would be seen to undergo a very large number of collisions each second. At each collision its velocity would change, so that for any one molecule, as for all the molecules at any instant, a "velocity distribution" and an "average velocity" can be spoken of. The velocity distribution is of course the well-known Maxwellian distribution law; namely, the fraction of the molecules having a velocity in the neighborhood of v is proportional to

$$\beta^3 V^2 e^{-\beta^2 v^2} \tag{8}$$

where $\beta^2 = m/2kT$, m is the mass of a molecule, k is the Boltzmann constant, and T is the absolute temperature. This means that a few molecules have very low velocities, a few have very high velocities, and most have velocities in the neighborhood of an average velocity given by

$$\bar{v} = \sqrt{\frac{8kT}{\pi m}} \text{ cgs units} \tag{9}$$

It is interesting to note in passing that $\bar{v}$ is about 30 per cent larger than the velocity of sound and has the same functional dependence on T and m. Values of $\bar{v}$ for various gases at 15°C are tabulated in Appendix D. It is seen that these velocities are large—of the order of 1 km/sec. These high velocities are very useful in the techniques of leak detection.

It is also shown by kinetic theory that in a mixture of gases, each gas has independently the same velocity distribution that it would have if it existed alone. Hence Eq. 9 can be used for any gas without regard to other gases present.

Throughout this chapter the word "velocity" is used to mean the "magnitude of the velocity vector." The word "speed" is usually used in this connection, but in the simple treatment given here no ambiguity will arise.

The Maxwellian distribution is a relatively sharp one. It is easily shown that about 75 per cent of the molecules have velocities between $\frac{1}{2}\bar{v}$ and $\frac{3}{2}\bar{v}$. This fact, together with other phenomena to be discussed later, means that the distribution function, although of fundamental importance to an understanding of the kinetic theory of gases, need not be taken into consideration in normal vacuum practice.

1.4 Mean Free Path. Although the molecules of a gas are traveling at velocities of the order of 1 km/sec at room temperature, each molecule usually travels only a short distance before colliding with another molecule or the walls of the container. The average distance traveled between collisions with other gas molecules is called the "mean free path" (m.f.p.). If the molecules of a gas are considered to be elastic spheres, then an elementary calculation based simply on a consideration of the target area of one molecule compared with the target area of a unit volume of molecules leads to the formula for the m.f.p. of a homogeneous gas, i.e.,

$$\lambda = \frac{1}{\pi n \sigma^2} = \frac{kT}{\pi P \sigma^2}$$

where k is the Boltzmann constant, T is the absolute temperature, P is the pressure in cgs units, n is the number of molecules per unit volume, and σ is the diameter of the molecule. The second form follows at once from Eq. 3 of Sec. 1.2, since $n = N/V$.

If the Maxwellian distribution of the velocities is taken into account, a rather lengthy argument leads to the well-known equation

$$\lambda = \frac{kT}{\sqrt{2}\pi P \sigma^2} \text{ cgs units} \tag{10}$$

In Appendix D, λ is tabulated for a number of gases at room temperature and 1 μ Hg pressure. A simple ratio then gives λ at other temperatures or pressures. It is very convenient to bear in mind that the m.f.p. for air is

$$\lambda_{air} = \frac{5}{P} \text{ cm}$$

where P is in microns of mercury. Then at 10^{-6} mm Hg pressure the m.f.p. is 50 meters, much larger than the dimensions of any normal vacuum equipment.

It is clear that at very low pressures most collisions are with the walls of the container and not with other molecules. Thus the average distance between collisions is no longer λ but is simply the average dimension of the container. This might lead to the supposition that the velocity distribution of the molecules would be changed at very low pressures. However, the temperature of a gas at equilibrium cannot be different from the temperature of its container, and from this it can be shown that the velocity distribution and the average velocity are unchanged.

Equation 10 applies to a homogeneous gas. Normally there is a mixture of gases, e.g., air. If an average value of σ is used in Eq. 10, an average value of λ will be obtained. This is what is done in getting the m.f.p. of air. It is possible to give general equations for the m.f.p. of each type of molecule in a mixture, but the general equations are not needed in this discussion. However, the following special case of a mixture of gases is of interest in vacuum work.

Consider two gases of molecular weights M_1 and M_2 and partial pressures P_1 and P_2. It is shown in kinetic theory that

$$\lambda_{1,2} = \frac{4kT}{\pi P_2(\sigma_1 + \sigma_2)^2(1 + M_1/M_2)^{1/2}} \tag{11}$$

It is clear that this reduces to Eq. 10 for the case $\sigma_1 = \sigma_2$ and $M_1 = M_2$. Now since

$$\lambda_2 = \frac{kT}{\sqrt{2}\,\pi P_2 \sigma_2^2}$$

then

$$\lambda_{1,2} = \frac{4\sqrt{2}}{(1 + \sigma_1/\sigma_2)^2(1 + M_1/M_2)^{1/2}}\lambda_2$$

Here $\lambda_{1,2}$ is the m.f.p. for molecules of type 1 colliding with molecules of type 2. But if $P_1 \ll P_2$, molecules of type 1 will make many more collisions with type 2 than with type 1 molecules; hence $\lambda_1 = \lambda_{1,2}$. Moreover, from Eq. 10

$$\frac{\sigma_1}{\sigma_2} = \sqrt{\frac{\lambda_2}{\lambda_1'}}$$

where λ_1' is the m.f.p. for a homogeneous mixture of gas of type 1 taken at the same pressure as λ_2 (i.e., at pressure P_2). So now

$$\lambda_1 = \frac{4\sqrt{2}}{\left(1 + \sqrt{\lambda_1/\lambda_2}\right)^2(1 + M_1/M_2)^{1/2}}\lambda_2 \tag{12}$$

To show the purpose of this equation, consider a mixture of a small amount of helium in air at low pressure. Then, from Appendix D,

$$M_1 = 4 \qquad \lambda_1' = 14.1$$

$$M_2 = 29 \qquad \lambda_2 = 4.86$$

Hence

$$\lambda_{He} = \frac{4\sqrt{2}}{(1.59)^2 \sqrt{1.14}} \lambda_2 = 2.1\lambda_{air} \qquad (13)$$

Thus the m.f.p. of the helium molecules, for a small mixture of helium and air, is about twice the m.f.p. of the air molecules, provided the pressure is great enough so that the m.f.p. of the air molecules is smaller than the dimensions of the container.

An interesting result of Eq. 12 is the m.f.p. of an electron in a gas. Then $M_1 \ll M_2$, $\sigma_1 \ll \sigma_2$, $\lambda_2 \ll \lambda_1'$; hence

$$\lambda_{electron} = 4\sqrt{2}\ \lambda_{gas} = 5.66\lambda_{gas}$$

1.5 Gaseous Diffusion. Consider a mixture of two gases of molecular weights M_1 and M_2, respectively, and suppose that the concentration of the gases is not uniform. Suppose further that a tube a few centimeters in diameter contains the gases, with almost pure helium at one end and almost pure air at the other. Then the pressure will be constant along the tube, but the partial pressures P_1 and P_2 will be a function of x, the distance along the tube. As a result of the random motion of the molecules, the gases will diffuse into each other and eventually establish a uniform concentration if no gases are added or allowed to leave the tube. It is shown in the kinetic theory that the rate at which the partial pressure of one of the gases is changing at any one point is given by

$$\frac{\partial P_1}{\partial t} = (\text{constant}) \frac{T^{3/2}}{P} \frac{\sqrt{1/M_1 + 1/M_2}}{(\sigma_1 + \sigma_2)} \frac{\partial P_1}{\partial x} \qquad (14)$$

where, of course,

$$P = P_1 + P_2 \qquad (15)$$

and where P is the pressure, σ is the diameter of a molecule, T is the absolute temperature, and t is time in seconds. Since P is not a function of either t or x, it follows that the same equation holds for P_2. The constant contains several other parameters, depending on the nature of the gases, but the effects of these are small and need not concern us here.

In vacuum practice the value of $\partial P_1/\partial x$ is never known, and hence Eq. 14 cannot be used quantitatively. But if the role of the different factors in the expression is understood, the significance of many phenomena occurring in the laboratory may be appreciated, in particular those which occur in modern leak-detection methods.

That the rate of diffusion is proportional to the gradient of the partial pressure, $\partial P_1/\partial x$, is not surprising. Diffusion would be expected to be very rapid if the concentration changed very sharply. But it should be remembered that the rate of diffusion will become very small as the gradient of the partial pressures becomes small. This means that under some circumstances it may take a very long time for diffusion to establish homogeneity, sometimes many hours or days.

The dependence of rate of diffusion on temperature and pressure is also easy to understand. A higher temperature means a greater velocity and faster diffusion. A higher pressure means a shorter m.f.p. and slower diffusion. When the pressure gets so low that the m.f.p. is of the order of the size of the container, the formula is no longer valid since molecular collisions are no longer of importance. However, at these low pressures, diffusion is virtually instantaneous since the molecules immediately go to the far corners of the container without interference.

The effect of the nature of the gas is contained in the factor

$$\frac{\sqrt{1/M_1 + 1/M_2}}{(\sigma_1 + \sigma_2)^2}$$

This factor has been tabulated in Appendix D, last column, for the common gases diffusing into air. The values shown have been arbitrarily normalized to make the factor for H_2 unity. It is interesting to note that hydrogen and helium are the only gases that diffuse appreciably faster than the average. This fact is utilized in modern leak-detection methods. The diffusion of neon is slightly more rapid than average because of the small diameter of its molecules, but this is not of much practical importance owing to its relative scarcity. Normally the pressure is the most important variable controlling the rate of diffusion, and, when the pressure is sufficiently low, all other considerations can be disregarded and diffusion can be considered to be instantaneous.

1.6 Thermal Diffusion. It is shown in a complete kinetic-theory treatment of diffusion that, if a temperature gradient exists in a container of gas, the heavier gases will diffuse toward the lower-temperature region, and the lighter gases toward the higher-temperature region. Thus in the absence of any pressure gradient a temperature gradient will set up a concentration gradient. The theory of this effect is very complex and will not be discussed here. It is usually a small effect, giving concentration differences of a few per cent for temperature differences of a few hundred degrees, and hence it can normally be disregarded. It is noted here only for the sake of completeness, in order that it will not be confused with the phenomenon of thermal transpiration, which is discussed below. In thermal transpiration a pressure gradient is established.

1.7 Thermal Conductivity of Gases. In vacuum work the rate of cooling of a hot object as a function of pressure is sometimes a matter of concern. At pressures around atmospheric and higher the main mechanism of gaseous cooling is convection. This is important at those pressures in which the gravitational forces arising from density changes due to temperature gradients are great enough to move masses of the gas and cause circulating currents. So many factors other than the nature of the gas are involved that it is not possible to make a quantitative theory of convective cooling. It is, of course, a very efficient method of transporting heat.

As the pressure is lowered, convection becomes less important and finally disappears. Cooling now takes place by a molecular process that can be treated by the kinetic theory. Molecules near the hot object acquire increased kinetic energy by collision with it and then impart this increased kinetic energy to the molecules of the cooler gases farther out, again by collision. An analysis of this process gives for the thermal conductivity

$$\kappa = (\text{constant}) \frac{\sqrt{T}}{\sigma^2 \sqrt{m}} \tag{16}$$

where T is the absolute temperature and σ and m are the diameter and mass of a molecule, respectively. This is only an approximation to the correct expression, but it illustrates the fact that the conductivity will increase with temperature and likewise will be largest for the small, light molecules. Moreover, the conductivity is independent of pressure over the region where molecular transport of heat takes place. This last, perhaps unexpected, conclusion has been verified experimentally down to about 100 μ Hg. It is obviously true that in some cases radiation may play a large part in the transfer of heat. This is the case where large temperature gradients exist, as for liquid-air traps.

In Appendix D are tabulated values of the thermal conductivity κ for various gases. Here κ is the heat transferred per square centimeter per second per unit of temperature gradient. It is valid only in the pressure region just discussed, i.e., in the region where the heat is transported only by intermolecular collisions of the cooling gas. The tabulated value may be corrected approximately to other temperatures by the relation given above.

In the pressure region just discussed the gas in the immediate neighborhood of the hot object takes on the temperature of the object, thus setting up a temperature gradient across which the heat is transported. If the pressure is still further lowered, the m.f.p. approaches the size of the container. Then the molecules that strike the hot object can travel through the gas to the walls of the container without striking other molecules and the heat is transported by the gas without setting up temperature gradients in the gas. It turns out that this process is actually less efficient than the previously described process of heat transfer, and hence the conductivity falls off. Moreover, in this region of pressure the thermal conductivity is proportional to the pressure and to the temperature difference between the hot object and the cool walls of the container. In addition, it depends on the shape and nature of the surface. This is due to the fact that a molecule does not come into equilibrium with a surface at a single collision, but after reflection it has an energy equivalent to a temperature intermediate between its initial temperature and that of the surface. Thus a rough and cavernous surface, which is hit many times by a molecule before it escapes to another surface, is more efficient in transferring its temperature to the gas molecules than a smooth and simple surface. The efficiency of heat transfer at a single collision (known in technical literature as the "accommodation coefficient") varies between 10 and 90 per cent, depending on the shape and nature of the surface, the nature of the gas, and the past history of the surface; consequently no general rule can be given. (At high pressures, where the m.f.p. is very short, this phenomenon can be disregarded since the molecules in the gas layer near the surface do in fact make many collisions with the surface.)

It is clear that this free-molecule conduction will be independent of the size of the system, provided the m.f.p. remains larger than the dimensions of the system. Now, since the heat conducted away from the hot object is independent of the size of the system and since there is no temperature gradient in the gas, a coefficient of conductivity of the gas in this pressure region cannot be spoken of. But thermal conductivity of the system approaches zero as the pressure approaches zero.

A simple Pirani gauge for reading pressure operates in the region just described. It functions from about 100 μ Hg, above which κ is insensitive to pressure, down to about 0.1 μ Hg, below which the thermal conductivity is very small.

The foregoing discussion makes it clear that if gas is let into a vacuum system for the purpose of more rapidly cooling a hot object there is no advantage in raising the pressure above about 1 mm Hg, since in the absence of considerable convection there will be no appreciable increase in the thermal conductivity above that pressure. Hydrogen would be the best gas for this purpose, but, for reasons of safety, helium is usually used.

1.8 Viscosity. Suppose a stream of gas is moving through a mass of stationary gas. Then molecules of the moving gas will diffuse into the stationary gas, owing to their thermal velocities, and will impart to the stationary gas some momentum in the direction of the stream. Likewise molecules of the stationary gas will diffuse into the stream, giving it, in effect, momentum in the reverse direction. This is a microscopic view of a phenomenon that, from a macroscopic viewpoint, can be described as saying that the moving gas exerts a drag upon the stationary gas, tending to pull it along in the direction of motion and likewise tending to slow itself down. This drag is known as the "viscosity" of the gas. It is defined as the tangential force per unit area of either of two planes at unit distance apart, one of which is fixed while the other moves with unit velocity, the space being filled with gas. The coefficient of viscosity η by kinetic-theory analysis is given as

$$\eta = \frac{1}{\pi^{3/2}} \frac{\sqrt{mkT}}{\sigma^2} \text{ cgs units} \tag{17}$$

where k is the Boltzmann constant, T is the absolute temperature, and m and σ are the molecular mass and diameter, respectively. This equation holds from about 10 atm down to the region where the mean free path is comparable to the size of the container. Actual values of the viscosity are given in Appendix D (1 poise = 1 dyne-sec/sq cm). It is noteworthy that the viscosity, like the heat conductivity, is proportional to $\sqrt{T}$ and independent of pressure over the whole pressure region where intermolecular collisions are the primary phenomenon.

At very low pressures, where intermolecular collisions disappear, one part of the gas exerts no drag at all on another part of the gas. Instead, the momentum of the moving gas is imparted directly to the walls. In this pressure region the phenomenon of "free-molecule viscosity" is spoken of. This is proportional to the pressure and independent of the size but not of the shape and nature of the surfaces. Thus even at very low pressures the viscosity has properties exactly analogous to those of heat conductivity.

The statement that free-molecule viscosity is independent of size means that if two surfaces in motion with respect to each other are separated by a gas at a pressure so low that the m.f.p. is greater than the distance of separation, then the momentum transfer between them does not depend on the distance between them. For example, the Langmuir viscosity gauge for measuring pressure consists of a quartz fiber that is set vibrating in the gas. In the region of free-molecule viscosity the rate at which the vibrations are damped is proportional to the pressure but is independent of the distance between the vibrating fiber and the fixed walls.

That the free-molecule viscosity depends on the shape of the surfaces means, for example, that the shape of the fiber in the Langmuir gauge will affect its rate of damping. The explanation of this is similar to the explanation of dependence on shape in the case of free-molecule heat conductivity. Here, a molecule on striking a surface obliquely transmits to that surface only a certain fraction, F, of its tangential momentum. If $F = 0$, the molecule is reflected with its tangential momentum unchanged, and the case of specular reflection obtains. If $F = 1$, the molecule loses all its initial tangential momentum and may come off the surface in any direction whatsoever, and the case of completely diffuse reflection obtains. If $F > 1$, the molecule would come off the surface with its direction reversed, which is conceivable with a saw-toothed surface and low angles of incidence. For all common surfaces and gases, the value of F is usually very close to 1. Thus it is usually satisfactory to assume completely diffuse reflection of molecules. In the case of the viscosity gauge, where the effect is critically dependent on momentum transfer, such an assumption might not be justified. As with heat transfer, a rough and cavernous surface would be more efficient than a smooth and simple one.

CHARACTERISTICS OF VACUUM SYSTEMS

1.9 The Vacuum Circuit: Definition of Impedance, Conductance, and Speed. In the remainder of the chapter the special forms that the laws of kinetic theory take when applied to vacuum systems are discussed. There is a very useful analogy between d-c circuit theory and vacuum systems that is helpful in understanding the characteristics of vacuum systems and allows certain well-known results of the electrical theory to be used. First the validity of the analogy will be established.

Consider a closed electrical circuit made up of sources of emf and resistances only. When equilibrium current is flowing, the circuit is characterized by two conditions: (1) current (which is electrons in motion) is neither created nor destroyed, and (2) the potential changes around the circuit but is continuous and single-valued. We define the resistance of an element of the circuit as the "potential drop per unit of current." It is an experimental fact (Ohm's law) that the resistance is independent of current for most substances, but this is not a necessary part of the analysis, nor is it in fact always true. From these considerations there follow at once Kirchhoff's laws and the well-known rules for combining resistance in series or in parallel.

Consider now a vacuum system consisting of a pump and some lines connecting this pump to a tank at high vacuum. Suppose that there is a small leak from the atmosphere into the tank. The air will then flow into the tank through the leak and through the lines and be ejected by the pump back into the atmosphere. Thus a closed circuit may be traced which is analogous to the electric circuit. The pressure will change as we go around the circuit but is continuous and single-valued, and hence it plays the same role as potential in the electrical case.

Suppose this vacuum system to be in equilibrium and at a uniform temperature. A quantity $Q = PV'$ to measure the flow must be defined. Here V' is the volume of gas flowing across any plane in the system per unit of time, and P is the pressure in that plane. Now from the gas law $PV = kNT$ (Eq. 3, Sec. 1.2) it follows that

$$Q = PV' = kN'T \tag{18}$$

where k is the Boltzmann constant, N' is the number of molecules crossing the plane per second, and T is the absolute temperature. Hence the gas current Q represents the molecules in motion and is neither created nor destroyed in the circuit. Consequently it is analogous to current in the electrical case.

The analogy may now be completed by defining the impedance (or resistance) of any segment of the system as the pressure drop per unit of current,

$$Z = \frac{P_1 - P_2}{Q} \tag{19}$$

where P_1 is the pressure on the upstream end, and P_2 is the pressure on the downstream end of the impedance. Clearly this is analogous to resistance in the electrical case.

In subsequent paragraphs it will be found that the impedance Z is sometimes a function of Q and P, and sometimes it is not. The terms "impedance" and "resistance" are used interchangeably in vacuum work. It is customary to introduce the notation of conductance, i.e.,

$$C = \frac{1}{Z} = \frac{Q}{P_1 - P_2} \tag{20}$$

Thus the conductance of a vacuum line at a given pressure is the amount of gas at the pressure which flows through the line per unit of pressure difference between the ends.

The electrical analogy allows application of the rules for combining impedances in series or parallel arrangements, i.e.,

$$Z_{\text{series}} = \Sigma Z_i \qquad \frac{1}{Z_{\text{parallel}}} = \sum \frac{1}{Z_i} \tag{21}$$

$$\frac{1}{C_{\text{series}}} = \sum \frac{1}{C_i} \qquad C_{\text{parallel}} = \Sigma C_i \tag{22}$$

Here Z_{series} means the effective impedance of several lines in series, the impedance of the separate lines being Z_1, Z_2, Z_3, etc. The meaning of ΣZ_i is simply $Z_1 + Z_2 + Z_3 + \ldots$.

In the following paragraphs, equations for computing impedances and conductances of lines and apertures will be given, always using the definitions in Eqs. 19 and 20.

The reader will find it useful to give some further thought to the analogy between electrical and vacuum systems. He will find that almost all vacuum phenomena have electrical analogies. These analogies are easily found for such things as the rise in pressure across a vacuum pump, the atmosphere at fixed pressure, leaks into vacuum systems at various places along the system, etc.

A vacuum pump is a device that uses external power to set up a flow of gas in the vacuum system. The pumping speed of such a device is defined in several different ways, but the simplest definition will be used, following Gaede: The speed S of a pump at pressure P is the volume of gas removed from the system per unit of time, measured at the pressure P. Clearly then $S = V'$, the volume flow through the throat of the pump. Since $Q = PV'$,

$$S = \frac{Q}{P} \tag{23}$$

This is the defining equation for the pumping speed S. The flow Q can be measured at any plane of the system, but the pressure P is to be measured at the inlet to the pump. Although there is no real distinction between S and V' as used here, the symbol V' will be used when referring to volume flow in a system, and S when referring to pumping action.

The defining equation (23) can be applied to a mechanical pump, a diffusion pump, a cold trap facing condensable vapors, or to an aperture connecting a system at pressure P to a system at lower pressure. More generally, any vacuum system with gas flowing can be said to have a pumping speed in any plane of $S = V'$, the volumetric flow across that plane.

The flow V' is usually given in liters per second, and the pressure usually in microns of mercury. Thus impedance has seconds per liter as units, but conductance and pumping speed have liters per second as units. Because they have the same units, conductance and pumping speed are often loosely used as synonymous terms. It will be seen later that they are sometimes numerically equal but never equivalent in meaning. Conductance is to be applied to impedances only, since it implies a pressure gradient and may be looked upon as a geometrical property of the impedance. Pumping speed, on the other hand, can be applied to any plane in the system that may reasonably be considered as a pump for that part of the system preceding it. Pumping speed may be looked upon as the ability of the system to remove gas and always implies an external source of power.

Consider an impedance Z connecting a tank at pressure P with a pump of speed S_p at pressure P_p. Let S be the pumping speed of the system at the inlet to the impedance. Then

$$\frac{1}{S} = \frac{P}{Q}$$

and

$$ZQ = P - P_p$$

from Eqs. 19 and 23; therefore

$$\frac{1}{S} = Z + \frac{P_p}{Q}$$

and

$$\frac{1}{S} = Z + \frac{1}{S_p} = \frac{1}{C} + \frac{1}{S_p} \tag{24}$$

where C is the conductance $1/Z$. In case the pump and the tank are connected by a complicated system of parallel and series lines, Z and C are the effective values, computed from Eqs. 21 and 22. Equation

24 is the fundamental expression for vacuum design purposes. It gives the effective pumping speed S of a pump of speed S_p working through an impedance Z. Clearly, if $1/Z = C \ll S_p$, then $S = C$, and the speed is limited by the line impedance. If $1/Z = C \gg S_p$, then $S = S_p$, and the speed is limited by the pump itself. In practice, C is usually taken somewhere between these limits.

There is no standard electrical concept analogous to pumping speed.

1.10 Flow through Thin Small Apertures. Consider a large region at constant pressure P_1, which is connected by a small hole of area A to a region where the pressure P_2 can be controlled. As the pressure P_2 is lowered to a little below P_1, which can be taken to be atmospheric pressure, stream lines are set up in the gas flowing toward the aperture. The gas acquires a velocity toward the aperture, so that on passing through the jet it reaches a minimum cross section on the low-pressure side, then expands again to a little over the cross section of the aperture, then contracts again, etc., as shown in Fig. 1.1. It may make as many as a dozen such oscillations before losing its identity by diffusion and turbulence. As P_2 is lowered, the amount of gas flowing through the aperture and the terminal velocity reached in the P_2 region both increase, until the ratio P_2/P_1 reaches a certain critical minimum. At this value the velocity through the aperture is the velocity of sound under the conditions of reduced pressure and temperature produced by adiabatic expansion through the aperture. Further reduction in P_1 produces no increase in either the outflow or the jet velocity, since no change in P_2 below this critical value can send a pressure wave back through the aperture and notify the P_1 region of a change in P_2.

Above the critical ratio the outflow is given by the equation

$$Q = \sqrt{\frac{2\gamma}{\gamma - 1} \frac{kT_1}{m}}\, r^{1/\gamma} \sqrt{1 - r^{(\gamma-1)/\gamma}}\, P_1 A \quad \text{cgs units} \tag{25}$$

$$r = \frac{P_2}{P_1} \leq 1$$

where A is the area of the aperture, γ is the ratio of the specific heats of the gas, k is the Boltzmann constant, m is the mass of the gas molecule, and T_1 is the absolute temperature in the P_1 region. (This equation is adapted from Prandtl,[8] p. 356, which should be consulted for a detailed study of this phenomenon.) Since for our purposes only the flow of air at room temperature need be considered in connection with high-pressure jets, set $\gamma = 1.403$ and $T_1 = 293°K$.

Then

$$Q = 76.6r^{0.712} \sqrt{1 - r^{0.288}}\, P_1 A \quad \mu\text{-liters/sec} \tag{26}$$

where P_1 is in microns and A is the area in square centimeters. If Q is considered to be a function of r, it has a maximum at

$$r_c = \left(\frac{2}{\gamma + 1}\right)^{\gamma/(\gamma-1)} = 0.525 \text{ for air} \tag{27}$$

Thus the flow Q is 0 at r = 1 and rises to $20AP_1$ liters/sec for $r \leq 0.525$. It is constant at and below the critical-pressure ratio.

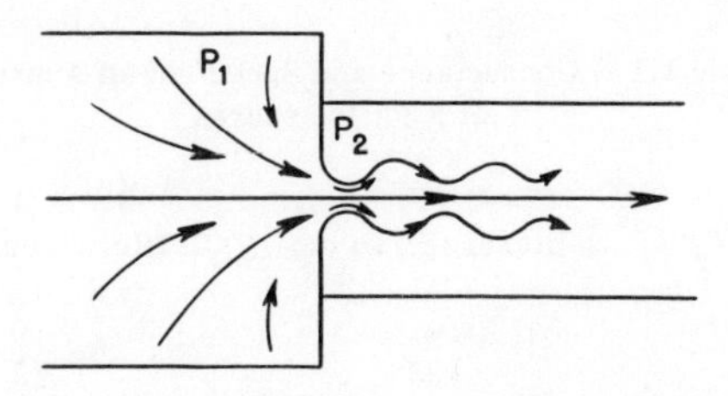

Fig. 1.1—High-pressure flow lines through a small aperture.

The impedance and conductance of the aperture are given by the equations

$$\frac{1}{Z} = C = \frac{Q}{P_1 - P_2} = 76.6\, r^{0.712} \sqrt{1 - r^{0.288}}\, \frac{A}{1 - r} \quad \text{liters/sec} \qquad r \gtrsim 0.52$$

$$\approx 20 \frac{A}{1 - r} \quad \text{liters/sec} \qquad r \lesssim 0.52 \tag{28}$$

$$\approx 20A \quad \text{liters/sec} \qquad r \lesssim 0.1$$

Thus the conductance of the aperture is a rather complicated function of the pressure ratio and is not even approximately constant until the ratio has dropped to about 0.1, i.e., for $P_2 \lesssim 0.1\, P_1$. Below that the conductance is independent of both pressure and the pressure ratio and thus can conveniently be used as an element in the vacuum circuit for purposes of design.

From the viewpoint of the region at pressure P_1, gas is disappearing into the aperture of area A so that the aperture is pumping gas out of the P_1 region, and from the P_1 side there is associated with the aperture a pumping speed.

$$S = \frac{Q}{P_1} = C\,(1 - r) = 76.6r^{0.712}\sqrt{1 - r^{0.288}}\,A \text{ liters/sec} \qquad r \geq 0.52$$

$$\approx 20A \text{ liters/sec} \qquad r \leq 0.52 \qquad (29)$$

Thus near $r = 1$ the pumping speed of the aperture is likewise a complicated function but assumes a constant value independent of pressure for values of the pressure ratio below the critical ratio. These equations are illustrated in Table 1.1, which gives values of the conductance and speed per square centimeter.

Table 1.1 — Conductance and Speed* of an Aperture at High Pressures

$r = P_2/P_1$	$C = Q/(P_1 - P_2)$, liters/sec/sq cm	$S = C\,(1 - r)$, liters/sec/sq cm
1.0	∞	0
0.9	123	12
0.8	80	16
0.7	62	19
0.6	49	20
0.525	42	20
0.5	40	20
0.3	29	20
0.1	22	20
≤0.03	20	20

*Multiply C and S by area in square centimeters to get value for a given aperture. Values are for air at 20°C.

It is quite common in the literature to fail to distinguish between conductance and pumping speed of an aperture, and it is clear from this table that under some special circumstances (fortunately rare in practice) this could lead to considerable confusion. This difference is particularly striking at $r = 1$. Then surely we would expect S to be zero because there will obviously be no flow between two regions at the same pressure. It would not be expected a priori that C would be ∞, but a value of ∞ should not be considered unreasonable. It simply means that for r very close to unity, i.e., for P_2 very near P_1, the ratio of flow to pressure drop is very great. It has the result that for a given pressure difference, $P_1 - P_2$, much more gas is pumped through the aperture if the pressure is high so that r is near unity, than if the pressures are low so that r is small.

The conclusions drawn thus far apply only to apertures small with respect to vessel size, and also thin and sharp edged. If the shape is very different from this, so that the stream lines are radically altered, the statements made here may not be correct. In addition, it should be noted that the speed and conductance values given thus far are valid even for values of P_2 so low that stream lines no longer exist in the P_2 region. But they hold only if P_1 is high enough so that the m.f.p. of the molecules in the P_1 region is small compared with the vessel and the aperture. When this is true the molecules disappearing into the hole will have come from its immediate neighborhood only. They will thus leave a low-pressure region around the hole, and then stream lines of flow will be set up in the P_1 region toward the aperture. Thus, gas some distance away from the aperture will be moving toward it, preparatory to going through, so to speak.

This process of flow and the equations given have been tested experimentally for values of P_1 in the neighborhood of atmospheric pressure. It may be expected that the equations are valid for values of P_1 down to a pressure where the m.f.p. becomes an appreciable fraction of the vessel or aperture dimensions. But, as the pressure is decreased still further, the mechanism for setting up flow lines ceases to operate. At very low pressures the molecules travel across the vessel without collision, and hence the molecules that disappear into an aperture may come from any part of the vessel. Thus no pressure gradients are established near the aperture, and hence there is no mass flow toward it.

It is shown in the kinetic theory that for an aperture of area A, the size of which is small compared to the vessel and to the m.f.p. of the gas, the amount of gas flowing through it is

$$Q_1 = \sqrt{\frac{kT}{2\pi m}}\, P_1 A \quad \text{cgs units} \tag{30}$$

If the restrictions mentioned apply to both sides, the net flow will be the difference between the two, which is

$$Q = \sqrt{\frac{kT}{2\pi m}}\, (P_1 - P_2)\, A \quad \text{cgs units} \tag{31}$$

or

$$Q = 11.6\,(P_1 - P_2)\, A \quad \mu\text{-liters/sec}$$

for air at 20°C, where A is the area in square centimeters and P is the pressure in microns of mercury. The assumption that the net flow through the aperture is just the difference of the two flows is justified by the restriction of a m.f.p. very large compared with other dimensions, since in this case, intermolecular collisions will be very rare, and the gas molecules will not interfere with each other in flowing through the hole.

Then for the conductance and impedance,

$$\frac{1}{Z} = C = \frac{Q}{P_1 - P_2} = 11.6A \quad \text{liters/sec} \tag{32}$$

for air at 20°C. Note that this is independent of pressure, which makes it very convenient for purposes of calculation. Using the argument that preceded Eq. 29 a pumping speed for the P_1 region may be assigned to the aperture. This speed is given by

$$\begin{aligned} S &= \frac{Q}{P_1} = C\left(1 - \frac{P_2}{P_1}\right) \\ &= 11.6A\left(1 - \frac{P_2}{P_1}\right) \text{liters/sec} \end{aligned} \tag{33a}$$

for air at 20°C. It should be noted that here P_1 is the upstream pressure and P_2 is the downstream pressure, on the two sides of the aperture. In the case of $P_2 \leq 0.1P_1$, which will be the usual case in high-vacuum practice, the equation becomes simply

$$S = C = 11.6A \quad \text{liters/sec} \tag{33b}$$

It should be emphasized that Eqs. 30 to 33b apply only to apertures much smaller than the m.f.p. and much smaller than the vessel size. Under these conditions the conductance is independent of pressure, but the speed, of course, depends upon the pressure ratio, reaching a maximum of 11.6 liters/sec/sq cm at large ratios. It is interesting to note that this is only a little over half the maximum speed of a high-pressure flow, which is 20 liters/sec/sq cm. Presumably this is due to the fact that the flow lines that occur at higher pressures make the process more efficient by transporting gas to the neighborhood of the aperture.

Equations 25 to 29 describe what is called the "viscous-flow" region, and Eqs. 30 to 33b describe "molecular flow." All these equations refer to apertures that are small compared with the vessel size. For pressure regions intermediate between the viscous-flow and the molecular-flow regions, no simple treatment is possible, but a reasonable interpolation between the equations given here must be made.

1.11 Flow through Thin Large Apertures. The term "large aperture" means an aperture of size comparable to the cross section of the vessel it faces. This definition is illustrated by the diagram in Fig. 1.2, where a very large vessel on the left is connected through a pipe of cross section A_0 to a very large vessel on the right, through an aperture of cross-sectional area A. Then A is to be considered a

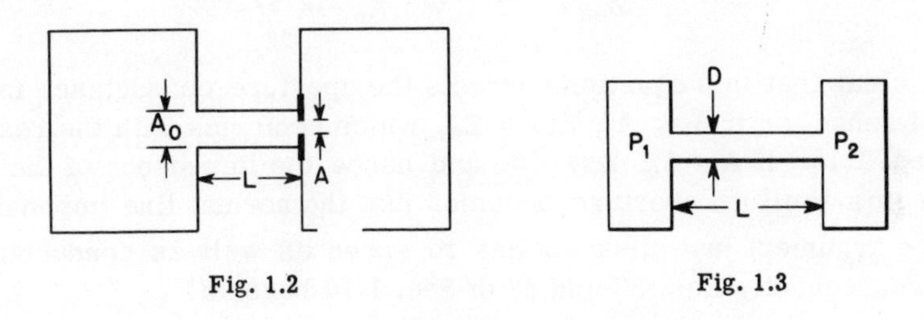

Fig. 1.2 Fig. 1.3

Fig. 1.2—Flow through thin large aperture.
Fig. 1.3—Flow through a pipe.

large aperture when approached from the left, but a small aperture when approached from the right. The gas in the vessel on the left must find the aperture A_0, then flow through the pipe L, and then find the aperture A. Thus the impedance from left to right is

$$Z = Z_{A_0} + Z_L + Z_{eff}$$

where Z_{eff} is the effective impedance of the aperture A within the pipe A_0. The gas flowing from right to left must first find the aperture A and then flow through the pipe L. All the gas flowing through A finds the pipe, and all the gas flowing through the pipe a distance L finds the left-hand vessel. Hence the conductance from right to left is simply

$$Z = Z_A + Z_L$$

But now the left-to-right conductance must equal the right-to-left conductance, in the molecular-flow region, for the flow out of either side is proportional to the conductance times the pressure on that side, and these two flows are independent. Hence, if the conductance were different in the two directions, there would be a net gas transfer starting from zero pressure difference, and this is not possible. It follows that

$$Z_{A_0} + Z_L + Z_{eff} = Z_A + Z_L$$

$$Z_{eff} = Z_A - Z_{A_0} = Z_A \left(1 - \frac{A}{A_0}\right) \tag{34}$$

and

$$\frac{1}{Z_{eff}} = C_{eff} = C_A \frac{A_0}{A_0 - A}$$

It is clear that this equation corrects the aperture conductance in the right sense, or if $A \ll A_0$, $Z_{eff} = Z_A$, which conforms with the results of Sec. 1.10. If $A = A_0$, $Z_{eff} = 0$, and hence the impedance of the line with this limiting aperture becomes just the normal line impedance.

The argument just given applies to speed as well as conductance, and consequently Eqs. 32 and 33 of Sec. 1.10 become

$$\frac{1}{Z} = C = \frac{11.6A}{(1 - A/A_0)} \text{ liters/sec} \tag{35}$$

and

$$S = C\,(1 - P_2/P_1) = 11.6A \frac{(1 - P_2/P_1)}{(1 - A/A_0)} \text{ liters/sec} \tag{36}$$

for air at 20°C. These give the speed and conductance of a thin aperture in the region of molecular flow, where the area of the aperture is A and the area of the region from which the aperture is conducting gas is A_0.

The arguments just given apply only to molecular flow. At higher pressures, where the m.f.p. is short, flow occurs only in the direction of the negative pressure gradient, and hence the conductance cannot be assumed to be the same in both directions. However, with viscous flow also the correction $A_0/(A_0 - A)$ gives the right value at the two limits $A \ll A_0$ and $A = A_0$, so that it is probably best to apply this correction to the pumping speeds and conductances of apertures in the viscous-flow region, too.

1.12 Flow through Pipes: General Discussion. Consider a pipe through which gas is flowing because of an applied pressure gradient. If the pressure and velocity of the gas are high enough the motion will be quite turbulent. The lines of flow are neither straight nor regular but turn and twist as the eddies appear and disappear. The velocity and the pressure at any point change with time, fluctuating widely about mean values. The flow, $Q = PV'$, of the gas through the pipe has been found experimentally to be approximately proportional to the square root of the pressure gradient. This is, in a general way, the nature of turbulent flow.

If the pressure and the velocity are now decreased, a point is then reached where the nature of the flow changes. The lines of flow become either straight or gently curved in the neighborhood of pipe irregularities. The lines of flow, the velocity, and the pressure are uniform with time. The amount $Q = PV'$ of gas flowing through the pipe is now proportional to the pressure gradient, since the energy available because of the pressure gradient is used only to cause the steady flow and is not used in creating random eddies. Near the walls the gas is almost at rest, but, progressing from the walls, the layers of gas slide over each other until at the center of the pipe there is a tube of gas flowing with maximum velocity. The flow in this pressure region is laminar in nature. Because the viscosity, i.e., the internal friction of the gas, is important in determining the nature and the amount of flow, it is called "viscous flow."

Clearly, viscous flow as described here can occur only when the m.f.p. of the molecules is very small compared with the pipe diameter. Only those molecules near the surface will actually collide with the surface, so that the size and shape of the pipe will affect the flow much more than the nature of the pipe surface. The flow arises because the applied pressure gradient causes adjacent layers of gas to exert pressure on each other in the direction of the negative pressure gradient. A velocity along the stream lines is superimposed upon the random Maxwellian velocities, and a mass flow is produced. In the neighborhood of bends, apertures, or other irregularities in the pipe the stream lines must contract somewhat, in order to carry the flow through without discontinuities. This means that the resistance to viscous flow of irregularities in the pipe will be somewhat greater than would be anticipated on purely geometrical grounds. Moreover, this resistance will depend on the shape of the irregularity, the velocity of the gas, and the pressure and consequently will be very difficult to treat quantitatively.

If now, still maintaining a pressure gradient along the pipe the pressure is lowered until the m.f.p. approaches the pipe diameter, the nature of the flow must change. The phenomenon of viscosity begins to disappear because the molecules collide less with each other than with the walls of the pipe. At sufficiently low pressures the molecules will migrate through the pipe independently of each other, and this is termed "molecular flow." It should be clearly understood that the nature of the flow is now entirely different from that in the viscous region. The phenomenon can be illustrated by the schematic diagram of Fig. 1.3, which shows a large vessel at pressure P_1 connected to another large vessel at pressure P_2, by a pipe of length L. Suppose that P_1 and P_2 are so low that the m.f.p. is large compared with the pipe diameter. Then the number of molecules going from P_1 region into the P_2 region is proportional to P_1 and depends upon L and D but is independent of P_2, because there are few intermolecular collisions. Likewise, there is a flow from the P_2 region into the P_1 region, which depends only on P_2 and not on P_1. Hence the net flow out of the P_1 region is proportional to $(P_1 - P_2)$, but even when $P_1 = P_2$ the molecules are still moving violently from the P_1 region to the P_2 region, and vice versa.

The reflection of a gas molecule by a solid has been shown experimentally to be essentially diffuse, as discussed in Sec. 1.8. Then the direction of the molecular velocity after reflection is unrelated to its direction before reflection. With viscous flow this affects only the molecules adjacent to the wall and gives rise to the phenomenon of "slip" at the walls, a phenomenon important in kinetic theory but not in vacuum practice. With molecular flow this diffuse reflection is very important because a molecule that enters the pipe from the P region and strikes the pipe wall stands just as good a chance of being reflected back into the P_1 region as of being reflected onward into the P_2 region. This means that molecular flow is strictly a matter of probability considerations based upon geometrical factors and consequently is capable of analytical treatment even in the neighborhood of irregularities. Molecular flow at bends in pipes is discussed in a later paragraph on this basis.

The criterion for determining the transition from turbulent to viscous flow is usually given in terms of the Reynolds number, defined by the equation

$$\mathrm{Re} = \frac{Dv\rho}{\eta} \tag{37}$$

where D is the diameter of the pipe, and v, ρ, and η are the velocity, density, and viscosity of the gas, respectively. It is easily seen that Re is a dimensionless ratio, and hence any consistent system of units may be used. It has been shown experimentally that the nature of gas flow, i.e., whether turbulent or viscous, can be predicted from the value of the Reynolds number. Although the results of different experiments have not been entirely consistent, the following rules have been found to be conservative statements of these results:

If $Re > 2{,}200$, the flow is turbulent

If $Re < 1{,}200$, the flow is viscous

If $1{,}200 < Re < 2{,}200$, the flow may be either turbulent or viscous, depending upon conditions at the inlet and the outlet (38)

In order to apply these criteria, the Reynolds number may be written in terms customary in vacuum practice as follows: From the equation of state, $\rho = mP/kT$. Dividing the volume flowing past any plane per second by the cross-sectional area for that plane gives the length of a circular cylinder that would pass that area in a unit time. Hence, for a circular pipe of diameter D,

$$v = \frac{V'}{A} = \frac{Q/P}{\pi D^2/4} = \frac{4Q}{\pi D^2 P}$$

and

$$Re = \left(\frac{D}{\eta}\right)\left(\frac{4Q}{\pi D^2 P}\right)\left(\frac{mP}{kT}\right) = \left(\frac{4m}{\pi kT\eta}\right)\left(\frac{Q}{D}\right) \tag{39}$$

where k is the Boltzmann constant, m is the mass of a molecule, and T is the absolute temperature. If values of the constants for air at 20°C are substituted, the equation becomes

$$Re = \frac{Q}{89D} \tag{40}$$

where Q is in micron-liters per second and D is in centimeters. Hence the rule for flow through a circular pipe is as follows: The flow is turbulent if

$$Q > 2 \times 10^5 D \tag{41a}$$

and the flow is viscous if

$$Q < 2 \times 10^5 D \tag{41b}$$

where Q is in micron-liters per second and D is in centimeters. For example, a very large diffusion pump, of 30,000 liters/sec speed and operating at the relatively high pressure of 1 μ, handles an amount of gas given by $Q = 3 \times 10^4$ μ-liters/sec. Then, clearly, turbulent flow need never be a cause for worry because the inequality

$$D > \frac{3 \times 10^4}{10^5} \text{ cm} \quad \text{or} \quad D > 0.3 \text{ cm} \tag{42}$$

needs only to be satisfied to guarantee viscous flow, and the actual pipe diameter connecting such a diffusion pump with its backing pump will be of the order of a hundred times this limit. Since at the present time 3×10^4 μ-liters/sec represents a safe upper limit in gas-handling capacity, it follows that all practical vacuum systems are operating at flows below the region of turbulent flow, which justifies giving attention in subsequent paragraphs to viscous and molecular flow only.

As the flow $Q = PV'$ is lowered, the transition from turbulent to viscous takes place rather suddenly, within a factor of 2 in the value of Q, as is indicated in Eqs. 41a and b. Moreover, this transition depends on the PV' of the flow and not on either the pressure or the volume flow alone. The transition from viscous to molecular flow, on the other hand, depends only on the pressure. As will be seen in the next section, for a circular pipe in which the average pressure is $\bar{P}$, the criteria may be stated as follows: The flow is viscous if

$$\bar{P}D > 500 \quad \mu\text{-cm} \tag{43a}$$

and the flow is molecular if

$$\bar{P}D < 15 \quad \mu\text{-cm} \tag{43b}$$

where D is in centimeters and $\bar{P}$ is in microns of mercury. For intermediate values of the product $\bar{P}D$ the flow is both viscous and molecular. This applies to air at 20°C, in the circular pipe of diameter D. Since for air the m.f.p. is given by $\lambda = 5/p$ cm, the rule is that the flow is viscous if

$$\lambda < \frac{D}{100} \tag{44a}$$

and the flow is molecular if

$$\lambda > \frac{D}{3} \tag{44b}$$

where D and λ are in any units. These rules, for a circular pipe, give results accurate to about 10 per cent. For noncircular geometrical forms no experimental results are available but it may be assumed that these limits hold roughly, if D is interpreted as the smallest linear dimensions of the pipe cross section. The transition from viscous to molecular flow is not sharp but occurs gradually in a region where the pressure changes by a factor of about 50.

1.13 Viscous and Molecular Flow through Long Circular Pipes. For the conductance of a long circular pipe Knudsen gave the following equation in 1909 (Loeb,[2] pp. 295 ff.)

$$C = \left(\frac{\pi}{128}\frac{D^4\bar{P}}{\eta L}\right) + \left(\frac{1}{6}\sqrt{\frac{2\pi kT}{m}}\frac{D^3}{L}\right)\left(\frac{1 + \sqrt{\frac{m}{kT}}\frac{D\bar{P}}{\eta}}{1 + 1.24\sqrt{\frac{m}{kT}}\frac{D\bar{P}}{\eta}}\right) \quad \text{cgs units} \qquad (45)$$

where D is the diameter of the pipe, $\bar{P}$ is the average pressure in the pipe, L is the length of the pipe, η is the viscosity of the gas, k is the Boltzmann constant, T is the absolute temperature, and m is mass of the molecule. Knudsen's equation is valid provided that (1) the flow is not turbulent in any part of the pipe (see discussion of previous paragraph) and (2) the pressure difference between the ends is not so great that the mechanism of flow (i.e., viscous or molecular) changes along the pipe.

If the pressure is very low the first member on the right-hand side can be neglected, the third member becomes unity, and the equation becomes one of molecular conductance

$$C = \frac{1}{6}\sqrt{\frac{2\pi kT}{m}}\frac{D^3}{L} \quad \text{cgs units} \qquad (46)$$

On the other hand, for very high pressures the third member becomes a constant independent of pressure, so that the last two members can be neglected. The equation becomes one of viscous conductance, i.e.,

$$C = \frac{\pi}{128}\frac{D^4}{\eta L}\bar{P} \quad \text{cgs units} \qquad (47)$$

Equations 46 and 47 are, in fact, the equations derived by the kinetic theory for the respective conductances. Equation 45 is a semiempirical combination of Eqs. 46 and 47, which Knudsen devised to represent his experimental data. It is said to be accurate throughout the entire region of viscous and molecular flow to within a few per cent.

In order to use Knudsen's equation, the values of the constants for air at 20°C are substituted. Then

$$C = \left(0.182\,\frac{D^4}{L}\,\bar{P}\right) + \left(12.1\,\frac{D^3}{L}\right)\left(\frac{1 + 0.256D\bar{P}}{1 + 0.316D\bar{P}}\right) \tag{48}$$

where D and L are in centimeters and $\bar{P}$ is in microns of mercury, or

$$C = 12.1\,\frac{D^3}{L}\,(J)$$

where

$$J = \frac{1 + 0.271D\bar{P} + 0.00479(D\bar{P})^2}{1 + 0.316D\bar{P}} \tag{49}$$

In Eq. 48 terms are grouped in parentheses to correspond to Eq. 45. Equation 49 is simply a rearrangement of the terms, so that J represents the correction to be applied to the molecular-conductivity formula. J is tabulated as a function of $D\bar{P}$ in Table 1.2. Note that for $D\bar{P} \leq 15$ μ-cm the error is not over 10 per cent in taking $J = 1$, i.e., assuming pure molecular flow. For very large values of $D\bar{P}$, the smaller terms in J may be neglected and the equation becomes

$$J = \frac{0.00479}{0.316}\,D\bar{P} = 0.0152D\bar{P}$$

and then Eq. 49 becomes

$$C = 12.1\,\frac{D^3}{L} \times 0.0152D\bar{P} = 0.182\,\frac{D^4}{L}\,\bar{P}$$

which indicates pure viscous conductance. From the tabulated values it is clear that the conductance may be taken to be viscous, to within an accuracy of about 10 per cent, for $D\bar{P} \geq 500$ μ-cm. This then is the origin of the limits on molecular and viscous flow stated at the end of the last section.

It has been said that in the transition region there is a certain fraction of molecular flow and that the remainder is viscous flow. It is easy to show that this is not quite accurate. If it were, the equation could be written

$$\left.\begin{array}{c} J = f_1 + f_2(0.0152D\bar{P}) \\ f_1 + f_2 = 1 \end{array}\right\} \quad f_1 \text{ and } f_2 \text{ each} \leq 1$$

and a quick examination of the tabulated values shows that these equations cannot be satisfied. The explanation, of course, is that the assumptions on which the equations for molecular and viscous flow depend are no longer valid in the transition region, where both the molecule-molecule and molecule-wall collisions are important.

Table 1.2

Region	$D\bar{P}$, μ-cm	J*	$0.0152D\bar{P}$
Molecular	≤10	1.0	0.15
Transition	20	1.1	0.3
	40	1.4	0.6
	60	1.7	0.9
	80	2.0	1.2
	100	2.3	1.5
	200	3.8	3.0
	400	6.9	6.1
Viscous	600	9.9	9.1
	800	13	12
	1,000	16	15
	2,000	31	30
	4,000	62	61
	10,000	153	152

*Equation 49.

1.14 <u>Viscous Flow through Pipes: General Discussion.</u> In the last section the conductance of a long round pipe in the viscous-flow region is given by

$$C = \frac{\pi}{128\eta}\frac{D^4}{L}\bar{P} \quad \text{cgs units} \tag{50}$$

where D is the diameter of the pipe, L is the length of the pipe, $\bar{P}$ is the average pressure, and η is the viscosity of the gas. For air at 20°C this becomes

$$C = 0.182\frac{D^4}{L}\bar{P} \quad \text{liters/sec} \tag{51}$$

where D and L are in centimeters and $\bar{P}$ is in microns of mercury. These equations are accurate to 10 per cent for $D\bar{P} \geq 500\ \mu$-cm, i.e., if $\lambda < D/100$ is the m.f.p. for air.

The limitation of these equations to a long pipe means that the pipe impedance is so large that the entrance-aperture impedance can be neglected. If the pipe conductance is comparable to the aperture conductance, then the entrance-aperture conductance may be computed from Eq. 28 of Sec. 1.10 and combined as described in Sec. 1.11. In terms of impedance, 1/C, then

$$Z_{eff} = Z_{ap} + Z_{pipe}$$

From the values of the viscosity of various gases given in Appendix D, Eq. 51 may be multiplied by a simple ratio to get conductances for other gases. Thus, for the ratio C_{gas}/C_{air},

$$\begin{aligned} C_{H_2} &= 2.1\ C_{air} \\ C_{He} &= 0.93\ C_{air} \\ C_{H_2O\ vapor} &= 1.9\ C_{air} \\ C_{Ne} &= 0.58\ C_{air} \\ C_{N_2} &= 1.04\ C_{air} \end{aligned} \tag{52}$$

Thus the viscous flow of helium and nitrogen is for all practical purposes the same as that of air, but that of hydrogen and water vapor is appreciably better, and that of neon is appreciably worse. Curves of conductance vs. length for round pipe of various diameters and for air at 20°C are shown in Figs. 1.4a to c. Two values of r, namely, 0.1 and 0.9, have been used, and a number of values of $\bar{P}$ have been used, chosen so that $D\bar{P} \geq 500\ \mu$-cm.

Since the viscous conductance is a function of pressure, it is often more convenient to give equations for viscous flow in terms of the pressure gradient. Since $Q = \bar{P}V' = (P_1 - P_2)\ C$, Eq. 51 gives

$$\frac{P_1 - P_2}{L} = 5.5\,\frac{V'}{D^4}\quad \mu/\text{cm} \tag{53a}$$

or

$$V' = 0.182\left(\frac{P_1 - P_2}{L}\right) D^4\quad \text{liters/sec} \tag{53b}$$

where P_1 and P_2 are upstream and downstream pressure, respectively, in microns of mercury, L is length of pipe in centimeters, D is the diameter of the pipe in centimeters, and V′ is the volume flow in liters per second in the middle of the pipe where the pressure is $\overline{P}$. Usually the difference between the volume flow in the middle of the pipe and the volume flow at either end can be disregarded, since the

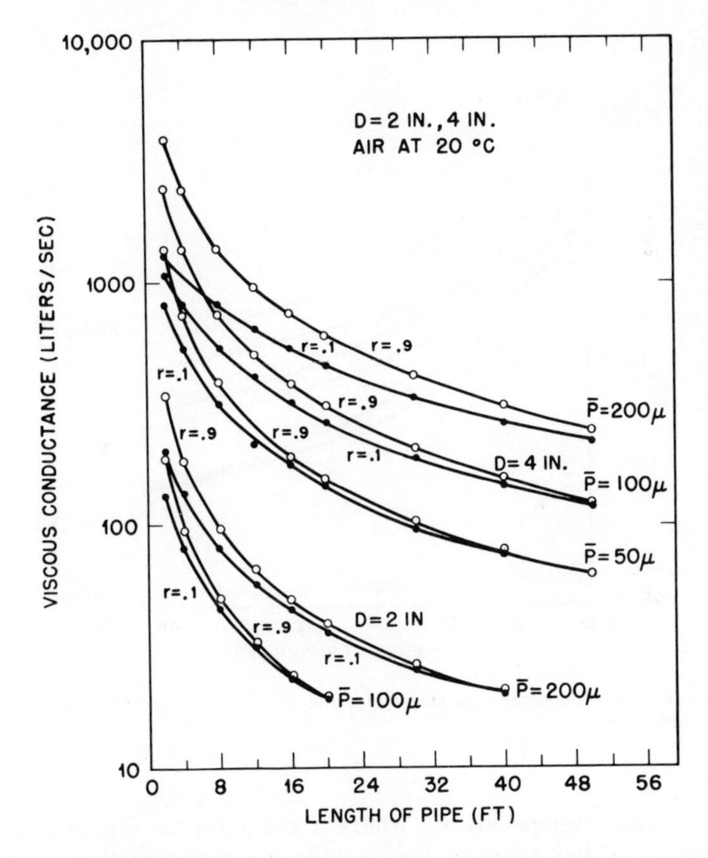

Fig. 1.4a—Viscous conductance of round pipe for various average pressures; diameter 2 and 4 in.; air, 20°C.

pressure drop along the pipe is usually small compared with the total pressure.

Relatively little data are available for viscous pipe conductances for noncircular cross sections. However, the following formula for the viscous conductance of a rectangular duct is offered:

$$C = 0.26Y \frac{a^2b^2}{L} \overline{P} \text{ liters/sec} \tag{54}$$

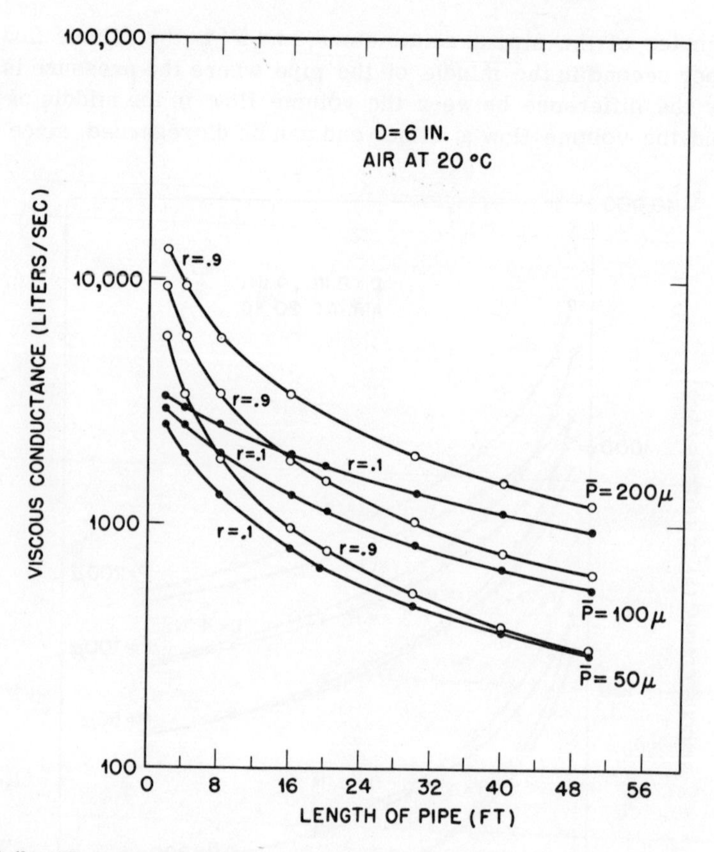

Fig. 1.4b—Viscous conductance of round pipe for various average pressures; diameter 6 in.; air, 20°C.

for air at room temperature. Where a and b are the dimensions, in centimeters, of the sides of the rectangular cross section, L is the length of duct in centimeters, and Y is taken from the accompanying table.

a/b	1.0	0.9	0.8	0.7	0.6	0.5	0.4	0.3	0.2	0.1
Y	1.00	0.99	0.98	0.95	0.90	0.82	0.71	0.58	0.42	0.23

Thus the conductance decreases markedly, for a given cross-sectional area, as the shape deviates from square.

Equation 54 can be rewritten in terms of volume flow V′ and pressure gradient $(P_1 - P_2)/L$ as before:

$$\frac{P_1 - P_2}{L} = \frac{3.8}{Y} \frac{V'}{a^2 b^2} \quad \mu/\text{cm}$$

$$V' = 0.26Y \frac{(P_1 - P_2)\, a^2 b^2}{L} \quad \text{liters/sec} \tag{55}$$

where a, b, and L are in centimeters and $\overline{P}$ is in microns of mercury.

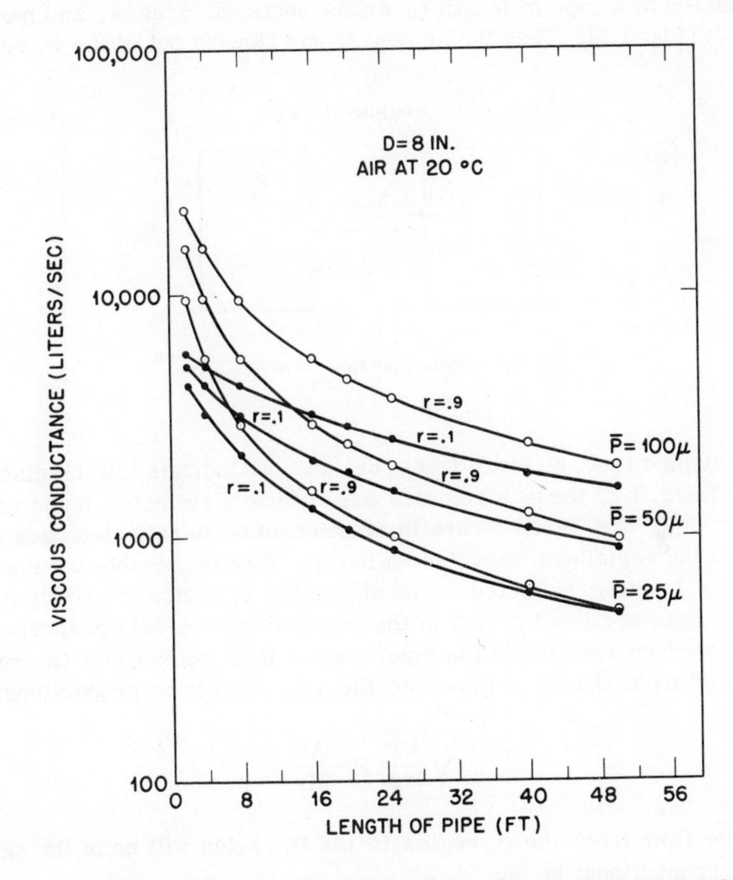

Fig. 1.4c—Viscous conductance of round pipe for various average pressures; diameter 8 in.; air, 20°C.

1.15 Molecular Flow through Pipes: General Discussion. (a) Knudsen's Formula. It is shown in kinetic theory that the amount of gas flowing out of a vessel, at pressure P_1, through an aperture of area A is

$$Q_1 = \sqrt{\frac{kT}{2\pi m}}\, P_1 A \quad \text{cgs units} \tag{56}$$

provided the size of the aperture is small compared to the vessel dimensions and provided the m.f.p. of the gas is large compared to the vessel dimensions. Here k is the Boltzmann constant, T is the absolute temperature, and m is the mass of a molecule. This is Eq. 30 of Sec. 1.10.

Consider, as in Sec. 1.12, two large vessels at pressures P_1 and P_2 connected by a pipe of length L, cross-sectional area A, and perimeter B (Fig. 1.5). Then the amount of gas flowing out of the P_1 region

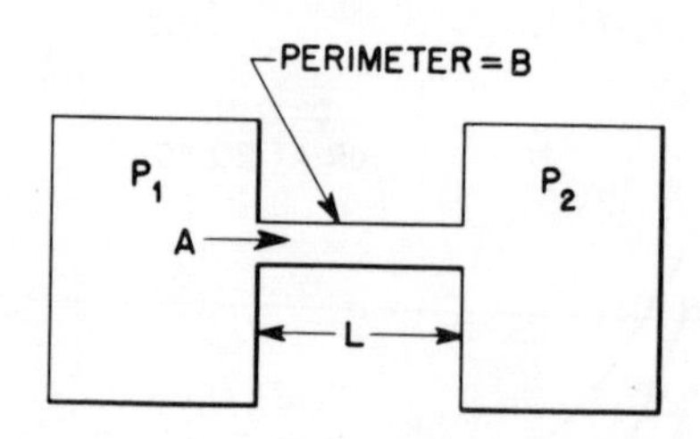

Fig. 1.5—Molecular flow through a pipe.

into the pipe is Q_1 as given in Eq. 56. But, as indicated in the discussion of Sec. 1.2, these molecules are diffusely reflected at the walls of the pipe, and hence a certain fraction of Q_1 is reflected back into P_1, and the remainder is reflected into P_2. It is reasonable to suppose that the fraction reflected forward into the P_2 region is proportional to the cross-sectional area A of the pipe and is inversely proportional to the surface area BL of the pipe. Hence it is reasonable to expect the flow from the P_1 region into the P_2 region to be proportional to

$$\sqrt{\frac{kT}{2\pi m}}\, P_1 \frac{A^2}{BL}$$

But the flow from the P_2 region to the P_2 region will be of the same form, proportional to

$$\sqrt{\frac{kT}{2\pi m}}\, P_2 \frac{A^2}{BL}$$

since the pressures P_1 and P_2 are assumed to be so low that intermolecular collisions are rare. Thus the net flow out of the P_1 region is

$$Q = (\text{constant}) \sqrt{\frac{kT}{2\pi m}}\, (P_1 - P_2) \frac{A^2}{BL}$$

This was first formulated in quantitative form by Knudsen, who gave $^{16}/_{3}$ as the constant of proportionality. For reasons that appear below, the constant of proportionality $^{16}/_{3}$ K will be used and then the conductance of the pipe is

$$C = \frac{Q}{P_1 - P_2} = \frac{16}{3} K \sqrt{\frac{kT}{2\pi m}} \frac{A^2}{BL} \text{ cgs units} \tag{57}$$

where K is a dimensionless constant, k is the Boltzmann constant, T is the absolute temperature, m is the mass of a molecule, A is the cross-sectional area of the pipe, B is the perimeter of the pipe, and L is the length of the pipe. The m.f.p. must be at least of the order of the cross-sectional dimensions of the pipe. Thus

$$C = 61.8K \frac{A^2}{BL} \text{ liters/sec} \tag{58}$$

for molecular conductance in air at 20°C and with dimensions in centimeters. In Knudsen's form of these equations, K is equal to 1 (Loeb,[2] pp. 290 ff.). But in the modern treatments of the molecular-flow equations there are certain integrals involved which depend on the geometrical form of the cross section. For a circular cross section, K is equal to 1, and the simple equation is correct. For a noncircular cross section, K is not generally equal to 1, because a rigorous evaluation of the integrals shows a deviation from the Knudsen equation that is sometimes quite appreciable (see Kennard,[1] p. 304, for derivation of the general equation). In the paragraphs that follow all the information now available on the best value of the correcting factor K will be presented.

(b) Circular Pipe. Here $A = \pi D^2/4$, $B = \pi D$, and $K = 1$.

$$C = \frac{\pi}{3} \sqrt{\frac{kT}{2\pi m}} \frac{D^3}{L} \text{ cgs units} \tag{59}$$

$$= 12.1 \frac{D^3}{L} \text{ liters/sec}$$

for molecular conductance in long circular pipe in air at 20°C and with D and L in centimeters. If the pipe is short the conductance of the entrance aperture must be included. Hence

$$\frac{1}{C} = \frac{1}{C_p} + \frac{1}{C_{ap}}$$

$$C_p = 12.1 \frac{D^3}{L}$$

$$C_{ap} = 11.6 \frac{AA_0}{A_0 - A}$$

$$= \frac{9.11D^2}{1 - (D/D_0)}$$

where D is the diameter of the pipe and aperture and D_0 is the diameter of the region from which the gas flows into the pipe. Substituting and solving,

$$C = \frac{12.1 \frac{D^3}{L}}{1 + 1.33 \frac{D}{L} \left(1 - \frac{D^2}{D_0^2}\right)} \tag{60}$$

or

$$C = 12.1 \frac{D^3}{L} \alpha \quad \text{liters/sec}$$

for molecular conductance of short pipe in air at 20°C and where α can be tabulated as a function of L/D. Now the equation is in fact not strictly accurate, because a kinetic-theory analysis of the end effects shows that considering the aperture as a series conductance is not quite right. Clausing[10] (discussed in Loeb,[2] p. 306) has determined the value of α with about 1 per cent accuracy. In Table 1.3, α is given as determined by Clausing and as computed here. Assume $D/D_0 \ll 1$.

The last line of Table 1.3 shows that for $L \leq 0.1D$, $\alpha = \frac{3}{4}L/D$, to within 10 per cent accuracy, which, if substituted in Eq. 60, gives only the aperture conductance. For $L > 20D$, use $\alpha = 1$, i.e., neglect the aperture, to within about 10 per cent. Clausing's value of α can be used for maximum accuracy. The values of Clausing's α have been computed from the equation

$$\alpha = \frac{15\left(\frac{L}{D}\right) + 12\left(\frac{L}{D}\right)^2}{20 + 38\left(\frac{L}{D}\right) + 12\left(\frac{L}{D}\right)^2}$$

which is taken from Kennard,[1] p. 308.

If $D < 0.2D$, then $(D/D_0)^2 < 0.04$, and the tabulated values of α are good to within at least 5 per cent. If, however, $D > 0.2D$, then the effective conductance of the aperture is larger, and the full formula for α from Eq. 60 must be used. Curves of conductance vs. length for round pipe of various diameters are shown in Fig. 1.6. In calculating these curves it has been assumed that $D/D_0 \ll 1$. Values of α calculated from Eq. 60 have been used.

Table 1.3

L/D	α*	α†	¾L/D
0.05	0.036	0.036	0.037
0.08	0.055	0.056	0.060
0.1	0.068	0.070	0.075
0.2	0.13	0.13	0.27
0.4	0.21	0.23	
0.6	0.28	0.31	
0.8	0.30	0.38	
1.0	0.38	0.43	
2	0.54	0.60	
4	0.70	0.75	
6	0.77	0.82	
8	0.81	0.86	
10	0.84	0.88	
20	0.91	0.94	
40	0.95	0.97	
60	0.97	0.98	
80	0.98	0.98	
≥100	1	1	

*Clausing.
†Equation 60.

(c) Circular Annulus. For the region between two circular concentric pipes (Fig. 1.7),

$$A = \frac{\pi}{4}(D_1^2 - D_2^2)$$

and

$$B = \pi(D_1 + D_2)$$

Hence Eq. 57 becomes

$$C = \frac{\pi}{3}\sqrt{\frac{kT}{2m}}\frac{(D_1^2 - D_2^2)}{(D_1 + D_2)L} K \quad \text{cgs units} \tag{61}$$

$$= 12.1 \frac{(D_1 - D_2)^2 (D_1 + D_2)}{L} K \quad \text{liters/sec}$$

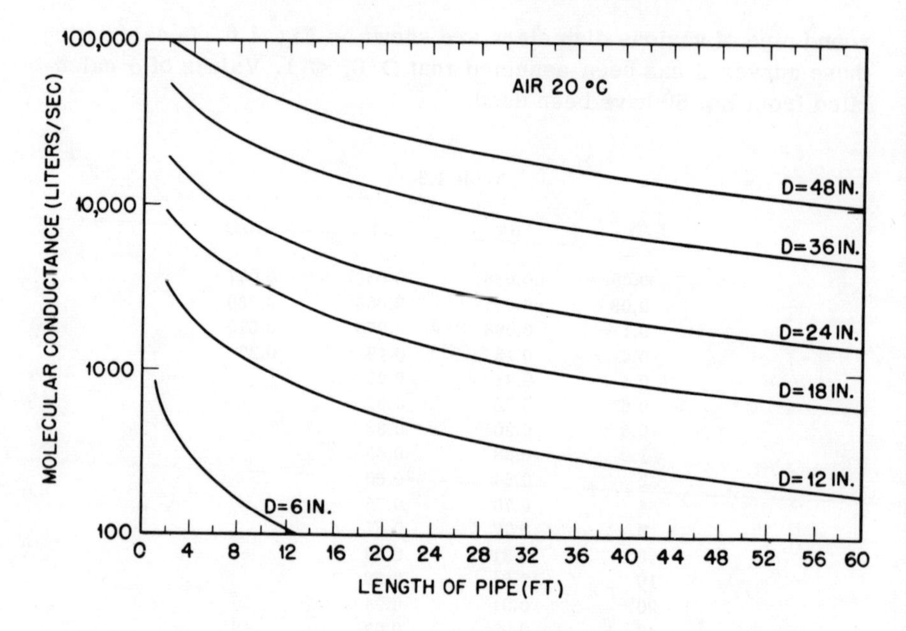

Fig. 1.6—Molecular conductance of round pipe for various diameters; air, 20°C.

for molecular conductance of annulus for air at 20°C, where D and L are in centimeters. For D = 0, this becomes Eq. 59, as it should. K is a function of D_2/D_1, as follows:

D_2/D_1	0	0.259	0.500	0.707	0.866	0.966
K	1	1.072	1.154	1.254	1.430	1.675

These values are taken from Barrett and Bosanquet.[11] They refer of course to a long annulus, for example, L > 20D. For shorter values the impedance of the entering aperture must be considered, i.e.,

$$Z = Z_{ap} + Z_{pipe}$$

(d) Rectangular Duct. In this case (see Fig. 1.8), A = ab, and B = 2 (a + b); hence Eq. 57 becomes

$$\begin{aligned} C &= \frac{8}{3}\sqrt{\frac{kT}{2\pi m}}\,\frac{a^2b^2}{(a+b)\,L}\,K \quad \text{cgs units} \\ &= 30.9\,\frac{a^2b^2}{(a+b)\,L}\,K \end{aligned} \tag{62}$$

for molecular conductance in a long rectangular duct for air at 20°C and with L, a, and b in centimeters, where K is given by the equation (from Clausing, quoted in Loeb,[2] p. 306)

$$K = \frac{3}{8}\frac{(1+r)}{r^2}\left\{ r \ln\left(r + \sqrt{1+r^2}\right) + r^2 \ln \frac{1+\sqrt{1+r^2}}{r} + \frac{1}{3}\left[1 + r^3 - (1+r^2)^{3/2}\right]\right\}$$

where

$$r = \frac{b}{a} \leq 1$$

Using this equation, the following values of K are computed (Barrett and Bosanquet[11]):

$r = b/a$	1	0.667	0.500	0.333	0.200	0.125	0.100
K	1.108	1.126	1.151	1.198	1.297	1.400	1.444

These values are, of course, for a long rectangular duct. If the conductance of the aperture is comparable to the conductance of the duct, it must be taken into account in the usual fashion.

(e) Equilaterally Triangular Duct. For this case K has been computed in Barrett and Bosanquet[11] to be 1.24. Now $A = \sqrt{3}a^2/4$, and $B = 3a$ (Fig. 1.9); hence, if $K = 1.24$, Eq. 57 becomes

$$\begin{aligned} C &= 0.413 \sqrt{\frac{kT}{2\pi m}}\frac{a^3}{L} \quad \text{cgs units} \\ &= 4.79 \frac{a^3}{L} \end{aligned} \tag{63}$$

for molecular conductance in a long equilaterally triangular duct for air at 20°C, where a and L are in centimeters. If the conductance of the aperture is comparable to the conductance of the duct, it must be included in the computation in the usual fashion.

(f) Thin Slitlike Tube. Now $A = ab$, and $B = 2\ (a + b) = 2a$, since $a \gg b$ (see Fig. 1.10). Hence

$$\begin{aligned} C &= \frac{8}{3} \sqrt{\frac{kT}{2\pi m}}\frac{ab^2}{L} K \quad \text{cgs units} \\ &= 30.9 \frac{ab^2}{L} K \end{aligned} \tag{64}$$

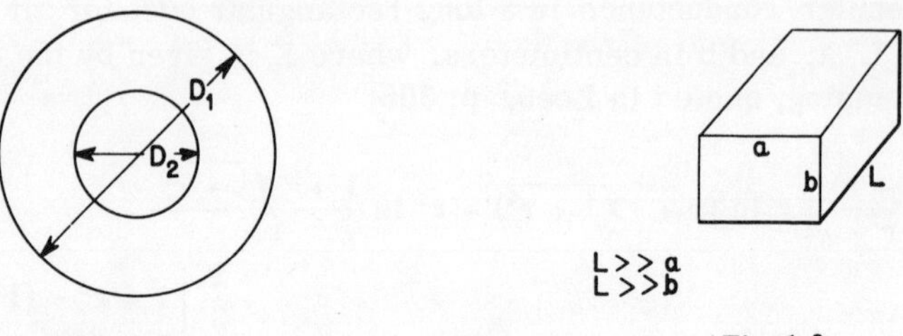

Fig. 1.7—Circular annulus.

Fig. 1.8—Rectangular duct. $L \gg a$; $L \gg b$.

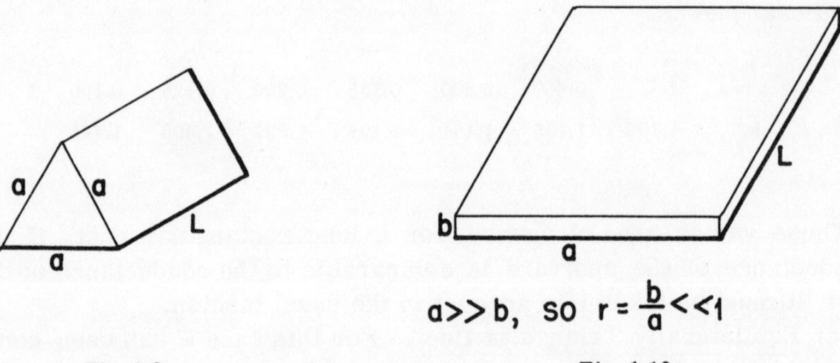

Fig. 1.9—Equilaterally triangular duct.

Fig. 1.10—Thin slitlike tube; $a \gg b$; hence $r = b/a \ll 1$.

for air at 20°C and with a, b, and L in centimeters. Clausing (quoted in Loeb,[2] p. 306) gives the following values of K:

L/b	0.1	0.2	0.4	0.8	1	2	3	4	5	10	>10
K	0.036	0.068	0.13	0.22	0.26	0.40	0.52	0.60	0.67	0.94	ln ⅜ (L/b)

Then, for a long slitlike tube,

$$C = 11.6 \frac{ab^2}{L} \ln \frac{L}{b} \quad \text{liters/sec}$$

$$= 27 \frac{ab^2}{L} \log \frac{L}{b} \qquad (65)$$

for air at 20°C and with a, b, and L in centimeters.

If the conductance of the entrance aperture is comparable to the conductance of the tube, it is included in the computation in the usual fashion.

(g) Ducts of Other Shapes. The mathematical aspects of the evaluation of the integrals involved in cross-sectional shapes other than those discussed here are very involved. Ordinarily a numerical solution of the equations is not worth the trouble involved. The best procedure for other shapes would be to estimate the factor K to be used in correcting Eq. 57. This estimate should be based on a study of the

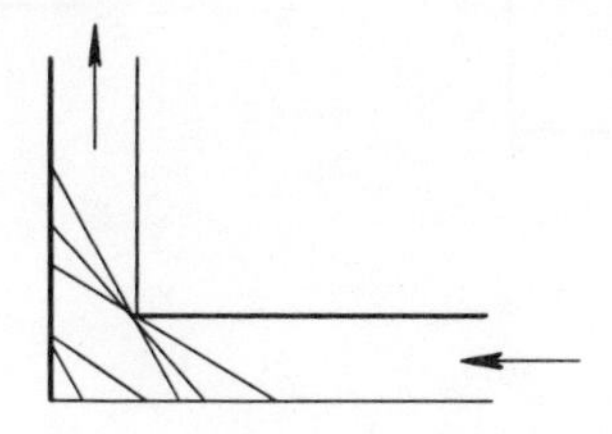

Fig. 1.11—Right-angle bend in pipe.

K factors given for the shape most nearly approximating the desired shape. Since most vacuum calculations do not require more than 10 per cent accuracy, this should usually be satisfactory.

(h) Bends, Elbows, etc. It is often assumed that bends in a pipe will introduce considerable resistance to molecular flow. Probably this is based on a visualization of the process of molecular flow as resembling viscous flow, with a contraction of the stream lines in the neighborhood of an obstruction. This is incorrect. Consider a pipe with a bend, as shown in Fig. 1.11. Gas molecules flowing from the left will be diffusely reflected by the walls near the bend, but, since the reflection is diffuse, the position of the wall doing the reflecting is not known and hence the probability of being reflected onward in the pipe is the same as the probability of being reflected backward, and the situation is no different from that in a straight pipe. But the m.f.p. of the molecules in the neighborhood of the bend is reduced, as indicated by the lines drawn in the figure. This will decrease the conductance in the neighborhood of the bend, so that it is reasonable to suppose that the effective length of the bend is greater than the axial length, i.e.,

$$L_{eff} > L_{axial}$$

Suppose now that the pipe is separated at the corner and connected into a large box as in Fig. 1.12. The gas will flow freely into the box, but the gas in the box must find the pipe opening before flowing downward, and therefore the conductance of one pipe aperture in the series conductance must be included, assuming the box to be so large that it

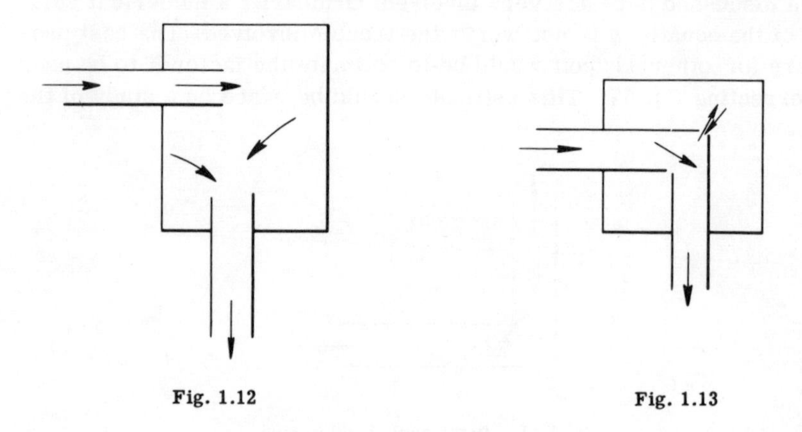

Fig. 1.12—Pipes at right angles leading into large vessel; wide spacing at ends.

Fig. 1.13—Pipes at right angles leading into large vessel; close spacing at ends.

has infinite conductance. But from Eq. 60 in the discussion of short circular pipes it follows at once that the effective length in this case is given by

$$L_{eff} = L_{axial} + 1.33D$$

Suppose, however, that the pipes are pushed almost but not quite together, as in Fig. 1.13. Now most of the gas flowing from the left goes into the downward pipe, so that the downward-flowing gas does not have to come entirely from the box. We should expect the conductance in this case to be somewhat greater than in the previous case, so that here

$$L_{eff} < L_{axial} + 1.33D$$

From these considerations, the general rule may be postulated that, for molecular flow around a bend of any angle, the effective length to be used in computing the conductance of the pipe is somewhere in the range

$$L_{axial} < L_{eff} < L_{axial} + 1.33D \qquad (66)$$

If there are n bends in series, then

$$L_{axial} < L_{eff} < L_{axial} + 1.33nD \qquad (67)$$

This equation will usually be an adequate guide for vacuum design purposes. L and D are in the same units.

Although no great amount of experimental data is available on molecular flow through bends and elbows, it has been shown (Klose[9]) that they do not offer large impedance under usual conditions, which is consistent with Eq. 66.

1.16 Thermal Transpiration and Diffusion through Porous Barriers. Consider a large volume of gas at pressure P_1 and tempera-

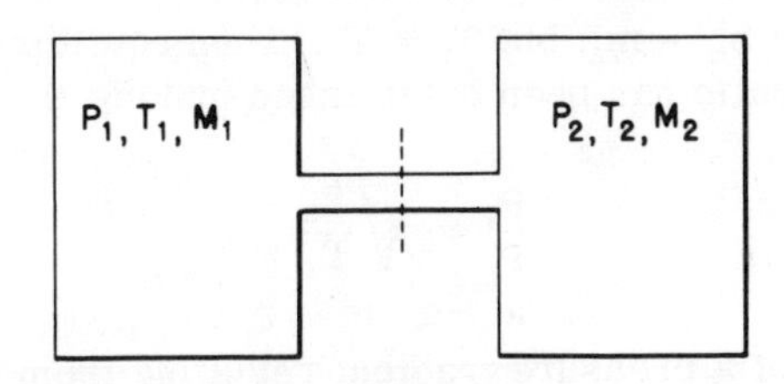

Fig. 1.14—Thermal transpiration and diffusion for two regions connected by a narrow tubulation.

ture T_1 with molecules of mass m_1, connected through a narrow tubulation to another large volume of gas at pressure P_2 and temperature T_2, and with molecules of mass m_2 (see Fig. 1.14). Suppose that initially there is a shutter at the center of the tubulation separating the two gases and that the m.f.p. of both gases is at least comparable to the size of the vessels. When the shutter is opened the molecules will flow in both directions. If $T_1 \neq T_2$, or $m_1 \neq m_2$, then the equilibrium condition is not necessarily equality of pressure but is instead the condition that an equal number of molecules cross the center plane in each direction. From the equation of state, Eq. 3 of Sec. 1.2, $Q = PV' = N'kT$, and from Eq. 56 of Sec. 1.15 and the subsequent discussion, it follows that the net number of molecules flowing from the P_1 region into the P_2 region is

$$N_1' - N_2' = \frac{Q_1}{kT_1} - \frac{Q_2}{kT_2} = \text{constant} \times \left(\frac{P_1}{\sqrt{m_1 T_1}} - \frac{P_2}{\sqrt{m_2 T_2}} \right) \qquad (68)$$

where N' is the number of molecules crossing the center plane per second, k is the Boltzmann constant, T is the absolute temperature, P is the pressure, and m is the mass of a molecule. The unspecified constant is a geometrical factor, depending on the size and shape of the tubulation.

First, suppose that the tubulation is a channel in a porous barrier in a vessel at a uniform temperature $T_1 = T_2$. Then if

$$\frac{P_1}{\sqrt{m_1}} = \frac{P_2}{\sqrt{m_2}}$$

there will be no transfer of molecules, and the two regions will be in equilibrium. Diffusion will be taking place but at an equal rate in the two directions. Likewise, if $P_1 = P_2$, at the start the transfer of molecules will be proportional to $(1/\sqrt{m_1} - 1/\sqrt{m_2})$, and gas will diffuse into the region of the heavier gas, raising the pressure there.

Second, assume $m_1 = m_2$, but $T_1 \neq T_2$. Then equilibrium will result when a pressure ratio has been established making $N_1' - N_2' = 0$. Then

$$\frac{P_2}{P_1} = \sqrt{\frac{T_2}{T_1}} \tag{69}$$

This phenomenon of a pressure gradient resulting from an established temperature gradient is known as "thermal transpiration." This can be of some importance in unequally heated apparatus. For example, a high-temperature vacuum furnace, operating at 2000°C, connected to a pressure-measuring device at room temperature will actually be $\sqrt{2273/293} = 2.8$ times higher in pressure than the reading indicates. Similarly a part of the apparatus that is at liquid-air temperature will actually be lower in pressure by the ratio $\sqrt{86/293} = 0.54$ than other parts of the apparatus at room temperature. Thus, when studying vacuum processes at very high or very low temperatures, thermal transpiration must be taken into account in determining true pressures.

Consider three regions connected by two narrow tubulations, as indicated in Fig. 1.15. Then from Eq. 69

$$P_1 = P_2\sqrt{\frac{T_1}{T_2}} \quad \text{and} \quad P_2 = P_3\sqrt{\frac{T_2}{T_3}}$$

therefore

$$P_1 = P_3\sqrt{\frac{T_1}{T_3}}$$

and thus the relation between regions 1 and 3 is not affected by the intermediate region 2. The following is, in fact, a general result: Any two low-pressure regions, connected by narrow tubulations, have their pressures and temperatures related by Eq. 69, independent of intermediate temperature conditions.

The last result is very convenient and justifies neglecting thermal transpiration for most applications. For example, a liquid-air trap

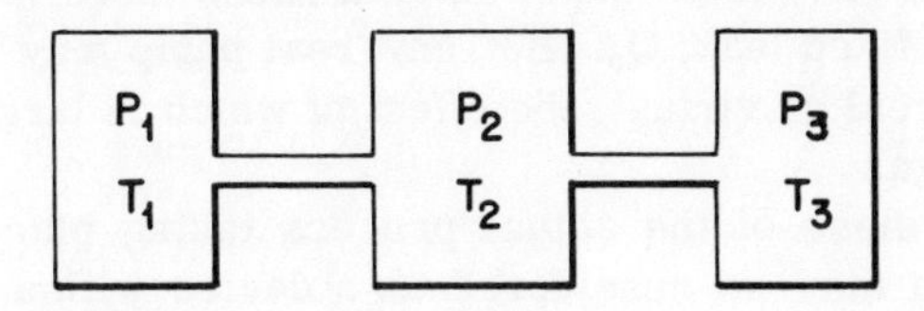

Fig. 1.15—Thermal transpiration and diffusion for three regions connected by narrow tubulations.

between a gauge and a tank does not falsify the pressure readings. The results of this section apply only when the m.f.p. is large compared with the apertures in question.

1.17 Pumping Speed of Vacuum Pumps. In Sec. 1.9 the pumping speed of a vacuum system was defined by the equation

$$S = \frac{Q}{P} \tag{70}$$

where $Q = PV'$ is the amount of gas flowing past any plane of the system. Hence $S = V'$, the volumetric flow past the plane in question. Since the flow Q has the same value everywhere in the vacuum circuit it can be measured in any part of the circuit, but the P of Eq. 70 must be measured in the same plane where the pumping speed S is required.

The mechanical pumps and diffusion pumps now in use are characterized by a pumping speed that is relatively constant over a wide range of pressure. In the case of a mechanical pump, an eccentric cylinder rotates with a frequency f and in each revolution sweeps out a certain volume of gas, V_1. Thus the speed of the pump is $S_p = fV_1$. In the case of a diffusion pump there is a constant speed S_p that depends on the velocity of the oil crossing the jets, which in turn depends on such things as the power input to the boiler, and the specific heat, specific gravity, and viscosity of the liquid (see discussion by Langmuir[12]).

On the other hand, there are certain processes in the pump that set a limit below which the system cannot be evacuated. In a mechanical pump a certain amount of gas is returned to the system each cycle, owing, for example, to the fact that oil which has been exposed momentarily to the atmosphere is carried around by the cylinder to the vacuum region and that there some of the dissolved gas escapes. Thus gas is being returned to the system at some fixed rate Q_0, independent of P. In the gas of a diffusion pump, the liquid that has been exposed to the backing pressure is returned to the system, and there some dissolved gas may escape. In both cases there is the equivalent of some small fixed leak, Q_0. But any real pump may very well have a small leak, real or virtual, the effect of which is larger than that of the dissolved gas.

Thus, regardless of the actual process taking place in the pump, any real pump may be considered as a device with a fixed speed S_p and a fixed leak Q_0. Then the net removal of gas from the system is

$$Q = S_p P - Q_0 = S_p P \left(1 - \frac{Q_0}{S_p P}\right)$$

The limiting pressure P_0 is reached when $Q = 0$, and hence $Q_0 = S_p P_0$ Then, setting $S = Q/P$, the equation becomes

$$S = S_p \left(1 - \frac{P_0}{P}\right) \tag{71}$$

Here S is the effective pumping speed at pressure P of a pump of speed S_p whose base pressure is P_0. The accompanying graph of Eq. 71, which is shown in Fig. 1.16, makes it clear that S must be considered to be different from the fixed speed of the pump S_p only when the pressure is near the base pressure, e.g., for $P < 10P_0$. In fact, Eq. 71 should be considered a representation of the effective pumping speed only in the neighborhood of the base pressure P_0. At much higher pressures other phenomena, too complex to be considered in the simple derivation of Eq. 71, enter into the picture, so that S_p is actually a function of the pressure under some circumstances.

It will be seen in the next section that the standard methods of measuring pumping speed actually measure S_p and not the effective speed S, regardless of the pressure at which the measurements are made.

Suppose now that a vessel at pressure P_1 is connected through an impedance Z to a pump of effective speed $S_2 = S_p[1 - (P_0/P_2)]$, where P_2 is the pressure at the entrance to the pump. The determination of the pumping speed S_1 and base pressure at the entrance to the impedance Z is desired. Then, from Eq. 24, Sec. 1.9,

$$\frac{1}{S_1} = Z + \frac{1}{S_2}$$

Since $P_1 S_1 = (P_1 - P_2)/Z(= Q)$, S_2 and then P_2 may be eliminated from the equation, making it

$$S = \frac{1}{Z + 1/S_p}\left(1 - \frac{P_0}{P_1}\right) \tag{72}$$

This, of course, is just the result that is to be expected, for it means that the base pressure in the vessel is just the base pressure of the

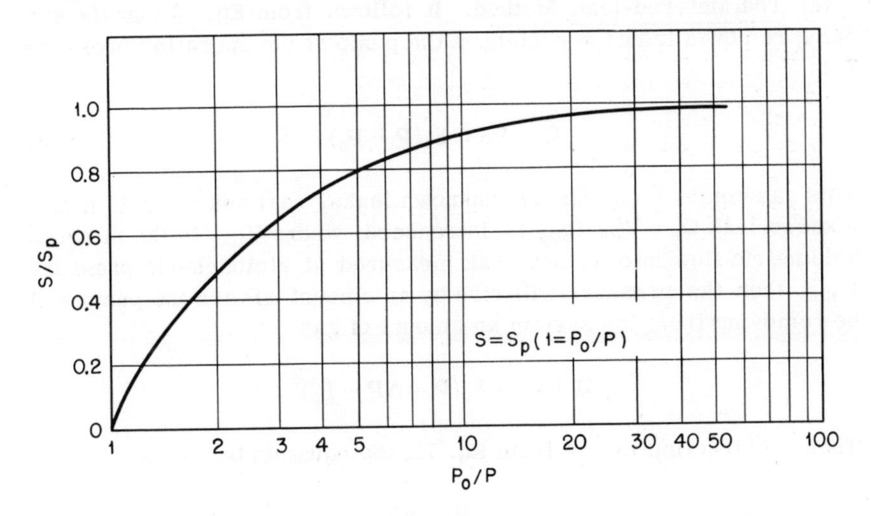

Fig. 1.16—Pumping speed of a pump near the base pressure P .

pump, while the pumping speed at pressures well above base pressure is that found by the usual equation, considering the pump of speed S_p to be in series with the impedance Z.

The equations developed in this section apply to either molecular or viscous flow, since they are based only on the assumption of a flow $Q = PV'$, which is constant throughout the vacuum circuit. A comparison of Eq. 72 with Eq. 33 of Sec. 1.10 shows that in the pressure region of molecular flow a pump is equivalent to an aperture and a series impedance, even in the neighborhood of the base pressure. This is also true in the pressure region of viscous flow, provided the pressure P_2 of Eq. 29, Sec. 1.10 is below the critical pressure.

1.18 Measurement of Pumping Speed. In this section, two standard methods of measuring the speeds of pumps will be briefly noted.

In Sec. 1.17 it was shown that, although pumps in general are characterized by a fixed pumping speed S_p, in the neighborhood of the base pressure P_0 the effective pumping speed is less and is given by

$$S = S_p \left(1 - \frac{P_0}{P}\right) \tag{73}$$

It will be shown here that what is actually measured is S_p and not S, even if the measurements are made near base pressure. It should be remembered that P_0 is the base pressure of the pump itself and not of the whole system, which may have a higher base pressure due to other leaks.

(a) The Metered-leak Method. It follows from Eq. 73 that the gas being removed from the system by the pump at the operating pressure P is

$$Q = PS = S_p(P - P_0) \tag{74}$$

This gas comes from various unknown leaks, real and virtual. If now a known leak $Q_1 = V'_{atm} P_{atm}$ is introduced, where V_{atm} is the metered volumetric flow into the new leak measured at atmospheric pressure P_{atm}, then the pressure will rise by an amount ΔP and the pump will be removing from the system an amount of gas

$$Q + Q_1 = S_p(P + \Delta P - P_0) \tag{75}$$

Then substracting Eq. 74 from Eq. 75, the equation becomes

$$S_p = \frac{P_{atm} V'_{atm}}{\Delta P} \tag{76}$$

This gives the pumping speed of the pump in terms of the pressure rise ΔP due to the metered leak V'_{atm} measured at atmospheric pressure P_{atm}. If P_{atm} and ΔP are in the same units, S_p will be in the units V'_{atm}, usually liters per second.

Thus the metered-leak method of pump-speed measurement requires a flowmeter for measuring V'_{atm} and a pressure gauge for measuring ΔP. The pressure gauge does not need a known zero point, but it requires a scale at least as good as the accuracy desired in S_p.

(b) The Rate-of-rise Method. Consider a vacuum system whose volume is V when the pump is closed from the system. The operating pressure is P_1 and the amount of gas due to all leaks, real and virtual, is Q_1. Then, as in Eq. 74, the pump is removing the gas in amount

$$Q_1 = S_p(P_1 - P_0)$$

If the pump valve is now closed, the pressure begins to rise at a rate P_1' given by

$$Q_1 = \frac{d}{dt}(PV) = V\left(\frac{dP}{dt}\right)_1 = VP_1' = S_p(P_1 - P_0)$$

If now a new leak Q_2 is added, the corresponding equations are

$$Q_1 + Q_2 = VP_2' = S_p(P_2 - P_0)$$

Hence, after combining equations,

$$S_p = \frac{P_2' - P_1'}{P_2 - P_1} V \tag{77}$$

This gives the pumping speed S_p in terms of the rate of rise of pressure P_1' due to leaks that give an operating pressure P_1, the rate of rise P_2' due to additional leaks that give an operating pressure P_2, and the known volume V of the system. This method has the advantage that the size of the leaks does not need to be determined, and the disadvantage that the volume V must be known. As before, the value of S_p is independent of the zero point of the pressure scale but now in addition is independent of any scale factor in the pressure gauge, provided that the pressure scale is linear.

1.19 Evacuation Rate. Consider a vessel of volume V being evacuated by a pump of speed S_p, which is taken to be the speed of the pump at the vessel through any connecting lines and not the speed at the inlet to the pump. Assume first that the base pressure of the pump and system is negligible. Then the flow of gas out of the vessel is $Q = PS_p$. As a result, the pressure must be dropping at a rate dP/dt given by

$$Q = -\frac{d}{dt}(PV) = -V\frac{dP}{dt}$$

Equating these gives the differential equation

$$\frac{dP}{P} = -\frac{S_p}{V}dt \tag{78}$$

which can be integrated to

$$P = P_1 e^{-S_p t/V} \tag{79}$$

Here P is the pressure at time t in a vessel of volume V that is being evacuated by a pump of speed S_p. P_1 is the pressure in the vessel at the initial time t = 0. The base pressure is assumed to be negligible. Equation 79 is equivalent to

$$t = \frac{V}{S_p} \ln \frac{P_1}{P} = 2.30 \frac{V}{S_p} \log \frac{P_1}{P} \tag{80}$$

From this it may be found that the pressure drops to half value in time

$$t_{1/2} = 0.69 \frac{V}{S_p} \approx \frac{2}{3} \frac{V}{S_p} \tag{81}$$

After that, the pressure reaches $\frac{1}{4}P_1$ at time $2t_{1/2}$ and $\frac{1}{8}P_1$ at $t = 3t_{1/2}$. In general

$$\text{Pressure} = \frac{1}{2^n} P_1 \qquad \text{at time } t = nt_{1/2} \tag{82}$$

This is a convenient rule to remember for quick mental estimates of evacuation rates. It applies only when the pressure is well above the base pressure of the system. This base pressure can be just the base pressure of the pump or more often will be due to leaks and water vapor in the vessel being evacuated.

The vapor pressure of water at 20°C is 17 mm Hg, so that a system which is moist at the start will not follow this exponential pump-down rule below 17 mm Hg, until the water vapor has been pumped out of the walls. Under some circumstances this takes a very long time.

Suppose now there is leakage into the system, resulting in a base pressure P_0 below which the system will not go. This could be a leak into the pump, as discussed in Sec. 1.17, or a leak into some other part of the system. In either case the effective pumping speed becomes

$$S = S_p\left(1 - \frac{P_0}{P}\right)$$

which is Eq. 71 of Sec. 1.17. The differential equation (78) then becomes

$$\frac{dP}{P - P_0} = -\frac{S_p}{V}\,dt$$

which can be integrated to

$$(P - P_0) = (P_1 - P_0)\,e^{-S_p t/V} \tag{83}$$

where P_1 is the initial pressure at time $t = 0$, P_0 is the base pressure of the system, P is the pressure at time t, and S_p is the speed of the pump at the vessel of volume V being evacuated. Normally $P_0 \ll P_1$, and hence

$$P - P_0 = P_1 e^{-S_p t/V} \tag{84}$$

which shows that the pressure approaches its lowest value exponentially, at a rate given by Eq. 82.

This discussion thus far has assumed a large vessel, all parts of which can be considered to have the same pumping speed. The evacuation of a long pipe, for example, in which some parts are separated from the pump by more impedance than are other parts, can be considerably slower.

1.20 Pumping Speed of Cold Traps. If there is a cold trap in a system, the molecules of a condensable vapor that hit the trap will stick to it, and at the same time molecules will be evaporating from the trap because of the finite vapor pressure of the substance at the trap temperature. Thus the trap will act like an aperture of some effective area A, with the condensable vapor at pressure P_1 on one side and P_2 on the other, where P_1 is the partial pressure of the vapor in the vacuum system at the trap and P_2 is the vapor pressure of that material at the cold-trap temperature. From Eq. 33 of Sec. 1.10, the speed of a cold trap for a condensable vapor is then

$$S = 11.6\sqrt{\frac{29}{M}}\left(1 - \frac{P_2}{P_1}\right) A \quad \text{liters/sec} \tag{85}$$

for molecular flow where A is some effective area and M is the molecular weight of the condensable vapor.

As an example, consider carbon dioxide, which sublimes at $-78°C$ and has a vapor pressure of 7×10^{-7} mm Hg at $-187°C$. If a system is imagined at a pressure of 10^{-5} mm Hg, with 10 per cent CO_2 vapor, then $P_1 = 10^{-6}$ mm Hg and $P_2 = 7 \times 10^{-7}$ mm Hg, and $M = 44$. Substituting in Eq. 85,

$$S = 11.6\sqrt{\frac{29}{44}}\left(1 - \frac{7 \times 10^{-7}}{10^{-6}}\right) A = 2.8A \quad \text{liters/sec}$$

This gives the rate at which the trap is pumping CO_2. Water has a vapor pressure of about 10^{-21} mm Hg at $-187°C$ and a molecular weight of 18 so that a liquid-air trap has a speed of $11.6 \times 1.27A = 15A$ for water vapor at all working pressures. But the vapor pressure of water at $-78°C$ is 5.6×10^{-4} mm Hg; therefore the pumping speed of a CO_2 trap for water goes to zero when the partial pressure of the water vapor reaches that value.

The exact value of the effective area A can be determined only experimentally. It may, however, be estimated from the situation of the trap. If the cold trap is located near the center of the vessel, so that gas has free access to all sides, A will be the full cold area. But if part of the trap is obscured by being near a wall, for example, then the effective area A will be less.

The reasoning leading to Eq. 85 cannot be applied to pressure in the viscous region. In the molecular region of pressure the molecules that hit the trap surface are exactly those which would go through an aperture at that point. But for viscous flow the stream lines of the whole gas do not converge toward the trap, because the noncondensable vapors are not condensing there, and, since the different gases do not flow independently, the speed of the trap will be much lower than would be assumed if the reasoning leading to Eq. 85 were followed. Thus it is clear that, if a cold trap is used for vapors at pressure in the viscous-flow region, the system must be so designed that the gas is forced to flow close to the cold surface over as large an area as possible.

1.21 Method of Adapting Numerical Results to Gases Other Than Air and Temperatures Other Than 20°C. Most of the equations in this chapter have been computed for air at 20°C. In order to get numerical results for other gases and other temperatures it is not necessary to repeat the calculation starting with the cgs formula. For example, all molecular-conductance equations are of the form

$$C = \sqrt{\frac{2\pi kT}{m}} \times \text{geometrical factor}$$

where k is the Boltzmann constant, T is the absolute temperature, and m is the mass of a molecule. Now, $m \propto M$, the molecular weight, and therefore molecular conductances for other gases may be obtained by a simple ratio, i.e.,

$$C_{He} = \sqrt{\frac{29}{4}}\, C_{air} = 2.7C_{air}$$

$$C_{H_2O} = \sqrt{\frac{29}{18}}\, C_{air} = 1.3C_{air}$$

$$C_{CO_2} = \sqrt{\frac{29}{44}}\, C_{air} = 0.81C_{air}$$

Thus there is quite an appreciable variation in molecular conductance with molecular weight. The same factors apply to molecular pumping speed of apertures. Similarly, for other temperatures the molecular conductances are

$$C_{-187} = \sqrt{\frac{86}{293}}\, C_{20} = 0.55C_{20}$$

$$C_{0} = \sqrt{\frac{273}{293}}\, C_{20} = 0.96C_{20}$$

$$C_{100} = \sqrt{\frac{373}{293}}\, C_{20} = 1.2C_{20}$$

$$C_{1000} = \sqrt{\frac{1273}{293}}\, C_{20} = 2.1C_{20}$$

Thus it is clear that fluctuations in room temperature can be neglected in these conductances, but very high or very low temperatures might be significant.

This method was used in the paragraph on viscous conductances to get the conductance of gases other than air. Viscous conductances at temperatures other than room temperature are seldom of interest.

It should be pointed out again that the method of getting the m.f.p. at any pressure is simply to take the value from Appendix D, tabulated there for 1 μ Hg, and divide by the pressure in microns of mercury.

$$\lambda = \frac{\lambda_{1\mu}}{P}$$

The m.f.p. at temperatures other than the tabular value of 15°C can be found by the same method. Since

$$\lambda = \frac{kT}{\sqrt{2}\,\pi P \sigma^2}$$

it follows that

$$\lambda_{-187} = \frac{86}{288}\lambda_{15} = 0.30\lambda_{15}$$

$$\lambda_{0} = \frac{273}{288}\lambda_{15} = 0.95\lambda_{15}$$

$$\lambda_{100} = \frac{373}{288}\lambda_{15} = 1.3\lambda_{15}$$

$$\lambda_{1000} = \frac{1273}{288}\lambda_{15} = 4.5\lambda_{15}$$

Occasionally the shortening of the m.f.p. in the neighborhood of liquid-air temperature may be of significance.

1.22 Sample Calculation of a Vacuum System. To illustrate the use of the equations developed in this chapter, the calculation of a vacuum system designed for a specific job will be undertaken.

Suppose the operation of an ion source in a vacuum is desired, e.g., with a mass spectrograph. Suppose that the conditions of the problem to be investigated and the physical layout impose the following requirements:

1. Ion source to operate up to 3 μ, in a vacuum at least as good as 0.1 μ Hg.
2. Opening from ion source into vacuum tank, 1 sq cm.
3. Distance between vacuum tank and diffusion pump, 3 ft.
4. Volume of vacuum tank, 25 liters (0.88 cu ft).
5. Distance from diffusion pump to backing pump, 12 ft.

The gas flow from the ion sources into the vacuum tank is, by Eq. 33,

$$Q = 34.8\ \mu\text{-liters/sec}$$

Since the pressure ratio across the opening in the ion source is 0.1/3 = 0.03, the P_2/P_1 term in Eq. 33 may be disregarded. Then the speed required at the vacuum tank is, by Eq. 23, S = 350 liters/sec. Clearly, a 500-liter/sec diffusion pump would not be adequate through a long line. Suppose that a commercial pump rated at 1,000 liters/sec is found to be available. To be conservative, suppose that it can be relied upon to have a rate of 800 liters/sec even when not operating at optimum conditions. Then, if Z is the maximum allowable impedance of the 3-ft line,

$$Z = \frac{1}{350} - \frac{1}{800}$$

from Eq. 24. Then $C = 1/Z = 620$ liters/sec. This, of course, is a minimum allowable conductance. Then, substituting $L = 3$ ft $= 91$ cm into Eq. 59,

$$D^3 = LC/12.1 = 4{,}700$$

$$D = 17 \text{ cm} = 6.7 \text{ in.}$$

This is the diameter of a circular pipe with a conductance of 620 liters/sec, neglecting the end effect, i.e., neglecting the conductance of the entrance aperture. Moreover, in practice a commercially available size would be used, e.g., brass tubing 7¼ in. O.D. with a ⅛-in. wall. This has an inside diameter of 7 in., which is equal to 17.8 cm. Its conductance is then, by Eq. 59,

$$C = 12.1\,\frac{(17.8)^3}{91} = 740 \text{ liters/sec}$$

To get the end correction, take $L/D = 36/7 = 5.1$. From Table 1.3, $\alpha = 0.75$, and the conductance becomes $740 \times 0.75 = 560$ liters/sec.

It is clear from Eq. 60 that the value 560 liters/sec applies only if the diameter of the vacuum tank is very large compared with the 7-in. line, i.e., if $D^2/D_0^2 \ll 1$ in Eq. 60. For example, if $D_0 \approx 20$ in., $D^2/D_0^2 = 0.09$, $D/L\ (1 - D^2/D_0^2) = 7/36\ (0.91) = 0.177$, or $L/D = 5.6$, and from Table 1.3, $\alpha = 0.77$. Consequently the conductance would be changed very little.

If, however, the vacuum tank is about 10 in. in diameter, $D^2/D_0^2 = (7/10)^2 = 0.49$, $D/L\ (1 - D^2/D_0^2) = (7/36)\ (0.51) = 0.1$, so one would get $\alpha = 0.84$ (the value from Table 1.3 with $L/D = 10$). Then the conductance of a circular pipe 7 in. in diameter and 3 ft long conducting out of a 10-in. tank is

$$C = 740 \times 0.84 \text{ ft} = 640 \text{ liters/sec}$$

Thus it appears that the 7-in. pipe would barely be adequate if the vacuum tank is only 10 in. in diameter but would have too small a conductance if the tank is larger.

In any event, it would probably be wiser to allow somewhat of a safety factor and use an 8-in. pipe. This has a conductance between 800 and 1,100 liters/sec, depending on the size of the vacuum tank itself.

Suppose the diffusion pump chosen requires a backing pressure of 100 μ Hg or better. Then, since the gas handled is 35 μ-liters/sec at most, the required pumping speed at the outlet of the diffusion pump is Q/P = 35/100 = 0.35 liters/sec. Now the question is, will standard 1½-in. pipe be adequate? This has an inside diameter of about 1⁹⁄₁₆ in. = 3.96 cm. Then, from Eq. 51,

$$C = 0.182 \frac{D^4}{L} \bar{P} = 0.12\bar{P}$$

since $D^4 = 245$ and L = 12 ft = 366 cm.

If now a rather small backing pump is used, e.g., 0.5 liters/sec, the pressure at the pump is 35/0.5 = 70 μ Hg. Then $C > 0.12 \times 70 =$ 8.4 liters/sec, and thus the conductance of the line is very much greater than the speed of the backing pump. Consequently the speed at the diffusion pump is about the same as the speed at the backing pump, and this line and pump are sufficient. In fact, from Eq. 53 the drop in the line may be computed as follows:

$$P_1 - P_2 = \frac{V'L}{0.182D^4} = \frac{Q}{\bar{P}} \frac{L}{0.182D^4} = \frac{290}{\bar{P}}$$

Then, since P_2 = 70 μ Hg P = 74 μ Hg if P_1 is taken to be 72 μ Hg. So again it may be seen that this rather small backing pump and line will carry the load. It should be noted particularly that the components on the backing side are far smaller than on the high-vacuum side. Using a faster backing pump will not improve the high vacuum.

In practice it would probably be better, if economy is not an essential factor, to use a slightly larger backing pump, e.g., 1.5 liters/sec in the present case. This would give a backing pressure of 35/1.5 = 23 μ Hg. Although this would not improve the vacuum, it would be somewhat safer, in the sense that a burst of gas would be less likely to send the backing pressure above the maximum and stop the diffusion pump.

It is customary, in systems of this size, to have a valve at the throat of the diffusion pump with a "by-pass" or "roughing-down" valve allowing the backing pump to be used to rough the system down to the pressure where it is safe to open the diffusion pump. In the present case, since the conductance of the long backing line is 0.12P, the roughing-down speed can be taken to be just the speed of the mechanical pump.

Now the total volume of the tank (specified as 25 liters) plus the high-vacuum line (about 22 liters) is approximately 50 liters. Then, from Eq. 81, the half-pressure time is

$$t_{1/2} = \frac{2}{3}\frac{V}{S} = 70 \text{ sec} = 1.2 \text{ min for } S = 0.5 \text{ liters/sec}$$

$$= 20 \text{ sec} = 0.4 \text{ min for } S = 1.5 \text{ liters/sec}$$

Atmospheric pressure is now 7.6×10^5 μ Hg. Hence roughing down must be by a factor of about 10 before the diffusion pump will take over. Since $2^{14} \approx 16{,}000$, about 14 half-pressure times will be needed. Thus the roughing-down time will be about

$$1.2 \times 14 = 17 \text{ min for } S = 0.5 \text{ liters/sec}$$

$$0.4 \times 14 = 6 \text{ min for } S = 1.5 \text{ liters/sec}$$

These are not unreasonable times, and consequently the roughing system may be considered satisfactory.

The half-pressure time is $t_{1/2} = (2/3)(50/400) = 0.08$ sec for the diffusion pump, and, since $10^2/0.1 = 10^3 \approx 2^{10}$, the diffusion pump will in theory take the pressure from 100 to 0.1 μ Hg in $10 \times 0.08 = 0.8$ sec.

The figures given here as pump-down times contain the implicit assumption that the system contains only clean, dry gases. If this condition exists, the simple considerations above are reliable. But if there is water, oil, alcohol, or any other substance with appreciable vapor pressure on the walls, the pressure will not decrease until the substance has been evaporated. If the system has been open to air for many hours, it will be found that enough water vapor has been absorbed on the walls to slow the pump-down appreciably from the geometrically computed values.

Moreover, if, in the operation of the vacuum tank, gas is evolved owing to heating of the components, or if leaks develop in the vacuum wall, the gas that must be handled will be considerably greater than the simple original estimate. The amount of gas that must be handled owing to these causes can only be estimated from the experience of similar systems.

REFERENCES

1. E. H. Kennard, "Kinetic Theory of Gases," McGraw-Hill Book Company, Inc., New York, 1938.
2. L. B. Loeb, "Kinetic Theory of Gases," McGraw-Hill Book Company, Inc., New York, 1934.
3. J. H. Jeans, "Kinetic Theory of Gases," Cambridge University Press, London 1940.

4. J. D. Strong, "Procedures in Experimental Physics," Prentice-Hall, Inc., New York, 1939.
5. G. W. C. Kaye, "High Vacua," Longmans, Green & Co., Inc., New York, 1927.
6. J. Yarwood, "High Vacuum Technique," Chapman & Hall, Ltd., London, 1945.
7. L. Dunoyer, "Vacuum Practice," D. Van Nostrand Company, Inc., New York, 1926.
8. L. Prandtl, "The Physics of Solids and Fluids," Part II, Blackie and Sons, Ltd., Glasgow, 1936.
9. W. Klose, Physik. Z., 31: 503 (1930).
10. P. Clausing, Physica, 9: 65 (1929).
11. A. S. D. Barrett and C. H. Bosanquet, "Resistance of Ducts to Molecular Flow," Imperial Chemical Industries, Ltd. (Billingham Division), Report BR-296, November 1944.
12. I. Langmuir, Gen. Elec. Rev., 19: 1060 (1916).

Chapter 2

ELEMENTS OF THE VACUUM SYSTEM

By William E. Bush

2.1 The Conventional System. Vacuum systems capable of producing pressures below about 1 μ Hg are generally classified as "high-vacuum systems," and those used to produce the very low pressures (10^{-3} to 10^{-5} μ Hg) sometimes required in the laboratory might be classified as "ultrahigh-vacuum systems." Those of the first category are the subject of this chapter.

Systems of the moderately high-vacuum class generally consist of all or most of the following elements:

1. A high-speed high-vacuum diffusion pump capable of producing the desired degree of vacuum on the high-vacuum side and capable of maintaining a discharge pressure up to 20 or 30 μ Hg.

2. A booster diffusion pump of lower speed but capable of maintaining a discharge pressure of about 100 μ Hg or more. The discharge of the high-speed pump is thus boosted to a higher pressure by this pump.

3. A backing pump capable of handling the booster discharge and delivering it at atmospheric pressure. For this purpose a mechanical pump is generally used. In some cases, where the amount of gas to be handled is very large, steam ejectors of three or four stages have proved satisfactory.

4. A cold thimble to supplement the high-vacuum pump in the removal of water and other condensable materials from the system. Such thimbles are generally desirable in addition to the high-vacuum pump. Liquid air or liquid nitrogen is usually used as the refrigerant in such thimbles.

5. In some processes where water vapor is present in abundant quantities it is necessary to have a refrigerant trap ahead of the pump to prevent water vapor from reaching the fore pump. The temperature of such a trap must be $-70°C$ or lower in order to be effective. Dry ice (CO_2) is frequently used as a refrigerant.

6. Miscellaneous valves, interlocks, and pressure gauges required for the correct operation and control of the system. These are necessary and should be included in the initial design.

A typical arrangement is schematically illustrated in Fig. 2.1. The graph represents an approximate distribution of pressure through the system. Any exact statement of this kind, however, would depend upon the specific equipment used and the particular circumstances under which it was operated.

If extremely low pressures were required, the arrangement would necessarily undergo alterations, and getters of some sort would be added to the high-vacuum side of the system. In addition, a complete trap to condense any vapors from the diffusion pump itself would be required since pressures lower than the vapor pressure of the oil or other pumping fluids can be obtained only in this way. Such a trap is not necessary in the case of high-velocity ejector pumps using steam, for example, as long as the pressures involved are sufficiently high that viscous flow and not diffusion is the mode of transfer.

2.2 Mechanical Pumps. Most backing pumps now in use are mechanical pumps of a volumetric-displacement type in several varieties and a wide range of capacities. The capacity of these pumps is stated in terms of the volume displaced by the pumping mechanism per unit of time. Consequently the capacity of such a pump is a function of the speed at which it is driven. Pumps of this kind are made in capacities of from a few tenths up to about 700 cu ft/min (cfm). Industrial systems are in use which utilize this entire range of sizes, the smallest being used on such equipment as leak detectors, mass spectrographs, metal-sputtering equipment, etc., and the larger sizes being used on process equipment of all kinds.

The principles involved in all the well-known makes are essentially the same, although the details vary with the manufacturer. Also, each general type will be found to have slightly different characteristics as to both performance and servicing requirements.

All the pumps use oil as a sealant and depend on close tolerances in a bath of oil for the prevention of leak-back or by-passing of gas. The degree of vacuum from them is dependent on the following items:

1. The vapor pressure of the oil and its contaminants.
2. The solubility of the gas being pumped in the oil.
3. The completeness with which gas is eliminated from the displacement volume at each cycle.
4. The effectiveness of the sealing against gas by-pass.
5. Freedom from leaks at bearings and elsewhere.

In general, mechanical pumps depend on rotating eccentric cams. They seal off either by virtue of the position of the cam surface with respect to the fixed cylinder in which it is rotated (Kinney), or by means of sliding vanes either bearing on the eccentric cam (Cenco) or riding the cam and bearing on the inner surface of the cylinder in which it rotates (Beach-Russ). In any event a copious amount of oil

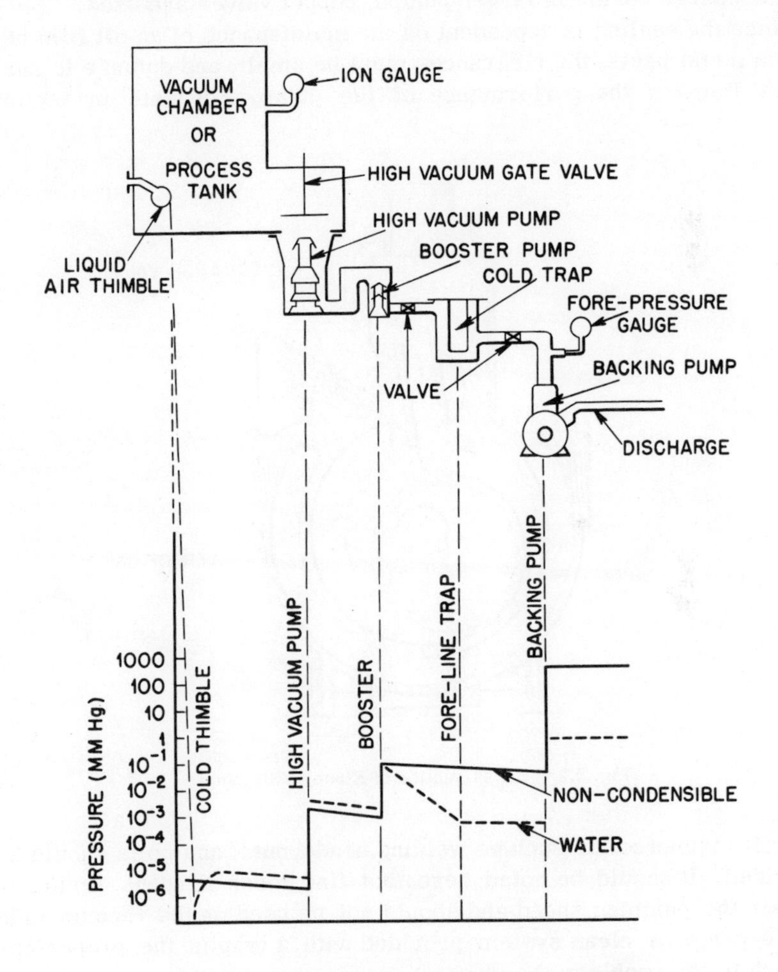

Fig. 2.1—The elements of a high-vacuum system.

is taken in with the expanding volume and is subsequently squeezed out with the entrapped gas as the volume becomes reduced to as near zero as possible on the discharge side. By this method the amount of residual gas remaining at the end of a cycle is very nearly zero, since the oil has filled the small space not actually filled by the cam.

The discharge side (see Fig. 2.2) is sealed off against gas returning from atmospheric pressure by some type of valve. In small pumps a so-called "feather valve" is generally used. It consists of a piece of thin spring steel lightly held on the ground surface of the outside of the discharge ports. In larger pumps, poppet valves are used.

Since the sealing is dependent on the maintenance of an oil film between metal parts, the clearances must be small, and damage to surfaces impairs the performance of the pump. Adequate protection

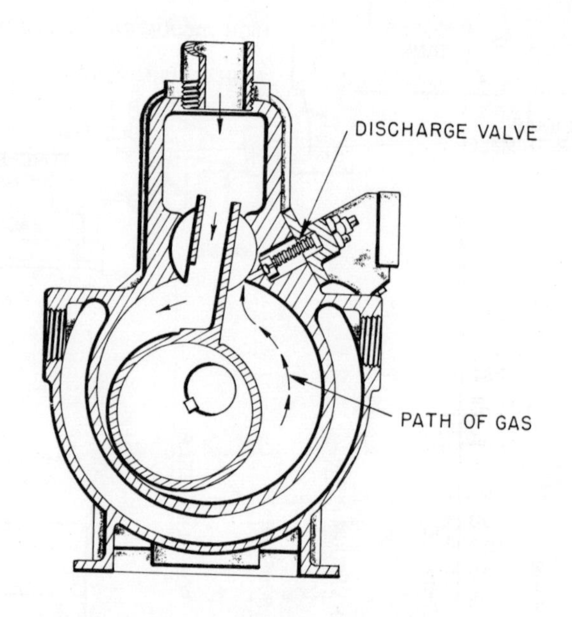

Fig. 2.2—Cross section of Kinney VSD pump.

against foreign solids such as welding beads, nuts, and bolts should be provided. It should be noted here that fine-mesh screens seriously impair the pumping speed and should not be used on the vacuum side of the pump. A clean system provided with a trap is the proper approach to the problem.

In all cases the rotating cam is driven by a shaft that must enter the vacuum region, since hermetically sealed motors have not come into use. Suitable provision must be made for packing, so that leaks will not occur. Two systems are used for rotating seals. One is to use a gastight packing capable of maintaining gastight contact between the shaft and the fixed shell. The other and more reliable seal, though perhaps not capable of being used on pumps to produce high vacuums, is that in which good bearing fits are made and are then followed by a packing of modest characteristics. Between the bearing and the packing a supply of oil is introduced at atmospheric pressure. Hence the bearing leaks oil into the system rather than air. In this case a certain amount of air, dissolved in the oil, is introduced into the system, but the amount is usually insignificantly small for practical purposes.

As previously mentioned, the capacity of such mechanical pumps is based on the volume swept out at each cycle of the cam. Thus if the volume swept out per cycle is V_1, the volumetric speed is $S_p = fV_1$, where f is the number of cycles performed per unit of time. Consequently, if V_1 is in cubic feet and f is in cycles per minute (usually the same as the revolutions per minute of the pump), S_p is the pumping speed in cubic feet per minute. If it is desired to know the mass of the gas, then it can be found from the relation $S'_p = f\rho V_1$, where ρ is the density of the gas.

It is to be noted that the mass speed S'_p is a function of the pressure at which the evacuation is taking place and consequently is not a constant for the pump at a given speed of rotation.

In actual practice the volumetric speed of the pump is not a constant either. This is due to the fact that the admittance of the apertures and ducts on the vacuum side of the pump becomes more important as the pressure is reduced (see Chap. 1) and tends to reduce the volumetric efficiency as the pressure is lowered. Figure 2.3 shows the volumetric speeds of two makes of industrial vacuum pumps as a function of pressure as determined in actual performance tests. Figure 2.4 shows the same data in terms of the volumetric efficiencies of the pumps.

Tests show that the actual pumping speeds of any of the pumps can be increased more or less linearly with the speed at which they are operated, but the likelihood of damage and serious wear is also greatly increased. It has been found that, in general, the manufacturer's specified speed is such that if it is exceeded by a very large factor (e.g., 50 per cent) the volumetric efficiency begins to decrease. It is also true that all these pumps consist of essentially unbalanced rotating parts, and increasing the speed greatly increases the amount of vibration they cause.

All larger types of mechanical pumps as well as some of the smaller ones utilize oil drawn from a reservoir other than the pump case. This reservoir may be a supplementary part of the installation. In any event the amount of oil (usually fed by gravity) allowed to enter the vacuum chamber through the bearing glands and direct feed lines is regulated by suitable valves. Generally speaking, the amount required is small, varying from a few pints to about 10 gal/hr, depending on the size of the pump and its condition. The oil entering the pumps is forced out through the gas-discharge line and is returned to the reservoir from a suitable trap and is recirculated. Thus the actual quantity of oil lost is small.

The amount of oil allowed to circulate through the pumps is sometimes determined by the particular use to be made of the pump. If the

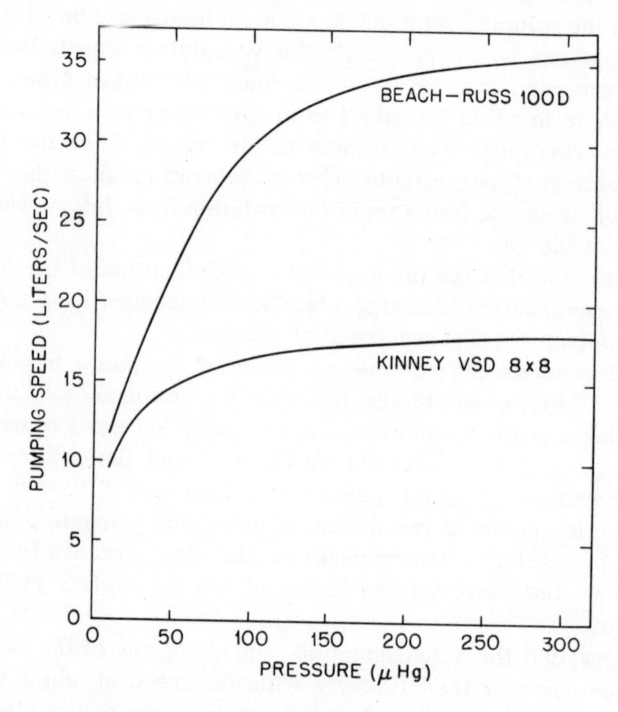

Fig. 2.3—Characteristics of Beach-Russ and Kinney backing pumps. The same manometer and McLeod gauge were used for both pumps.

oil is adjusted for the production of the lowest base pressure, i.e., the lowest pressure the pump can produce when no air is being pumped through it, then the amount of oil will usually be insufficient to seal the moving parts effectively when gas is actually being handled.

Tests have been made on the operation of different 105-cfm Kinney pumps when adjusted for best base pressure as compared to their operation when adjusted to a more copious oil supply. The amount of difference is not critical unless the lowest base pressure is desirable. Actually the usual requirement is for the maximum speed at higher pressures, i.e., these near the cutoff of the booster diffusion pumps, so that the base pressure is unimportant. It will be noted that when they were adjusted for lowest base pressure most of these pumps had only half the speed under a load producing 100 μ Hg as when ample oil was used.

The fact that a minimum amount of oil produces a lower base pressure than a larger amount is probably a result of the gases being in

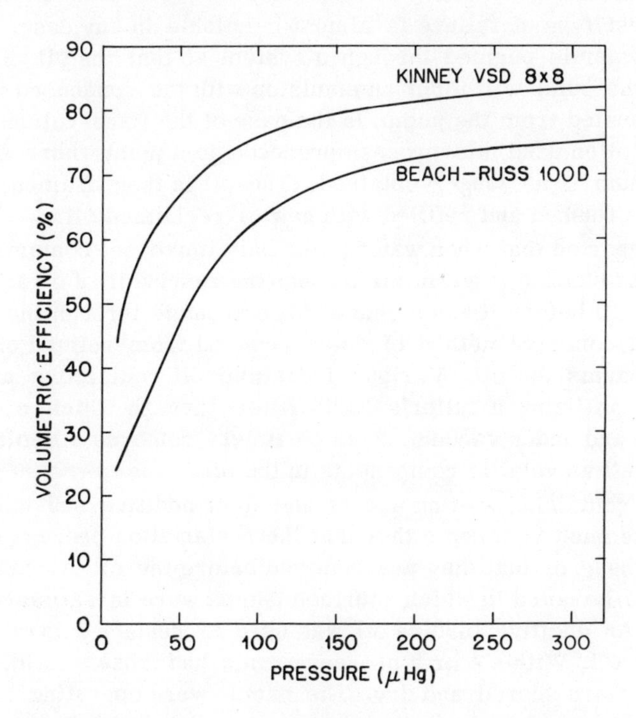

Fig. 2.4—Volumetric efficiency vs. pressure for Beach-Russ and Kinney backing pumps.

solution in the oil when it enters the pump. The less oil introduced, the less gas there is to come out of solution in the expansion part of the pumping cycle.

Large pumps (50 cfm or larger) are generally jacketed so that they may be cooled with water. The cooling requirements are usually very small, 1 or 2 gal/min being adequate even for the largest sizes under normal operating conditions. Small models depend upon air cooling. The heat generated is limited to that due to mechanical friction except when a large amount of gas is being handled, as, for example, when first pumping down a system (roughing). Such friction heat can be considerable, but in any real case this condition persists for only a very short time, and is unimportant.

One of the chief causes of unsatisfactory operation, and sometimes of total failure, of vacuum pumps of the types considered here is oil contamination. This gives rise to two types of failure, that of high vapor pressure in the oil, causing excessively high base pressures, and that of corrosion and gumming of critical surfaces in the pump.

The first type of failure is almost inevitable in any case. Usually enough water is pumped through a system so that the oil circulated through the pump will form an emulsion with the condensed water as it is exhausted from the pump. In the case of the fixed-volume reservoirs so often used this process proceeds to a point where satisfactory vacuum is no longer obtained. The oil is then drained, and the system is flushed and refilled with new or reclaimed oil.

It is reported that when water is the only important contaminant the continuous blowing of warm air through the reservoir of oil adequately dries the oil before it has a chance to recirculate through the system. This is a common method of water removal from refined oil and in no way harms the oil. Various industrial oil-reclaiming units are available utilizing a fuller's-earth filter through which oil passes while hot and under vacuum. This treatment removes all solid material as well as volatile components in the oil.

If oils containing wetting agents and other additive substances are used, care must be taken either that the reclamation process does not remove these or that they are renewed before the oil is reused. One case is to be noted in which fourteen pumps were in satisfactory operation. An additive turbine oil was used to replace a straight SAE 20 motor oil. Within 4 or 5 hr every pump had frozen solid, and the surfaces were scored and dry. The pumps were operating on a continuous-oil-circulation system passing through one of the fuller's-earth units described. Upon changing back to the original oil, satisfactory operation was resumed.

The causes for the second type of failure mentioned, that of corrosion and gumming, are sometimes not so easily eliminated as the water problem. The pumps themselves are commonly made of cast iron fitted with steel shafts, valves, and springs, and with bearings of bronze. All these, as well as the oil itself, are subject to action by strong oxidizing agents such as sulfur dioxide, chlorine, fluorine, and the acids of which these are anhydrides or derivatives.

The corrosion of the metal resulting from concentrations of oxidizing agents usually encountered seems generally to be negligible except for the steel valves. Many failures of feather-type valves have been noted which result from etching of the surfaces. In some cases etching of the cast iron forming the valve seat has also been so bad that remachining has been required.

The more common occurrence, however, is the destruction of the oil by oxidation and the deposition of a gum residue on the surfaces of the pump. In extreme cases the gum forming on the rotating cam assembly finally causes the pump to stick tightly. The pump must then be taken apart, and each part carefully cleaned. Since no suitable solvents have been noted, the usual method has been that of scraping the surfaces clean with a soft-metal scraper.

Pumps threatening to stick can sometimes be located by observing overheating or slipping belts and certainly by abnormal power loading. If a pump is stopped intentionally when in such a condition, it will probably stick so tightly that it cannot be started again. Disassembly and cleaning is then usually required. Some operators have felt that they had prevented the sticking of pumps which had to be stopped by turning off the cooling water during the shutdown, thus keeping the pump warm. This is possibly true, but no reliable data are available to prove or disprove the point.

It does seem true, however, that if a pump which is gummed is not stopped and if the oil is changed a few times during the course of a day or so, the parts tend to become clean by themselves. Evidence also seems to indicate that new pumps are more subject to sticking than old ones that have been in use for some time. This probably results from clearance being increased by wear.

The usual power consumption is about 1 hp for each 20 cfm. However, when sticking is about to occur, a 5-hp motor on a 100-cfm pump occasionally burns out. Ordinarily, such a ratio of power to pump capacity is completely satisfactory.

Mechanical pumps are tested by measuring the base pressure that the isolated pump will produce. The base pressure varies somewhat with individual pumps and with the particular make. A McLeod or Pirani gauge is suitable for the purpose. Industrial pumps using good grades of motor oil of about SAE 20 generally have a base pressure between 5 and 20 μ Hg. A base pressure much higher than this might be due to one of the following causes:

1. Water in the oil. A change of oil will show if this is causing the high pressure. Badly contaminated oil looks cloudy.

2. The sealing oil valves may be set so that too little oil is circulating through the pump. If the pump has been operating satisfactorily with the setting being used, this is not likely to be the cause of the high pressure.

3. The valves may be damaged, owing to corrosion, or they may have dirt under them. The latter condition has been noted a number of times. Usually a blast of air allowed to go through the pump will momentarily alter the apparent base pressure of the pump. If corrosion is causing the trouble, the difficulty will have developed over a period of time rather than suddenly.

4. The pump may leak or the test apparatus may leak. Pumps sometimes leak owing to poor assembly but seldom develop leaks after operating satisfactorily.

The speed of a displacement pump, once determined, can be relied upon to remain constant for any one pressure (see Fig. 2.3). Tests sometimes do, however, reveal failures that otherwise would go unnoticed. A leak of known size is admitted into the system, and the resultant rise in pressure is noted. The speed is then

$$S_p = \frac{760V'_{atm}}{\Delta p} \tag{1}$$

where S_p is in liters per second, Δp is the observed change in pressure in microns of mercury and V'_{atm} is the atmospheric leak rate introduced in cubic centimeters per second.

Oil adjustment should be made on the basis of maximum speed at a given maximum allowable pressure.

In several instances errors in pump assembly have been noted during speed measurements. Large-sized Kinney pumps, for example, are partially compensated with respect to the unbalanced eccentric moving parts by being built in the form of two parallel pumps 180 deg out of phase. If one of the eccentric-piston assemblies is put in backward, the air-intake parts will be on the wrong side, and that section of the pump will not pump. The over-all apparent pumping speed of one of these pumps so assembled is just half what it should be. Noting the time to evacuate a vessel of known size to a certain pressure would, of course, indicate the same thing.

A well-installed mechanical pump, typical of industrial models now available, requires very little attention. Particular features of installation are as follows:

1. The pump should be very firmly mounted on a concrete pier.

2. Approximately 1 hp per 20 cfm should be allowed. Suitable overload protection should be provided.

3. No remote starting switches should be allowed. A stuck pump is likely to be unnoticed, and damage will result.

4. Ample room for servicing, such as oil changing, should be provided.

Other refinements such as automatic- or continuous-oil-change and oil-reclamation installations are probably justifiable in some cases. It is highly advantageous to include a refrigerant trap to remove water before it gets to the pump. These will be discussed later in the chapter.

The properties of oils for use in mechanical pumps have apparently not been exhaustively investigated. In general, a medium-weight turbine-type oil is suitable. Certain properties desirable in oils to be used are as follows:

1. The clearances involved in pumps in general use usually require an oil with an SAE number of 15 to 20. The temperature ranges in actual operation are not very great, and the viscosity index is not critical.

2. Good lubrication is essential. Some very stable oils that might be favored because of their oxidation resistance are not suitable without the use of additive wetting agents.

3. The tendency of the oil to emulsify with water should be minimum. Most oil-circulation systems provided with the pumps include a settling system for separating excesses of water from the oil. Incidentally, these provide insufficient separation when fairly low pressures are required of the pump.

4. The oil should be resistant to oxidation from the particular gases being handled. Chlorinated or fluorinated oils can be used but are expensive. Tricresyl phosphate has in some cases been successfully used as a sealant in mechanical pumps. This compound is sometimes used as an additive substance in motor oils to increase their stability. Diesel and turbine motor oils have been found to be satisfactory oils in most cases.

5. The oil should not contain volatile components whose presence in the oil cause a vapor pressure above the desired base pressure.

The rate of deterioration of the oil varies greatly with the use to which the pump is put. Some pumps used primarily for holding a vacuum on tight systems through which only air has been passed have been known to run continuously for many months without any noticeable deterioration. On the other hand, pumps used to exhaust very wet tanks sometimes require oil replacement within a few hours, owing to the formation of a water emulsion with the oil. If chlorine is passed through the pump the oil turns to a dark color (brown, purple, or blue-black) because of the suspended materials, which are oxidation products. This does not seriously alter the vacuum produced, but gumming of the pump eventually makes the pump inoperable. If a pump is employed under such conditions, very frequent oil change is necessary. A number of oils often used are listed in Appendix E.

Large pumps are sometimes damaged by improper starting procedure. When a Kinney pump, for example, is stopped under vacuum the evacuated section tends to fill with oil, since the oil source is at atmospheric pressure. Most installations provide an electromagnetic check valve, which cuts off the oil supply when the power is turned off. These frequently leak, and great reliance on them is not justified. If any considerable quantity of oil does get into the pump while it is stopped, this oil must be ejected from the pump through the discharge valves on the first revolution of the mechanism. This cannot be done when the pump is operating at high speed. Consequently a pump into which oil has leaked should be turned over by hand once or twice before an attempt is made to start the motor. Rather frequently keys have been sheared or castings broken as a result of the sudden hammer action applied by the motor as the puddle of oil is struck.

In order to avoid filling the pump and possibly a part of the vacuum system with oil, the pump should be let down to atmospheric pressure as soon as it is stopped. Even the small self-contained-reservoir-type pumps have been known to allow oil to run back into the system they had evacuated, despite advertising to the contrary.

2.3 General Design of Diffusion Pumps. Diffusion pumps are relative newcomers to the industrial field, and their development has therefore been largely carried on by scale-up and empirical testing rather than by theoretical design. The cyclotron has made ever-increasing vacuum demands, and, with recent developments in vacuum distillation of such products as magnesium, penicillin, and vitamins, the demand is for better vacuum in larger tanks.

A diffusion pump, as shown in Fig. 2.5, consists essentially of a water-cooled jacket in which a suitable boiler and nozzle assembly is so arranged that oil or other suitable substance can be boiled off the bottom, and the resulting vapor can be ejected at high velocity in a downward direction against the cold jacket and be recondensed. Gas molecules entering the jet from region A become entrained in the vapor jet and are carried to the lower part of the pump where they are removed by a second pump, usually of the type described in the preceding pages. In general, the exact mechanics of the jet action is not known. However, it can be seen that the action of the pump is to transfer the momentum of the jet to the gas coming in at A.

Pumps of this type are essentially low-pressure pumps, usually requiring that the discharge pressure be no higher than 100 to 200 μ Hg. Nevertheless, the pressure to which they will reduce a nonleaking system seems to be dependent only on the vapor pressure of the cold oil thrown out above the nozzle. For most purposes, diffusion pumps are built as multistage devices having several nozzles in series. Specific characteristics can be built into a pump in this manner.

Consider now the operation of a diffusion pump. In general the vacuum at the input A is such that the mean free path of the molecules of gas is sufficiently long that they seldom collide with each other but do collide with the side walls of the ducts (see Chap. 1). Furthermore, mass flow of gas is not the way transfer of momentum is accomplished. The only reason that a given molecule goes into the pump is that it chances to be traveling in that direction. The probability that

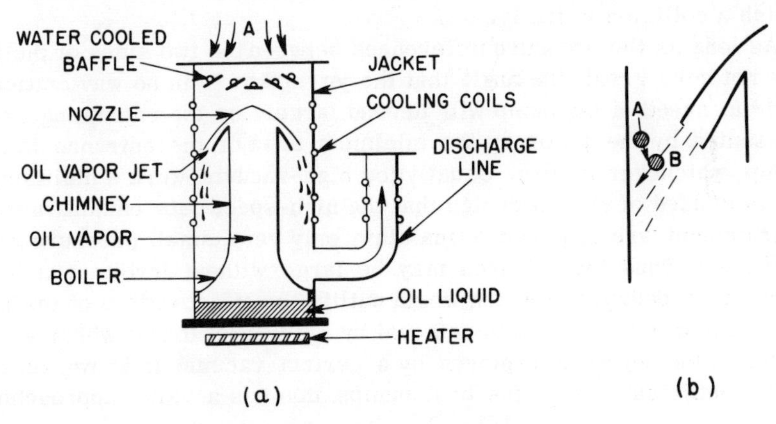

Fig. 2.5—View of single-jet diffusion pump.

any particular molecule will enter the pump from a given point is essentially the solid angle intercepted by the pump from that point divided by 4π. In addition, a molecule has actually to enter the jet stream before its chances of entrainment rise above this value.

It is also true that even though a gas molecule A (Fig. 2.5b) experiences a collision with the oil molecule B in the jet, this collision might result not in entrainment but in rejection, since the molecule A might be thrown away from the jet instead of into it. However, once molecule A does become involved in a collision in which it is thrown deeper into the jet, its chances of return to the side from which it came are essentially zero, since the density of the oil stream is so high that a collision is inevitable.

If one considers the molecule A at rest and being subjected to a chance collision with B, then the chance that the momentum transferred to A will be on a specified side of a plane through the original trajectory of B is 0.5. Since all molecules A being pumped come from outside the pump, they will always arrive at the jet with some downward momentum. Thus the chances of momentum transfer toward the jet rather than away from it are somewhat greater than 0.5, although probably not much greater when the whole process is considered.

The jet itself is pointed away from the side being evacuated, since not only is the jet itself somewhat diffuse, but the transfer of momentum to a pumped gas molecule in the direction of the high-pressure region means transfer to the oil molecule in the opposite direction. In order for a substantial pressure difference to be maintained between the upper and lower side of the jet it is necessary that the component of momentum toward the high-pressure side be equal to or greater than that of any gas molecule in the opposite direction with which a collision is likely.

As long as the pressure differences between the two sides of the jet are not very great, the angle that the jet makes is in no way critical, and the speed of the pump will depend largely on the entraining area presented by the jet or by the minimum area of the entrance to the pump, whichever is less. Usually for high-vacuum work a multistage pump is used of such a design that the high-speed jets causing initial entrainment are required to maintain only very small pressure differences. Thus the jet area may be large without involving a long duct, the impedance of which would nullify the effectiveness of the jet. The ratio of the rate of gas removal by a given jet to that which would occur if the jet were replaced by a perfect vacuum is known as the "Ho coefficient." For the best pumps this has a value approaching 0.4.

The molecular weight of oils used for pumping is fairly high, e.g., 200 or more, and the temperature of the vapor is much higher than that of the average molecule being pumped. Also the oil vapor is forced up the chimney under a pressure usually ranging from 1 or 2 mm Hg up to 1 cm Hg or more (oil head). The jet velocities in this case are very high.

The foregoing discussion suggests that the Ho coefficient for all well-designed pumps should be the same and that all pumps should be capable of producing a vacuum equal to the vapor pressure of the pumping fluid at the temperature of the walls of the system ahead of the pump. This tends to be true when the pump is properly installed. The gas-handling capacities of the pumps per unit of size vary greatly, as do other characteristics.

Gas molecules entering the jet of a diffusion pump are either thrown through the jet or simply entrained in the vapor stream until they strike the cold jacket wall. Here the oil condenses and runs down into the bottom of the pump, where it is reheated, and the cycle is repeated. When the oil condenses, the entrained gas is apparently nearly completely liberated. A patented two-stage design known as a "fractionating diffusion pump" is shown in Fig. 2.6. The initial intent of this design seems to have been to effect a separation of low-pressure oil from high-vapor-pressure oil by the following means: The high-vacuum high-speed nozzle A is fed from a boiler in the center of the pump, and the low-speed high-pressure bucking nozzle B is fed from the outer boiler. These boilers are concentric, and oil returning down the sides is first heated at the periphery of the pump and thus is first boiled in the outer boiler. If there are light fractions in the oil they will largely be evaporated in this area. By the time the returning oil

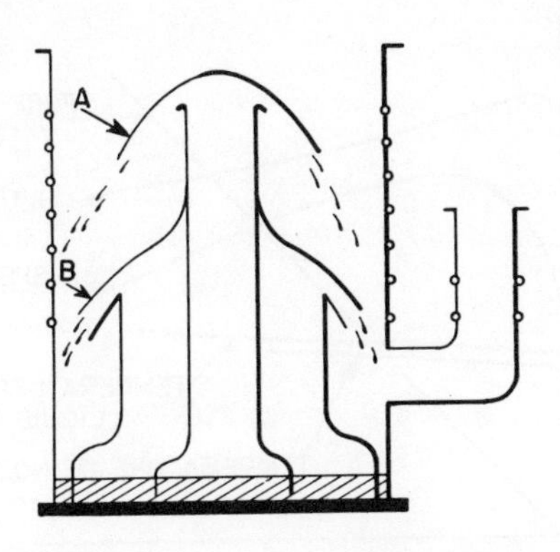

Fig. 2.6—View of fractionating diffusion pump.

has reached the center boiler that feeds the high-vacuum jet the more volatile compounds will have been eliminated. Whether this is important has not been conclusively shown. However, it undoubtedly does give greater opportunity for entrained gases to come out of solution without being returned to the high-vacuum region of the pump.

The walls of diffusion pumps must be cooled in order to condense the oil and thereby keep the pressure below the jets as low as possible. Cooling of the jacket in the region of impingement of the top jet should be such as to produce a temperature as close to that of the pour point of the oil as possible, since the ultimate vacuum obtained definitely depends on the vapor pressure of the oil in this region, as does also the oil migration back into the vacuum chamber. The cooling of subsequent jet-impingement areas needs only to be sufficient to afford condensation of a large percentage of the oil. Cooling of the oil below necessary temperatures is a waste of power, for it has to be reheated.

As a matter of fact, practically all the heat put into a diffusion pump is either lost to the cooling water by contact and condensation of the oil or by radiation from the boilers, chimneys, nozzles, and base of the pump. The amount utilized in actual pumping is negligible in even the very largest pumps.

The heat requirements of a diffusion pump vary greatly with its size, design, and use. Fundamentally the problem is that the heat input must be sufficient to (1) supply enough vapor to the nozzles for the maintenance of adequate jets, (2) supply enough additional vapor to

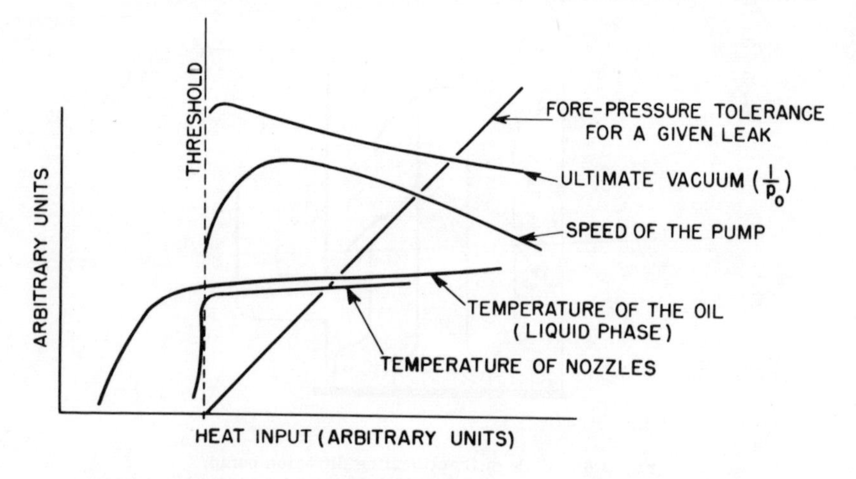

Fig. 2.7—Effect of change in heat input on performance of diffusion pump.

keep the nozzle and chimney assembly at operating temperature (i.e., that of the vapor), and (3) take care of direct heat losses through radiation and convection from the base of the pump, heater housing, etc. All these considerations can be objects of economy of design and operation far beyond the actual practice to date.

Of primary interest is the quantity of heat required to produce vapor sufficient to maintain adequate jets. If any real pump is set into operation and then the heat supplied is very gradually reduced, a number of changes in the performance of the pump will take place until finally it fails completely. These are represented quantitatively in Fig. 2.7. An investigation[1] of these properties in the case of several types of pump has shown that, although individual cases differ, the variations are minor. In all cases a fairly sharp threshold value of heat input exists, below which no pumping is accomplished. This value, it has been shown, agrees closely with the heat that would be expected to be radiated from the nozzle and chimney assembly if this assembly were at the temperature of the boiling oil and radiating as a black body to the jacket.

It is improbable that this type of loss can be reduced very much by the use of shiny surfaces since even a thin oil film on the surface increases the emissivity to almost black-body values. Multiple wall assemblies have a chance of success since inside and outside stack pressures are considerably different and since surfaces protected from mechanical spraying would tend to remain free of oil. Such an arrangement is being partially utilized on some of the pumps manufactured by Distillation Products, Inc.

An investigation[2] of the temperature distribution in a four-stage high-vacuum pump has shown that the actual temperatures from place to place within the liquid- and vapor-filled regions vary considerably. Cooled oil runs down the sides of the jacket, and consequently, if the bottom of the pump is more or less uniformly heated, the peripheral section of the boiler would be expected to be cooler than the center. Also the fact that an oil of complex composition fractionates, causing a similar distribution, increases this effect.

Since the metal-to-oil heat-transfer coefficient varies with the flux density, the difference between the temperature of the bottom plate and the oil itself varies. A considerable drop in the temperature of the vapor itself occurs as it expands up the stacks.

An experimentally determined temperature profile is produced in the isothermal diagram of a 32-in. pump, Fig. 2.8. All these temperatures increase as the power input is increased, owing to the fact that the boiling point of the oil is raised when the vapor pressure in the jets is increased as the result of the augmented supply of vapor.

Similar measurements[3] made on an 8-in. booster using Litton Molecular C oil show a rather constant difference of about 20°C between the surface of the bottom plate and the oil at the center of the pump. This difference remained essentially unchanged as the power input was varied from 1,400 to 2,500 watts, although the plate-surface temperature changed from 226 to 233°C.

It will be noted that for a given pump there is an optimum power input, which yields the highest speed. The results of pump tests concerning this point[1] are shown in Fig. 2.9.

The power requirements of some pumps will differ considerably, depending on the conditions under which they are installed. Thus pumps installed and rated to consume 7 kw were found to be working so close to the threshold value that the variation in performance was extreme. The rating had been determined in a shop and with the bottom of the pump close to the floor. No adequate insulation was provided around the bottom, and the heat loss was greatly increased when the pumps were installed high in the air and amidst a ventilating sys-

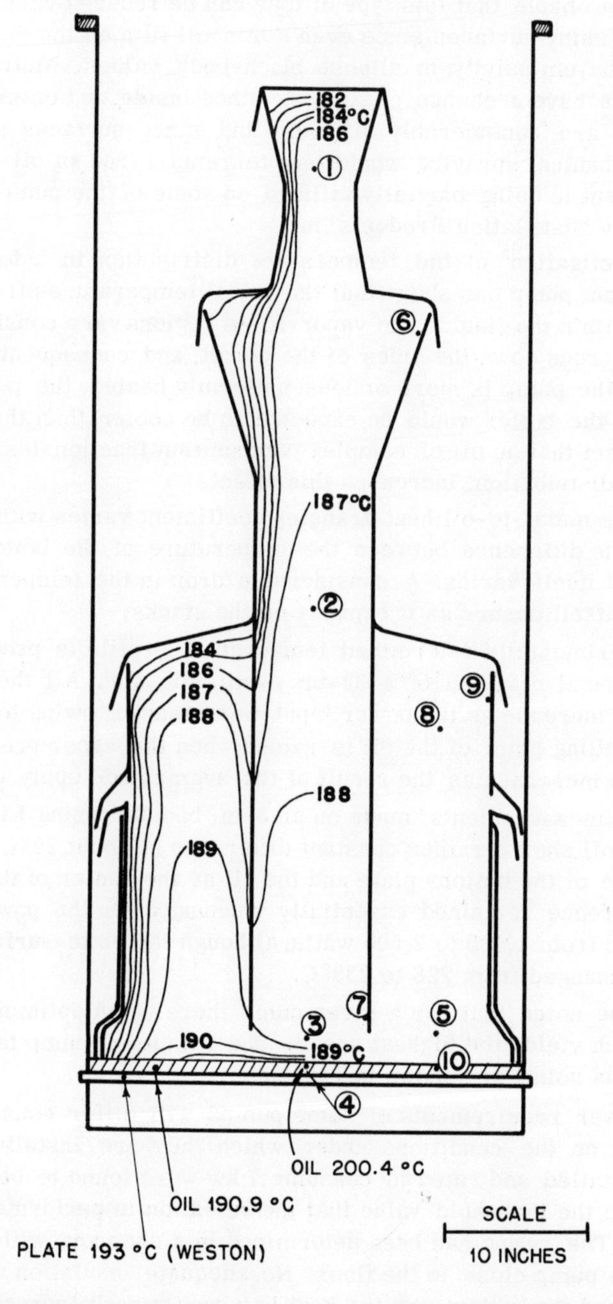

Fig. 2.8—Isothermal diagram for 32-in. diffusion pump. The numbered dots represent the location of the thermocouples used in the measurement.

tem. Table 2.1 shows the change in speed resulting from the installation of rock-wool pads about the bottoms of these pumps.

Thus the threshold might be at one value for the pump under one circumstance and have some new value when the pump is moved. The temperature and quantity of the cooling water will also have an effect.

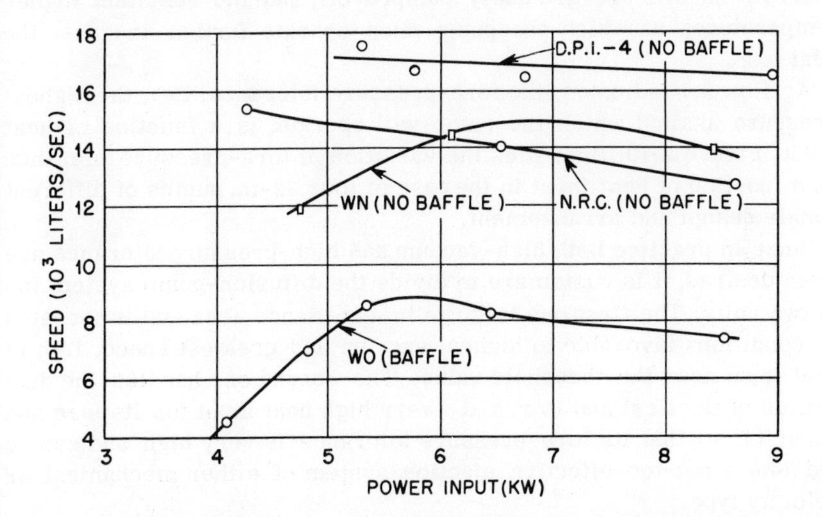

Fig. 2.9—Pumping speeds vs. power input for a number of 32-in. diffusion pumps. D.P.I., Distillation Products, Inc.; N.R.C., National Research Corporation; WO, Westinghouse, old design; WN, Westinghouse, new design.

Table 2.1—Effect of Insulation on Pump Speed*

Insulation	Power input, kw			Temp. at base,† °C			Speed measured at ionization gauge on valve No. 1, liters/sec				
	Pump 1	Pump 2	Pump 3	Pump 1	Pump 2	Pump 3	Pump 1	Pump 2	Pump 3	Sum of 1, 2, 3	Measured total
No	6.48	6.57	6.58	210	203	208	4,780	3,030	2,040	10,080	9,850
Yes	6.48	6.58	6.58	226	219	224	4,760	2,920	2,920	10,000	10,600
Yes	8.66	6.58	8.67	240	238	236	6,150	3,460	3,160	11,550	12,770

*Taken from Chupp.[4]

†Temperature measured in well in base plate with mercury thermometer (for a Weston thermometer subtract 7°C).

Why most pumps show a drop in speed when a given value of heat input is exceeded is not clear. There is, however, the possibility that, as the boiling of the oil is increased and the heat transfer between the heater and oil becomes less efficient, cracking due to local high temperature will set in, yielding volatile products, which result in poorer vacuum.

It should also be noted that there is some evidence that pumps require less heat when newly put into operation than they do later. This is due to two facts: (1) a certain amount of coke gradually forms on the stack assemblies, and the emissivity and hence the radiation heat loss increases; and (2) in the process of use the lighter-boiling fractions of the oils are gradually pumped off, and the resultant higher temperatures at which the pump must operate further increase the heat loss.

As Fig. 2.7 indicates, the fore-pressure tolerance, i.e., the highest pressure against which the pump will operate, is a function of heat input. Figure 2.10 illustrates the variation of fore-pressure tolerance as a function of heat input in the case of four 32-in. pumps of different nozzle design and arrangement.

Since in practice both high-vacuum and high-pressure tolerance are often desired, it is customary to divide the diffusion-pump system into two units. The first one is large in admittance area and is operated at conditions favorable to highest vacuum and greatest speed, i.e., at heat input near the threshold value. The second one handles the discharge of the first and is run at a very high heat input for its size and capacity, so that its fore-pressure tolerance is very high and can be fed into a not-too-effective ejection system of either mechanical or velocity type.

Thus two distinct types of diffusion pumps are used, each of which has its own set of characteristics. The complete vacuum system can be properly designed only when these characteristics are combined to match the requirements of the particular system as a whole.

The high-vacuum high-speed pump has these characteristics:

1. Large admittance areas.
2. Nozzles of the deflection type that are designed to furnish only a high-velocity umbrella of low density and a pumping component.
3. A small pressure drop across the high-speed jets, so that high jet density is not required.
4. The use of several stages, each progressively slower but capable of maintaining greater pressure differentials.
5. A relatively low vapor pressure (heat input) to maintain oil jets of the order of a few millimeters of oil.

A booster pump, on the other hand, has these characteristics:

1. A relatively small admittance area.
2. Nozzles designed to produce as high a fore-pressure tolerance as possible for a given jet velocity.
3. A high pressure (2 or 3 cm of oil head) and a large volume of vapor through the jets. In the case of the so-called "ejector-type" booster, the oil head may be several feet.

A review of the performance characteristics of each type of pump will facilitate design of a high-vacuum–booster combination that will meet the requirements of a specific problem.

Before discussing the characteristics of these two types of pumps in more detail, a word will be said regarding diffusion-pump oils.

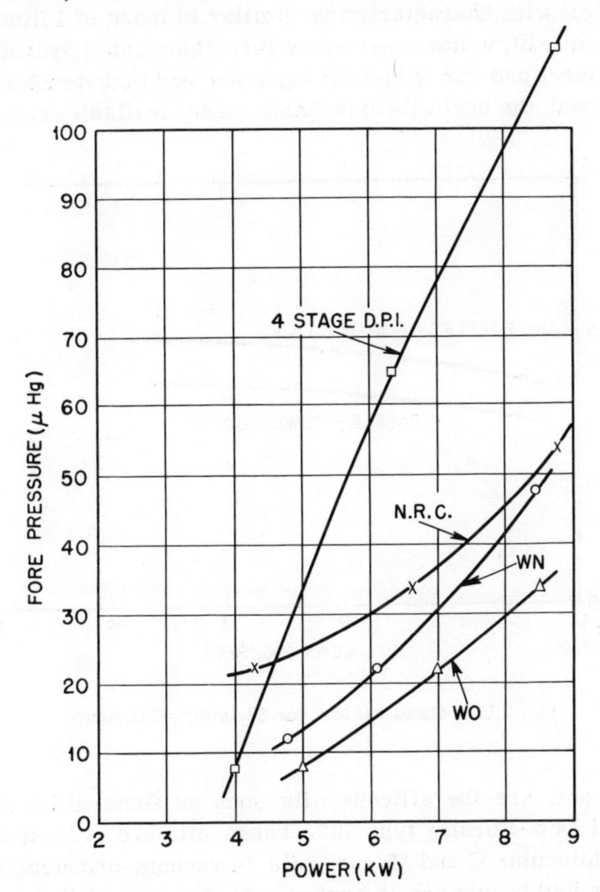

Fig. 2.10—Fore-pressure tolerance for 32-in. pumps, no leak. D.P.I., Distillation Products, Inc.; N.R.C., National Research Corporation; WO, Westinghouse, old design; WN, Westinghouse, new design.

Most of the experimental work at the University of California Radiation Laboratory was carried out with Litton Molecular C oil, owing to its availability, relatively low cost, and general suitability. Some of the characteristics of this oil, as well as those of a number of other oils, are listed in Appendix F. Some oils not listed in the appendix have now become available, including Myvane oil (originally DP-20) of Distillation Products, Inc., Narcoil-10 of National Research Corporation, type A diffusion-pump oil of Eitel-McCullough, and Pancro oil of Central Scientific Company. Myvane oil is a vacuum-distilled petroleum oil with characteristics similar to those of Litton Molecular C. Narcoil-10, a low-vapor-pressure chlorinated hydrocarbon, is relatively inert and can withstand exposure and high-temperature operation. About the best oils now being made available, although still

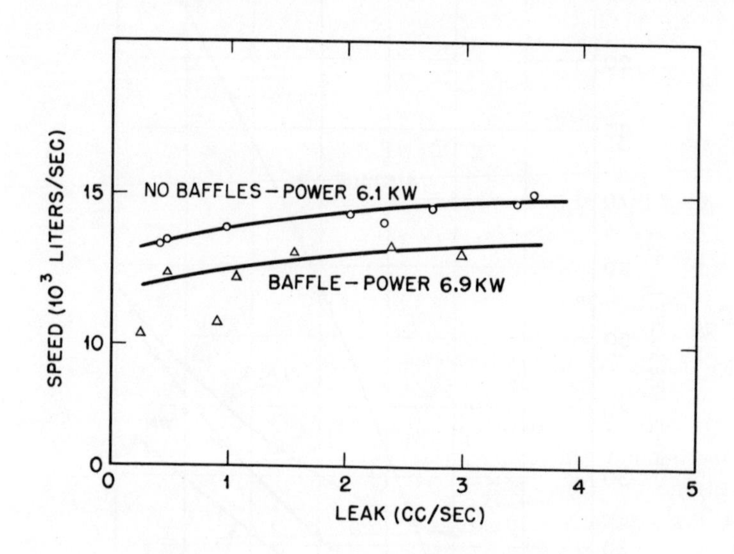

Fig. 2.11—Speed vs. leak for 32-in diffusion pump.

at a high cost, are the silicone oils such as General Electric type ZV5289 and Dow-Corning type 703. These oils are at least the equal of Litton Molecular C and Myvane oils in vacuum-producing properties and are highly immune to exposure to air even at their operating temperatures.

2.4 High-vacuum Pumps. The high-vacuum pumps having the general characteristics of structure mentioned in Sec. 2.3 have a certain definite and reasonably predictable behavior.

(a) Speed. The volumetric speed is essentially a constant over the useful range of the pump. This means that the pressure in the system is a linear function of the leak. Figure 2.11 shows a typical speed curve obtained by admitting a known leak into a suitable test dome and noting the rise in pressure ahead of the pump. Such a curve is then calculated from the definition of speed,

$$S_p = \frac{\Delta V_p'}{\Delta p} \tag{2}$$

where $\Delta V_p'$ is the admitted leak and Δp is the resulting change in pressure.

Calculated on this basis, the speed of the pump is constant until the base pressure P_0 is reached. No evidence has been collected to justify a different interpretation. On the other hand, curves are often presented showing the speed falling off gradually to zero. These are based on speed as calculated from the relation

$$S_p' = \frac{V_p'}{P} \tag{3}$$

where V_p' is the total leak admitted, and P is the total pressure. Since the total leak V_p' is never known, the definition of Eq. 2 is the more practicable, and its constancy in high-speed pumps is a convenient basis for design calculation.

The Ho coefficient is generally calculated on the basis of the area of the annular aperture between the top nozzle and the jacket walls. Other approaches might include the use of the area of the jet, but this is indefinite in most cases. Furthermore, evidence points to the conclusion that jets which have large area by virtue of being long cones coaxial with the jacket do not have higher speed than those which are ejected more nearly normal to the jacket surface.

Consider the case of a four-stage pump having a jacket 32 in. in diameter and a top nozzle 10 in. in diameter. This gives an annular aperture of 726 sq in. If this area were to open into a perfect vacuum, the number of molecules disappearing into it at room temperature would amount to about 75 liters/sec/sq in. The measured speed of the pump is 18,000 liters/sec. Since the theoretically perfect pump would remove about $75 \times 726 \approx 54{,}400$ liters/sec, the Ho coefficient is

$$\text{Ho} = \frac{18{,}000}{54{,}400} = 0.331$$

For large pumps this is a very good value. Small pumps sometimes have slightly larger coefficients.

The speed remains essentially constant, sometimes increasing slightly as the size of the leak is increased, until the pump fails completely as the pressure differential on one or more jets exceeds its tolerance.

(b) Base Pressure. The base pressure of a pump is that pressure which is attained when the pump is operated on a system having no leaks of any kind, either real or virtual. This requires not only a tight system but also a completely outgassed one. Close approaches to this are realized in small all-glass systems, but large metal systems are virtually sources of gas, generally from both outgassing and small leaks. The lowest attainable pressure in a leaking system is

$$P = \frac{760V'_{atm}}{S_p} + P_0 \tag{4}$$

where P and P_0 are the actual and base pressures in microns of mercury, V'_{atm} is the leak (real or virtual) in cubic centimeters per second at atmospheric pressure, and S_p is the pumping speed in liters per second. Thus the observed P is the base pressure when V'_{atm} is zero.

Base pressures are associated more with pumping fluids than with pumps. Thus a pump that gave consistent base pressures of 10^{-5} mm Hg with Litton Molecular C oil, a straight-petroleum-base oil, gave a base pressure below 5×10^{-7} mm Hg with a silicone fluid. In all probability these results represent the vapor pressures of the two fluids at the temperature of the cooled surfaces of the pump. The technical difficulty of determining the base pressure is discussed later in more detail.

The base pressures obtainable with most commonly used oils range from about 10^{-5} to 10^{-7} mm Hg, the lowest pressures being obtained with silicones.

(c) Gas-handling Capacity. The gas-handling capacity of a pump depends on (1) the heat input, and (2) the speed of the backing system.

As the size of a leak is increased, the pressure below each jet increases. The pump does not fail as long as a certain maximum is not exceeded. This maximum value depends on the design of the nozzle and on the momentum of the vapor ejected through it. Of this more will be said under the subject of "pressure tolerance." As already noted (Fig. 2.7) the pressure tolerated by a jet increases with heat input. For this reason the gas-handling capacity of a pump is increased if the heat input is increased. Likewise if the speed of the backing system is increased the capacity of the system will be increased, since the back pressure resulting from a given throughput of gas will be reduced.

For high-speed pumps the backing system is usually the limitation on the gas-handling capacity. For example, a good 20-in. pump having a speed of 7,000 liters/sec can be made to operate satisfactorily up to pressures of about 1 μ Hg if it is suitably backed. Thus 7,000 μ-liters is being handled. This corresponds to an atmospheric leak of

$$V'_{atm} = \frac{7{,}000 \times 1.0}{760}$$

$$= 9.2 \text{ cc/sec}$$

For example, if a booster must not allow the second discharge pressure of the high-vacuum pump to exceed 30 μ Hg, then its speed will have to be

$$S_p = \frac{760V'_{atm}}{\Delta p} = \frac{760 \times 9.2}{30} = 233 \text{ liters/sec}$$

at this pressure (30 μ Hg).

To pursue the problem further, suppose that the booster will operate only to 150 μ Hg when this amount of gas is passing through it. The mechanical pump must be fast enough to remove 9.2 cc/sec when the pressure is only 150 μ Hg. The base pressure of the pump is probably 20 μ Hg. Hence the pump required has a minimum speed of

$$S_B = \frac{760 \times 9.2}{130} = 53.8 \text{ liters/sec}$$

The system will operate under this load only in the event that all these requirements are met.

The pressure tolerance of a system of jets, and no doubt of a single jet, tends to decrease as the amount of gas entrained by it increases. This is much more apt to be the case on booster designs than on high-vacuum types. Thus complete performance curves on all pumps to be included in a system are required before a vacuum system can be designed intelligently. Figure 2.12 illustrates tests of fore-pressure tolerance made as a function of leak throughput for a high-vacuum-type pump of usual characteristics. It will be noted that only slight dependence seems to exist. This is in contrast to the performance of booster-type pumps shown in Fig. 2.13.

2.5 Booster Pumps. (a) Design. The design of booster pumps involves (1) a first jet with sufficient speed to back the high-vacuum pump at the greatest leak throughput demanded of the system and (2) a final jet capable of enough speed to back the jet ahead of it and with a high enough pressure tolerance to allow a specified mechanical pump to remove the required gas load without exceeding the tolerance limits.

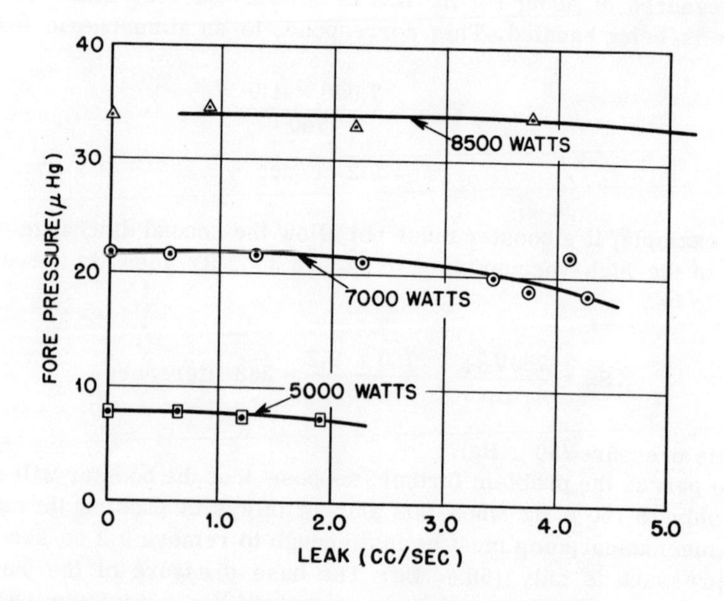

Fig. 2.12 — Fore-pressure tolerance vs. leak for 32-in. diffusion pump.

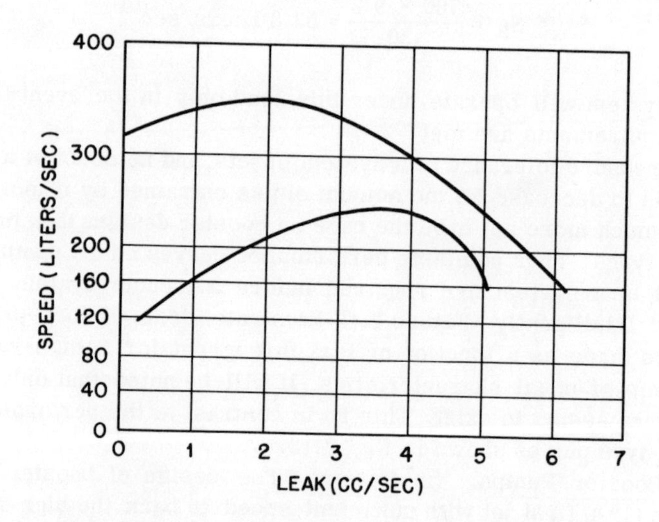

Fig. 2.13 — Speed characteristics of 8-in. booster pumps.

The first requirement is generally accomplished with a fairly dense jet of small proportions allowing an Ho coefficient of about 0.1 for the annular space between the nozzle and the walls. A directed jet is not usually used, but large volumes of vapor are employed. Thus, typically, a pump jacket 6 in. in diameter will have a nozzle aperture with a periphery of 10 in. and a throat of 1/16 in. or more and will operate on vapor held at a 2 or 3 cm head of oil. This quantity is obtained either by a very high heat-input flux by using a boiler of much larger dimensions than the jacket, or by a combination of the two methods.

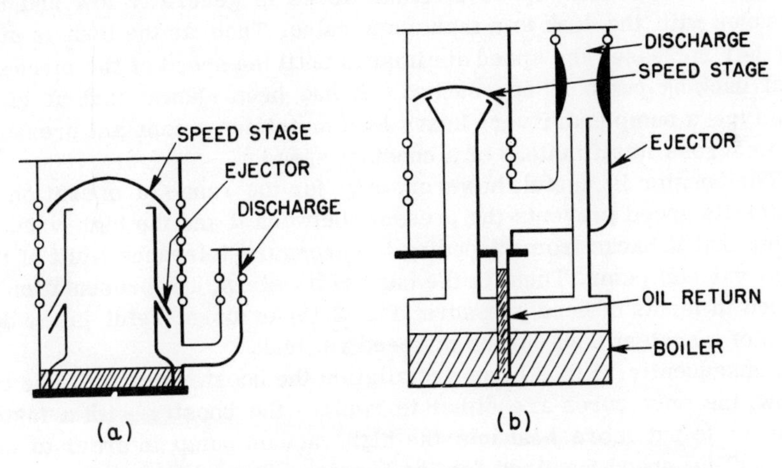

Fig. 2.14—General arrangements of two types of booster pumps.

The second requirement, i.e., extremely high-pressure tolerance for the output stage, is met by the use of an ejector nozzle with only small clearances to the walls or by use of a venturi-and-ejector system. The principles of these alternates are similar, but the construction is modified to meet the structural design in each case. The general arrangements of the two types are shown in Fig. 2.14. Although type a is good, the advantages offered by type b are many. Greater use of type b may well be expected.

The advantages of arrangement b are that a very much greater pressure of oil vapor may be obtained by just lowering the boiler and that the amount of heat put into the system may be increased indefinitely by enlarging the boiler, since it does not intimately affect the shape of the nozzle assemblies. Boosters of this type can be produced capable of handling large amounts of gas against fore pressures of 1 mm Hg or more.

Ejector stages of the type a are difficult to keep in reasonable alignment since the distance from the nozzle to the jacket is only about ⅛ in. in any case. The jackets are usually of rolled and welded construction, and close tolerances are not feasible. Pumps of this kind have recently been designed and operated against pressures up to 400 μ Hg when small leaks are handled.[3,5]

(b) Speed. The speed characteristics of the semiejector jets of boosters present quite a different picture from those of the high-vacuum diffusion type previously mentioned. Figure 2.13 illustrates a typical case. The speed at small leaks is generally low and increases with the leak to a maximum value. Then as the leak is still further increased the speed diminishes until the speed of the mechanical backing pump is approached. It has been shown[5] that at least the type a pump under very heavy load maintains a constant pressure drop across itself instead of a constant speed.

The booster is useful, however, only for the range of operation in which its speed prevents the pressure between it and the high-vacuum pump that it backs from exceeding the pressure-tolerance limit of the high-vacuum pump. Thus, in the case of boosters, a representation of speed in terms of head pressure (Fig. 2.15) is more useful in the design of a system than curves of speed vs. leak.

Consequently, if in a given installation the booster proves to be too slow, the only cures are either to replace the booster with a faster one, or to put more heat into the high-vacuum pump in order to decrease the speed required for the booster. The latter solution might not always be feasible.

As in the case of the high-vacuum pumps the speed is a function of heat input. Figure 2.16 shows that as the heat input is increased the speed is somewhat reduced. Since speed is important only at the maximum leaks to be handled, the only concern of the designer is the speed at this critical situation.

(c) Base Pressure. Booster pumps produce low base pressures if the heat input is kept low. When this is done they lose their usefulness as boosters because they will not withstand high fore pressures. Hence, boosters as actually used do not produce very high vacuums. Base pressures of most boosters noted range from about 0.5 μ Hg to 1 or 2 μ Hg, depending on the conditions of operation. No concern is ever given to this feature since it does not enter into the performance of the pumping system. Boosters are not made in fractionating designs because this feature would add only expense to the system.

(d) Fore-pressure Tolerance. As previously mentioned, the fore-pressure tolerance of a booster determines the capacity of a mechanical pumping system that will be required to handle leaks of a given size. In a multiple-pump system, such as is described elsewhere, the pressure tolerance becomes the limiting factor on the amount of gas that can be handled by a header and very often dictates operational procedure.

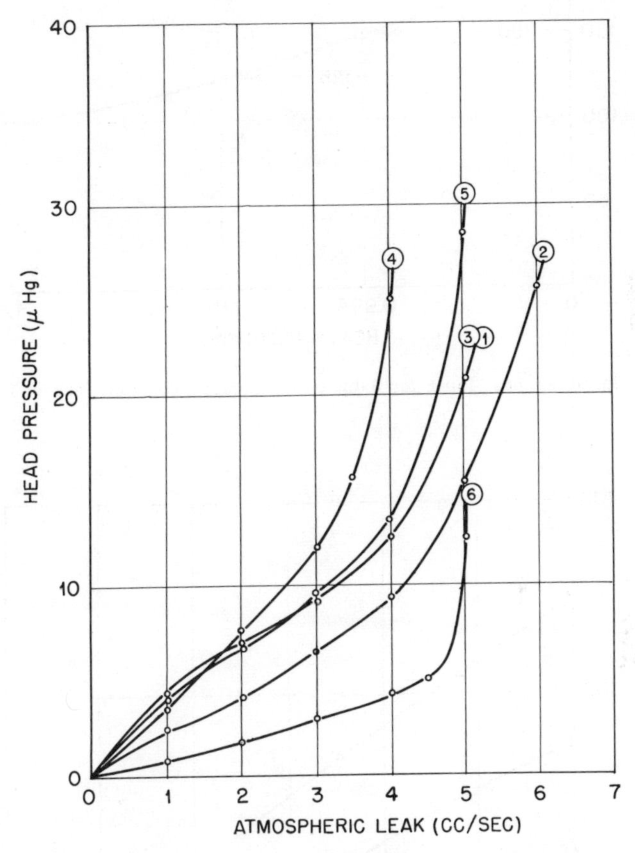

Fig. 2.15—Head pressure vs. leak for 8-in. booster pumps.

For all vacuum systems consisting of complete units, such as the one shown in Fig. 2.1, the highest fore-pressure tolerance at all leak rates is bound to produce the most efficient and trouble-free system. In cases where a number of systems are maintained by one header, the desirable situation is that of high fore-pressure tolerance for zero throughput but rather rapidly decreasing tolerance as the throughput is increased.

Aside from initial design of the nozzles, the heat input determines over a wide range what the fore-pressure tolerance will be. Figure 2.17 shows the dependence of the fore-pressure tolerance on the

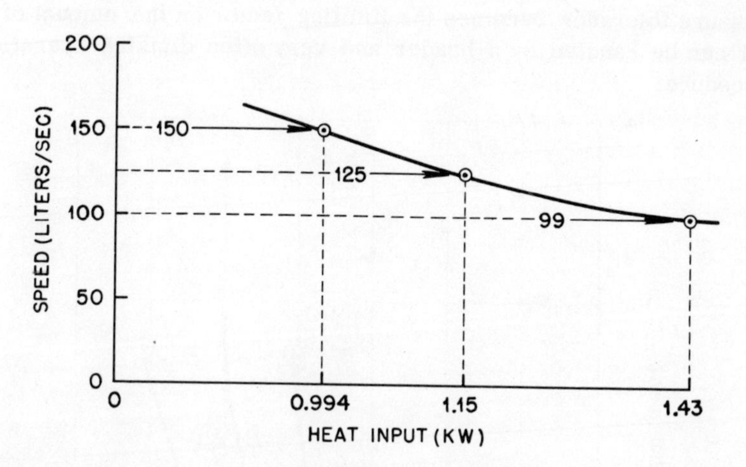

Fig. 2.16—Speed vs. heat input for 6-in. booster pump (constant leak of 1 cc/sec at 1 atm).

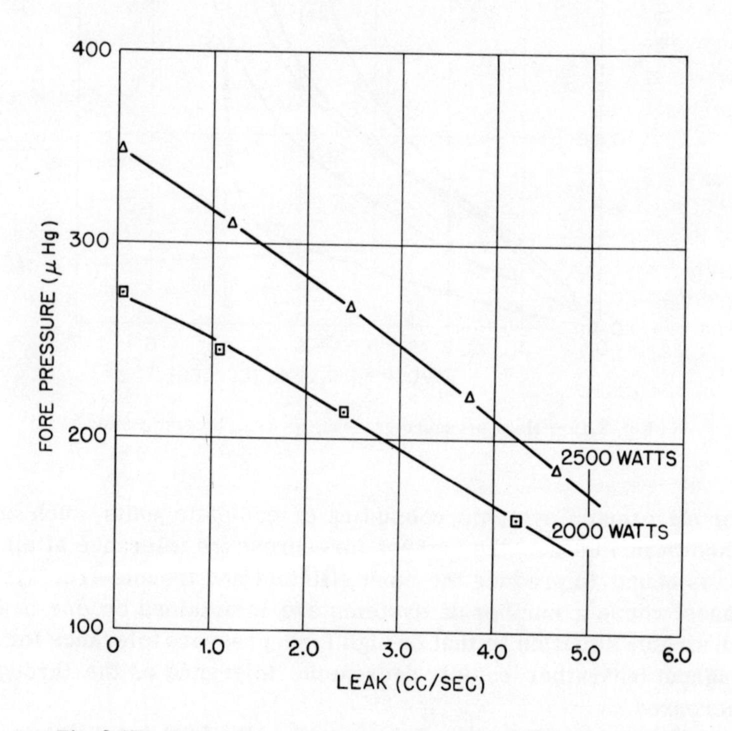

Fig. 2.17—Dependence of fore-pressure tolerance on heat input.

heat input. The maximum heat that will be effective is determined by the ability of the heaters to deliver the heat through a small area and by the heat-transfer coefficient between the metallic surfaces and the oil.

In those boosters in actual use it has been found that, unless good insulation is provided around heaters and boilers, considerable external heat loss occurs owing to radiation and convection. In the case of 8-in. boosters this loss amounts to 400 to 500 watts or about 25 per cent of the normal input of such a pump.[3] One inch of magnesia insulation around the bottom of the pump has been shown to reduce this to a negligible value.

2.6 Oil-migration Problems. (a) General. In the normal operation of any diffusion pump there is a continuous loss of pumping fluid from the pump, both to the chamber being evacuated and to the discharge system. This is a disadvantage both from the standpoint of the loss of the fluid from the pump and the damage caused by the fluid to the process or apparatus with which it is associated.

In the case of oil diffusion pumps, the loss of oil to the discharge system does no particular harm except to make replacement of the oil necessary. Migration can be prevented almost completely by making the discharge line rise vertically for a distance of 3 or 4 ft before returning it to the exhausting pump. This vertical section should be cool so that condensation is fairly complete. Normal air cooling of the pipe is usually sufficient, but if there is any doubt about the temperature in a given installation, water cooling should be applied.

The migration of oil into the high-vacuum side of the system is not so simply controlled, and solutions so far devised are makeshift at best. Although some studies of this problem have been made, the mechanisms of the migration of oil from the jets exposed to the high-vacuum side of the system are not clear. However, oil leaves the pump and passes into the high-vacuum chamber by two processes, namely, (1) evaporation of oil (or other fluid) from the upper surfaces of the pump walls and (2) direct ejection from the jet as the oil traverses the region between the nozzle and condensing wall.

Consider the second method first inasmuch as the fluid initially reaches the exposed areas only by this process. It is generally assumed that, owing to intermolecular collisions within the jet itself as well as to turbulence in the vicinity of the nozzles, some oil leaves the main jet stream in the direction of the vacuum chamber. In order to prevent this a baffle of some sort is usually placed between the first-stage nozzle and the vacuum chamber.

The design of such a baffle is based on the reduction of optical paths from the first jet into the vacuum system to zero, the conductance of the system being kept as high as possible. One of the most successful designs consists of a series of concentric water-cooled cones placed just above the top nozzle. Figure 2.18 illustrates a typical example of this design (see also Fig. 2.19b).

Baffles of the design illustrated sometimes reduce the speed of a pump in a very serious way. Thus the 20-in. pump for which this baffle (Fig. 2.18) was designed had a speed of about 5,200 liters/sec when

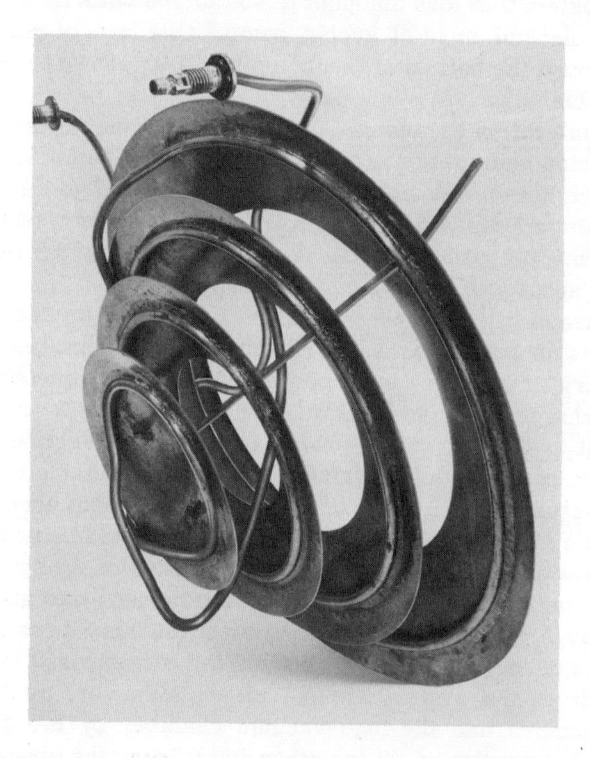

Fig. 2.18—Typical example of water-cooled cones used to reduce oil migration.

used without the baffle, but the effective speed of the same pump with the baffle installed was reduced to about 4,000 liters/sec.

The baffle should be designed not as part of the pump design but as part of the system design. If a large disk valve is used in conjuction with the pump, it has been found feasible to assume that this is effective as part of the baffle and that the baffle plates are needed to protect only that part of the system not shaded by the valve and valve-seat assembly.

In all cases provision should be made for oil-return spouts so located that the returning oil does not drip on the top nozzle or other heated parts of the pump (Fig. 2.19a). If this happens the oil is immediately reevaporated into the system.

The distribution of oil thrown from the jets is a matter of uncertainty and probably depends on (1) the nozzle design, (2) the gap between the nozzle and condensing wall, (3) the jet velocity, and (4) the gas pressure around the jet. Evidence indicates that, for nozzle designs studied, a large part (perhaps half) of the thrown vapor comes

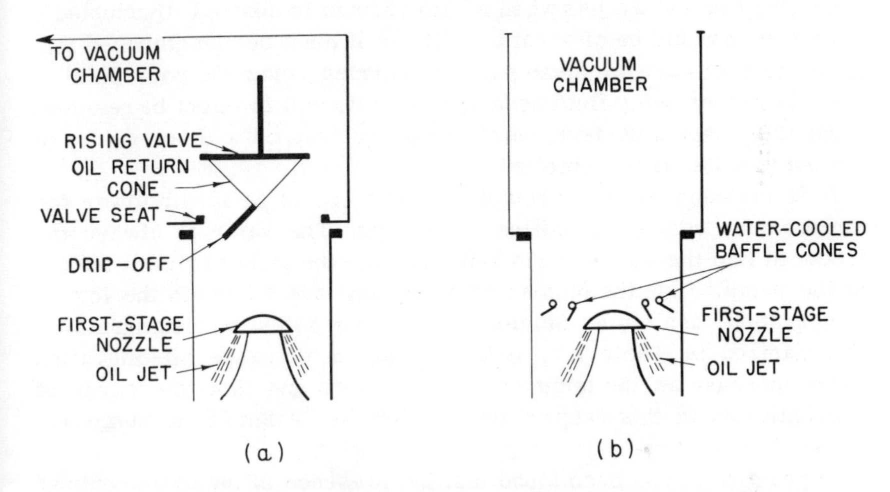

Fig. 2.19—General arrangements used to reduce oil migration. (a) Utilization of valve assembly for baffling; (b) utilization of baffle only for control.

from the vicinity of the edge of the nozzles. This is probably due to turbulence at that point. Since oil migration usually must be reduced only to certain definite values, some pumps require optical barriers only in the region of the nozzle edge to achieve the specifications demanded.

Once a baffle system has been decided on for the control of optical-path projection of oil from the jets, the first-mentioned mode of oil transfer becomes the major problem, namely, the evaporation of oil from the surfaces upon which it has collected.

Under high-vacuum conditions the loss of material by evaporation is very great, even though the vapor pressure of the material is fairly low. This problem has been specifically dealt with by Hickman[6,7] and others[8] and is the basis of molecular distillation processes.

Since at low pressures the m.f.p. of evaporated particles is very long, evaporation from a surface is uninhibited except in so far as the vapor pressure is low. Hence, once it is collected upon baffles, etc., the oil must be quickly drained back into the pump or be kept cool enough to make the evaporation rate negligible. It has been found that the ultimate vacuum produced by a pump depends greatly on the temperature of the baffles and other parts on which oil is collected. It is probably true that the ultimate vacuum produced is essentially the vapor pressure of such oil deposits.

This situation suggests refrigeration of baffles and pump walls above the first-stage jets when a high vacuum is desired. Undoubtedly refrigration would be of great benefit, but it must be remembered that if the temperature of these parts is carried below the pour point of the oil or other pump fluid used, the deposits will in effect be removed from the pumping system, since the oil so trapped will not return to the pump boiler until remelted.

It is common to use circulating water cooled in a rain tower for temperature control of baffles and pumps. The water is always introduced into the baffles first and then into the jacket coils at the top of the pump. Thus the high-vacuum regions are cooled to the lowest temperature available. Studies concerning rates of oil migration,[1] summarized in Table 2.2, indicate that in all cases oil-migration rates increase as the temperature increases and that the degree of susceptibility in this respect depends on the design of the pump and baffle.

In practice it has been found that the presence of small amounts of oil within the systems is not harmful, and consequently the retention of the oil in the pump is the primary purpose of any baffling. However, in the case of the small mass spectrographs for analytical work and for leak hunting the presence of oil soon causes the apparatus to be inoperable. The apparent cause of failure of such apparatus is the formation of a hard insulating film on the surfaces of electrodes, which causes them to act as charge accumulators rather than conductors.

When total oil exclusion is required the baffling must be essentially complete, and optical traps, such as are used on ionization gauges (Chap. 3), cooled with liquid air or liquid nitrogen are almost mandatory. Such provision should be made only when necessary, since the impedance of such devices is always high, and, if the system is large, the expense involved is great.

(b) Interpump Oil Migration. Some combinations of high-vacuum pumps and boosters show a strong tendency for one to lose its oil to the other. The best solution for this seems to be the establishment of the boilers of the two pumps at the same level and the connection of the boilers by a small tube to equalize the oil levels.

This method imposes two limitations on the system, namely, that the same pump fluid must be used in both pumps and that the booster boiler pressure must not be so great as to cause all the oil to be blown out of the booster into the larger pump. If the latter case seems to be a factor of importance, it can be compensated for by suitable adjustments in boiler level corresponding to the difference in head required.

In the event that different fluids are to be used in the two pumps, suitable baffling between the pumps will be required.

Table 2.2—Oil-migration Rate

Cooling-water temp., °C	No baffles, cc/hr		With baffles, cc/hr	
	Pump 1	Pump 2	Pump 1	Pump 2
10	1.6	3.2	0.2	0.28
30	2.5		0.25	0.77

2.7 Performance Testing of Diffusion Pumps. (a) Testing Equipment. Associated with any vacuum-pump-design program there must be a testing laboratory of some kind. This means that certain types of instruments and controls must be provided such that all desired measurements can be easily made. Laboratory equipment should include the following:

1. Power-control panel. A power-control panel capable of delivering currents at voltages applicable to the heating units involved and continuously variable from zero to the maximum values to be used should be available. It should be possible to read the current and voltage accurately.

2. Cooling-water supply. A reliable source of cold water (preferably of controlled input temperature) equipped with thermometer wells for measurement of input and output temperatures is necessary. In the event that heat-balance problems are to be attempted, a flowmeter should be included.

3. Mechanical pump. A large-capacity mechanical vacuum pump capable of base pressures down to about 20 μ Hg should be connected by a manifold to several outlets so that more than one pump can be tested at once if so desired.

4. Test domes for the sizes of pumps to be tested. These domes should be fitted with gauge openings, leak entries, and oil-collection equipment.

5. Ionization gauges. For measurement of pressure on the high-vacuum side of the pumps, reliable ionization gauges and power sup-

plies should be used. It is recommended that at least two always be used simultaneously, since reliability for such equipment is not high.

6. McLeod gauges. These gauges (see Chap. 3) are absolute-calibration instruments and within certain limits are highly valuable.

7. Pirani gauge. A Pirani gauge of good quality should supplement the McLeod gauge, since it is a continuous-reading gauge.

8. A calibrated manometer. For measuring leak rates a calibrated manometer is necessary.

9. Leak valves. Leak valves (see Chap. 4) of good design are among the most important pieces of apparatus in a vacuum-testing laboratory.

10. Interval timer or stop watch. A typical pump test setup is represented schematically in Fig. 2.20. In addition to the equipment shown, an additional leak assembly is frequently desired between the booster and the high-vacuum unit or in the foreline. The specific use of the equipment depends upon the features being investigated. The characteristics usually measured are those noted previously in this chapter.

If accurate results are to be obtained, certain precautions must be exercised as follows:

Introduction of the Leak. In testing the speed of a pump an attempt is made to obtain a measurement characteristic of the pump itself and independent of the equipment with which it is used. To this end care must be taken to see that gas introduced as an artificial load enters the pump without directional characteristics different from those occurring without the leak. In this respect a dome of the same or greater diameter than the pump is used rather than a cover plate. The height of this dome should be one or more diameters. Furthermore, the leak itself must not be introduced as a jet straight down into the pump. A simple and effective method has been found to be introduction of the leak through a tube directed at the top of the dome.

Differences of as much as 25 per cent in measured speed, caused by changing the direction of the introduced leak, have been noted. The dependence varies with the geometry of the pump and baffle.

Position of Ionization Gauges. Since it is desired to know the speed of the pump, the gauges should be placed as close to the pump as is feasible because the conductance of the dome itself is not zero. It has sometimes been desirable to measure not the speed of a pump but the effective speed of a pump and disk-valve assembly together. In this case a mock valve seat, disk, and drip cone may be inserted in the dome in their correct relative positions. The gauges should be above such an assembly.

Investigations concerning effective pressures as a function of the distance from the axis of the pump have not suggested significant differences. The direction of the gauge entry into the system has been regarded as significant by some investigators, but the author's experience indicates that if the leak is initially well distributed the differences are at least fairly small at pressures under 0.1 μ Hg.

Anomalous results have been reported by investigators who measured pressure by inserting tubes into the spaces between jets in a multistage pump. The usual results are that excessively high speeds

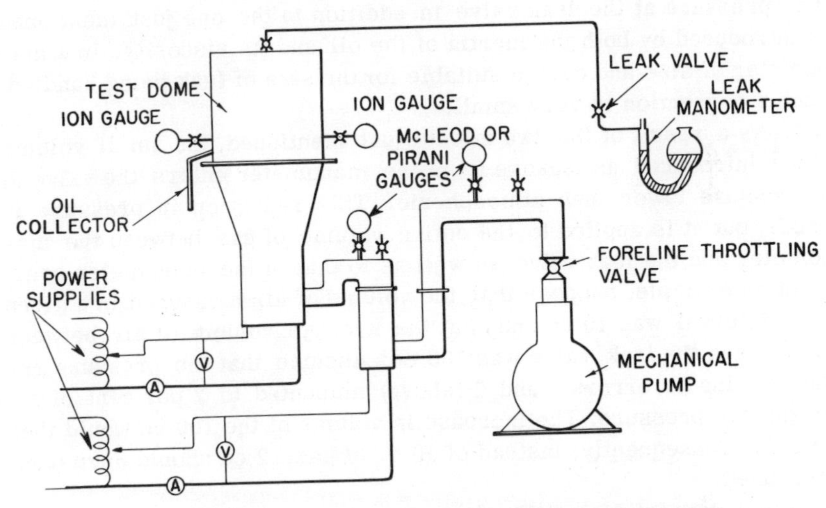

Fig. 2.20—Test setup for high-vacuum pumping system.

are reported for the jets involved. This is probably due to the fact that the leak introduced in these cases was ahead of the pump and that a fairly large part of the gas introduced became entrained in the oil from the first-stage jet and hence was never handled by the second.

Location of McLeod Gauges. In general, all gauges must be applied at the point where it is desired to know the pressure. Errors in readings will be introduced by both line drop and accumulation of condensable vapors in a region where the gauge is applied.

The latter phenomenon has been noted in measuring booster foreline tolerances by use of a foreline leak. If the gases being pumped are essentially condensable and if the foreline leak is introduced near the mechanical pump but the gauge is applied near the booster, the condensable gases are backed up into the booster but do not show on the McLeod gauge. When the leak is introduced just ahead of the gauge, true readings are obtained.

Controlled Leak and Manometer. The usual manner of introducing a known leak is to connect a U manometer containing oil in series with the leak valve. The rate of rise in the calibrated arm is noted. The following errors are introduced by this method. All of them may be neglected if design is suitable.

1. The difference in height of oil in the two arms of the manometer causes the air to be measured at other than atmospheric pressure. Correction may be made for this by subtracting the average oil head from the atmospheric pressure.

2. If the acceleration or motion of the oil is rapid, an error in actual pressure at the leak valve in addition to the one just mentioned is introduced by both the inertia of the oil and its viscosity. In a manometer of size and design suitable for the size of leak being handled, such a correction is very small.

3. As a result of the two effects just mentioned, the small volume of air introduced as leakage from the manometer enters the valve at a pressure lower than atmospheric. This reduction in pressure is small, but it is applied to the entire volume of gas between the manometer and the leak valve as well as to that in the manometer area.

As an example, suppose that the volume of air measured in a given time interval was 10 cc and that the average volume of air between the oil and the leak valve was 100 cc. Assume that the pressure reduction due to errors 1 and 2 (above) amounted to 2 per cent of atmospheric pressure. The increase in volume of the 100 cc would then be 2 cc. Consequently, instead of 10 cc of gas, 12 cc should have been measured.

Actual correction is difficult to calculate since it varies with each leak rate, but it may be made to introduce only a negligibly small error if the volume of air between the leak valve and the oil surface is kept no larger than absolutely necessary.

(b) Speed Measurements. The speed of a pump is measured by introducing a leak of known amount and noting the increase of pressure caused by the leak. Then, according to the theory developed in Chap. 1, the speed is calculated from the formula

$$S_p = \frac{760V'_{atm}}{P - P_0}$$

where V'_{atm} = volume of air in cubic centimeters admitted per second at atmospheric pressure (760 mm Hg), P is the pressure in microns of mercury observed with the pump handling the leak V'_{atm}, and P_0 is the pressure reading in microns of mercury on the ionization gauge when the leak is zero.

Since the speed of most pumps is constant over fairly wide ranges, small leaks in the system or in the ionization gauge do not change the value of S_p obtained as long as the total gas being handled does not approach the maximum that the pumping system as a whole can handle. This point has been carefully checked and well verified.

If the pressure is plotted as a function of the leak admitted, the slope of the line so plotted is the effective speed of the pump. This is a common method of representing such data even though the speed may not be read directly from such a representation.

(c) Fore-pressure Tolerance. The fore-pressure tolerance of a diffusion pump under any particular leak-load conditions is best measured by introducing a leak between the pump discharge and the mechanical pump and increasing the leak very slowly until the diffusion pump fails. In general, failure of the pump is indicated by a sudden rise in pressure on the high-vacuum side. The pressure on the vacuum side will be unaffected by rising fore pressure until total breakdown of the jet occurs.

In the event that booster fore-pressure tolerance is being measured in conjunction with a complete system including a high-vacuum pump, the head pressure should be that of the booster only. The pump-failure point should not be decided by noting the high-vacuum-pump failure. If the tests include the high-vacuum pump, the results will depend on its heat input since the failure of the booster is not sharply a function of the fore pressure.

An alternative method to admitting a leak into the foreline is simply to throttle the foreline by partially closing a valve in the line until the pressure to the cutoff valve rises, owing to the reduced gas-removal rate. This is a more difficult procedure since considerable time is required before a steady state is reached.

(d) Total Gas-handling Capacity. The gas-handling capacity (maximum leak) of a system depends upon the failure of that element of the system having the lowest capacity. In most systems failure occurs owing to the low speed of the mechanical pump. Booster cutoff is usually reached before any other element of the system fails.

The gas-handling capacity of any system depends on the whole system and is calculable on the basis of material already presented. An empirical test consists in admitting a larger and larger leak until suddenly the increase in pressure rises excessively with increased leak. The system is then said to have failed. Use of the instrumentation described will reveal the cause of breakdown in any case.

(e) Diffusion-pump Failure. Diffusion pumps can fail to operate in any one of several ways, namely, (1) failure to pump at all, (2) low gas-handling capacity, (3) low fore-pressure tolerance, (4) high base pressure, and (5) low speed. Generally there is a combination of two or more of these factors, and the causes are usually easily determined. The following analysis may be applied to pumps behaving abnormally.

Failure to Pump at All. This may be caused by (1) no oil in the pump, (2) insufficient heat in the pump, and (3) fore pressure too high owing to poor operation of the backing pump. These causes can be checked. The presence of oil in the pump can be checked by measuring the temperature of the bottom of the pump. If the pump is dry, the temperature will be considerably higher than is normal.

Low Gas-handling Capacity. The causes of low gas-handling capacity are (1) too low heat input into the pumps, (2) foreline pressure excessively high, and (3) a leak within the pump itself, which must be handled by the booster.

Low Fore-pressure Tolerance. The causes of low fore-pressure tolerance are (1) too low heat input into the booster, and (2) lack of oil in the booster pump.

High Base Pressure. A high base pressure is caused by (1) cooling water too warm or lacking, (2) high heat input into the high-vacuum pump, (3) lack of oil in the high-vacuum pump (this will also result in the loss of speed), and (4) pump fluid contaminated with high-vapor-pressure constituents.

Low Speed. Low speed indicates lack of vapor supply to the first stage of the system. This can be caused by (1) lack of oil in the high-vacuum pump and (2) heat input of high-vacuum pump too low or lacking altogether.

Any of these causes of failure can be quickly checked, and the necessary corrective steps taken. Pumps should be designed for easy checking.

2.8 Refrigerants as Pumps. In many vacuum systems where a pressure of the order of 10^{-6} mm Hg is to be maintained, it has been common practice to use cold traps or suitable absorbing materials between the vacuum chamber and the diffusion pump in order to lower the pressure due to condensable vapors. In some cases it is desirable to protect the mechanical pumps from condensable vapors, which may be corrosive or harmful to the pump oil, by the use of cold traps between the fore pumps and diffusion pumps. Since much experience was gained in the application of refrigerants to vacuum systems, it is considered advisable to record some of this experience in this section.

If a cooled surface is inserted in a system, the surface becomes a sink for all vapor-phase molecules whose vapor pressure from the liquid phase is above the temperature of that surface. Thus, if a container filled with liquid nitrogen is inserted into the system, a vacuum equivalent to the vapor pressure of the highest-vapor-pressure materials within the system at the boiling point of nitrogen will ultimately result, even though no additional pumping is done. Water may be effectively removed by liquid-nitrogen temperatures down to pressures of the order of 10^{-7} mm Hg. Consequently, for water removal and protection of equipment from water, liquid nitrogen has been extensively used. Until the vapor pressure of water at liquid-nitrogen temperature is approached, the pumping speed of the cooled area is essentially that of a perfect vacuum (see Chap. 1). Thus the speed may be considered to be about 95 liters/sec/sq in.

Since during preliminary pump-down of most systems a large fraction of the gas to be removed is water, a refrigerated surface can add greatly to the speed with which the operation takes place. It has been common practice to use thimbles having areas of about 50 sq in. per 1,000 liters of tank volume. Suppose the speed of pumps used on the systems varies from 2,500 to 5,000 liters/sec. Since a 100 sq in. thimble filled with liquid nitrogen has a speed of about 9,500 liters/sec (for water only) it can readily be seen that, as long as water is a large portion of the gas to be removed, the use of the thimble is even more effective than the use of pumps.

One great drawback in using refrigeration is that, once vapor has been condensed, it must be held on the surface until the entire operation being undertaken is completed. A number of designs for removable thimbles have been proposed (see Chap. 4). These would enable the removal of the thimble entirely once the concentration of water has been sufficiently reduced. All designs involve seals of some kind, and the possibility of their being troublesome is far from negligible.

A thimble that could be completely isolated from the high-vacuum system has been designed and actually operated.[9] Performance of this equipment indicates that, although the system may be operated without the presence of the thimble, sudden overheating from any cause quickly throws water into the system at a rate that makes the pumps inadequate. If, on the other hand, the thimble is retained, the water-removal speed is always high.

The location of refrigerant thimbles within the system is worthy of some consideration. In some types of industrial vacuum equipment economy of refrigerant has demanded a compromise in this respect. If thimbles are placed in their most effective location, they will be as close to the sources of water vapor as possible. However, the sources of water evolution are generally associated with parts heated to high temperatures. Since heat shielding of the thimble at close quarters also means decreased pumping speed, a compromise is generally necessary.

In any event the thimbles should be as close to the region of required low pressure as possible, since pressure gradients, even in fairly open equipment, are high when high-speed sinks such as thimbles are applied.

The performance of a refrigerant trap may be predicted, and design may be varied to meet any specific requirements. The actual requirements for a given process are generally only very roughly known; hence trial-and-error installations are common. Among the points that must be considered are the following:

(a) Speed. As previously mentioned, the speed of a thimble acting as a sink for a specific vapor being condensed is effectively that of an aperture of the area of the thimble (see Chap. 1). However, the effective gas removal from the processing region must be calculated by including the impedance of the line or chamber space between the thimble and the process region.

In the event that diffusion pumps remove gas over the same path at the same time (the usual case) the pressure drop across all lines should be calculated from the total gas-removal rate. The area required for effective removal rate can be calculated by considerations of this sort.

(b) Refrigerant Consumption. The rate at which the refrigerant is boiled off is governed by two factors, namely, the difference between the temperatures of the refrigerant and of the enclosure wall, and the quantity of vapor being condensed.

The heat absorbed by the refrigerant is due almost entirely to radiation, since the heat conduction by the atmosphere within a high-vacuum chamber is essentially zero. This heat may be calculated from the equation

$$H = EA\,(T_2^4 - T_1^4)$$

where H is the heat absorbed per unit of time, E is the constant of emissivity, A is the area of thimble in contact with the refrigerant, T_2 is the wall absolute ambient temperature, and T_1 is the refrigerant absolute temperature. In general, the constant E refers to black-body radiation, since as soon as a layer of condensate accumulates on the thimble the original surface of the thimble is no longer a factor.

Thus, if the latent heat of the refrigerant used is l, the weight consumed per unit of time is

$$W = EA\,\frac{T_2^4 - T_1^4}{l}$$

This is an accurate expression for thimbles open to air, since the vapor resulting from the boiling refrigerant is ejected from the thimble to the atmosphere at essentially the temperature of the boiling refrigerant.

(c) Conservation Methods. It has been shown experimentally that there can be very effective shielding against radiation without seriously decreasing the effectiveness of the refrigerant thimbles. By lining the walls of the vacuum chamber in the region surrounding the thimble with aluminum foil or sheet aluminum, savings of from 40 to 60 per cent in refrigerant could easily be made. Other experiments, involving a movable insulating shell that could be made to enclose the thimble when pumping was not required, showed that refrigerant consumption could be reduced to about 5 per cent of that consumed when no shields were used. The latter system removes the pumping value of the thimble when the shields are closed upon it.

As mentioned before, the loss of refrigerant is essentially proportional to the area of the thimble that is in actual contact with the refrigerant. Thus a thimble nearly empty will not evaporate the refrigerant as rapidly as when full. However, once vapor is condensed upon a surface, that surface must be kept cold or reevaporation will take place.

A number of constant-level control devices have been designed, but no large-scale use of them has been tried.

(d) Construction. Refrigerant thimbles have generally been made of stainless steel. Safety of design is imperative since the sudden bursting of a large thimble filled with liquid nitrogen into a vacuum system containing hot metal parts would undoubtedly produce damage.

Experimental thimbles have generally been made of roll-up stainless-steel sheet in cylindrical form with either conical or reinforced flat ends. The whole assembly must always be welded and adequately pressure-tested before use. Support of the thimble itself is usually made primarily by the filling neck, although supplementary support is sometimes desirable (see Fig. 2.21).

2.9 Refrigerant Traps. In many cases it is desired to prevent a condensable vapor from entering a given section of the system, such as the mechanical pumps and ionization gauges. In the case of the ionization gauges, liquid-nitrogen temperatures are usually required, but the mechanical pumps are, in general, adequately protected with dry ice (CO_2).

The principle used in the design of such traps involves simply the reduction of the optical-entry path to zero. Various patterns are in use. A typical glass trap is shown in Fig. 2.22. Stainless-steel traps have been used on industrial installations and are satisfactory, although their refrigerant-consumption rate is always high because of the conduction of heat through the metal stems.

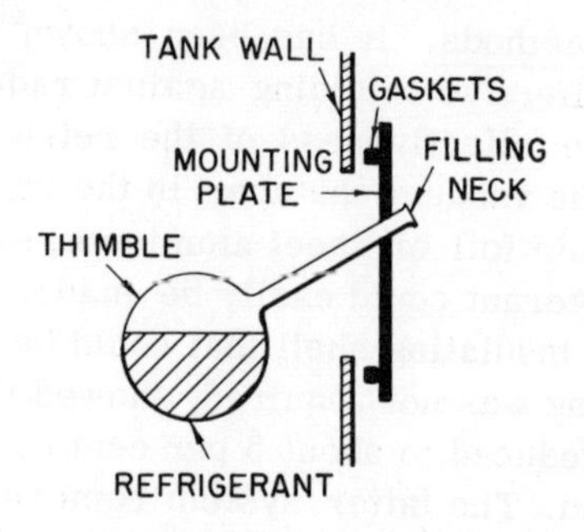

Fig. 2.21—Method of support of thimble.

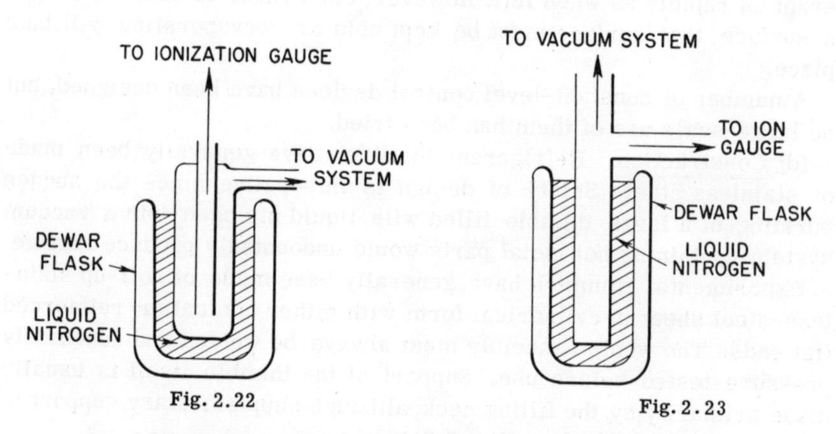

Fig. 2.22—Typical glass cold trap for protection of ionization gauge.

Fig. 2.23—Thimble used for protection of ionization gauge.

In some cases thimbles of the type shown in Fig. 2.23 were used instead of ionization-gauge traps. These are not effective in protection against reentry of condensable gases and are not to be recommended.

Traps are in some cases used to prevent the entry of water vapor into mechanical pumps. Water entering the pumps is retained in the oil and causes the base pressure to which the pump is effective to be very high.

Extremely low temperatures of liquid air or nitrogen are not necessary for the protection of mechanical pumps. The practice is to use either mechanical refrigeration or traps utilizing dry ice as a refrigerant.

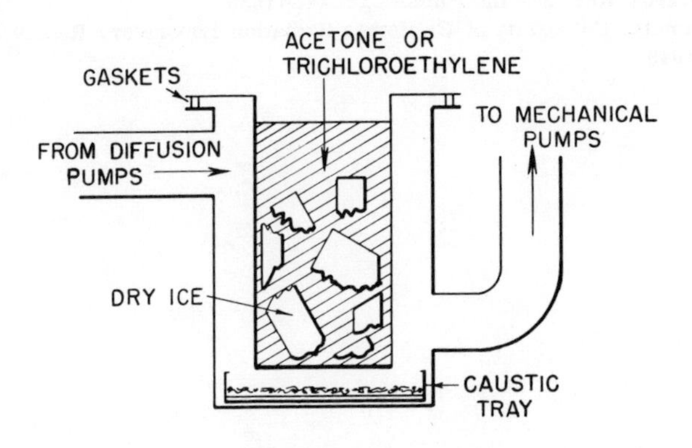

Fig. 2.24—Dry-ice trap for protection of mechanical pumps.

At the temperature of dry ice (−70° C) the vapor pressure of water is about 0.5 μ Hg. Since mechanical pumps are not required to produce pressures below 10 or 20 μ Hg, this protection is adequate. On the other hand, if mechanical refrigeration is used, temperatures of at least −50 to −60° C must be used in order to obtain adequate removal.

The exact requirements are, of course, dictated by the fore-pressure requirements of the diffusion pumps being used in the system (see Fig. 2.24).

The use of dry ice requires that a heat-transfer liquid also be used. A number of liquids including acetone and trichloroethylene have been found satisfactory. The vapors from these are dangerous, and therefore good ventilation should be provided.

REFERENCES

1. W. E. Bush and K. M. Simpson, University of California Radiation Laboratory Report RL 20.6.40, June 15, 1945.
2. W. E. Bush, University of California Radiation Laboratory Report RL 20.6.37, May 30, 1945.

3. K. M. Simpson and W. E. Bush, University of California Radiation Laboratory Report RL 20.6.35, Jan. 20, 1945.
4. W. W. Chupp, University of California Radiation Laboratory Report XL 20.6.802, Dec. 12, 1944.
5. K. M. Simpson, University of California Radiation Laboratory Report RL 20.6.39, May 18, 1945.
6. K. C. D. Hickman, J. Franklin Inst., 221: 383 (1936).
7. K. C. D. Hickman, J. Applied Phys., 11: 303 (1940).
8. H. W. Edwards, Rev. Sci. Instruments, 6: 145 (1935).
9. Alan J. Samuel, University of California Radiation Laboratory Report RL 20.6.14, Nov. 11, 1943.

Chapter 3

VACUUM GAUGES

By Kenneth M. Simpson

3.1 Introduction. It is customary to regard measurement of the vacuum obtained in a vessel as equivalent to measurement of the pressure exerted by the enclosed gas. The terminology appropriate to this conception is very well established. When a slight proportion of the gas has been removed a Bourdon gauge or mercury U tube is used, and the pressure is read. When almost all the gas is out of the vessel some other effect related to pressure is measured, e.g., the thermal conductivity of the gas, and the gauge is calibrated in terms of pressure. It frequently turns out, it will be seen, that pressure is often not the most relevant measurement, yet it is the traditional one and will do as a basis for discussion.

3.2 Types of Gauges. It is convenient to classify vacuum gauges according to the effect or property used in their operation. All the gauges considered here appear to fall into six such classes:

1. Hydrostatic pressure gauges. This class includes all gauges that depend for their action on the actual force exerted by the gas. Examples are the mercury U tube, the Bourdon gauge, the inclined oil manometer, and the click gauge. The various types of McLeod gauges also come under this heading.

2. Thermal-conductivity gauges. The Pirani and thermocouple gauges make use of the fact that the thermal conductivity of a rarified gas varies with the pressure.

3. Viscosity gauges. Langmuir's viscosity gauge is an example of viscosity gauge. These gauges depend on the fact that the viscosity of a rarified gas varies with the pressure.

4. Gauges depending on the radiometer effect. The Knudsen gauge is the only important example of a gauge that depends on the radiometer effect.

5. Ionization gauges. A number of types of gauges depend on measuring the ion current produced in a rarified gas by a variety of agencies. Examples are Dushman's triode ionization gauge, the Philips ionization gauge, and the Alphatron.

6. Discharge tubes. The physical characteristics of a high-voltage discharge produced in a tube attached to a vacuum system may be used to give a measure of the gas pressure in the system.

The operator of a vacuum system will want to know the range of a gauge, whether it reads pressure or molecular concentration, whether the calibration is linear, and how its readings depend on the gas. On a more practical level, he will want to know whether the readings are continuous or intermittent, whether it will read pressures due to vapors, whether it should be connected to the vessel by a tube or placed within the vessel, whether it is remote reading, the possibility of using it as a leak-detecting instrument, and the effects of temperature and of magnetic fields on the gauge. On a still more practical level, there is considerable interest in the cheapness, ruggedness, and availability of the gauge. These questions will be kept in mind in the following expositions.

3.3 Hydrostatic Pressure Gauges. Of the hydrostatic pressure gauges the most important thus far utilized in vacuum work are the various varieties of McLeod gauges, but before discussing them a word or two will be said about some others.

When dealing with pressures in the micron range it is convenient to remember that a pressure of 1 μ Hg is approximately 1 dyne/sq cm. To make any direct measurement of pressures in the region below 1 mm Hg thus requires very sensitive equipment. The measurement of the small forces involved means that any mechanical system used must be very sensitive. The low-pressure side of the instrument must also be maintained at a fixed low pressure. A number of types of differential manometers have been described in the literature, several references being listed at the end of this chapter.[1,2] The difficulties involved have led in almost all cases to the use of other methods. However, in the case of vapor-pressure measurements these other methods sometimes have such difficulties of their own that mechanical diaphragms have been used. The click gauge described in physical-chemistry texts employs such a diaphragm—a thin flattish bubble of glass that snaps inside out at a critical pressure. Another method has been to use a vane hung on a torsion suspension. Close clearances around the vanes cut the leakage, and fast pumping keeps the pressure to a negligible value on the low-pressure side.

For slightly higher pressures an inclined U tube containing some low-vapor-pressure low-viscosity fluid such as butyl phthalate or butyl sebacate may be used. The low-pressure side must have a known pressure if more than pressure differences are to be obtained. The use of oil produces a gain of a factor of about 15 over mercury, and inclining of the tube gives a gain of a factor of 5 or 10. Readings

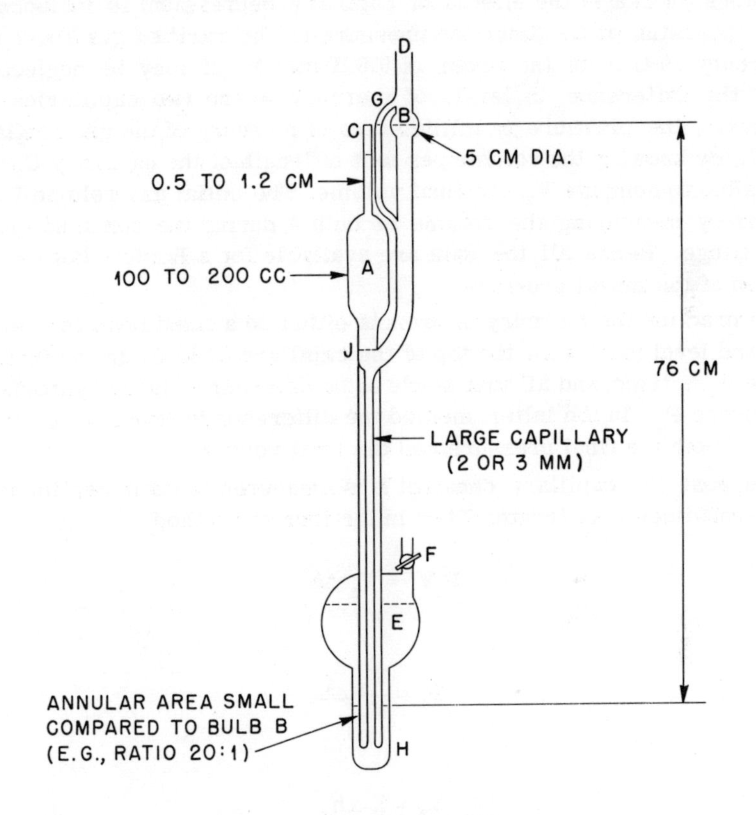

Fig. 3.1 — Form of McLeod gauge.

of 50 μ Hg are possible. Hickman,[3] Hickman and Weyerts,[4] Malmberg and Nicholas,[5] and others[6,7,8] have described the use of oils in manometers.

(a) McLeod Gauges. In the typical McLeod gauge, a known large volume V_1 of rarified gas at pressure P_1 is compressed into a known small volume V_2 at a pressure P_2 that is large enough to be measured hydrostatically. If the Boyle's law relation, $P_1V_1 = P_2V_2$, is used, then P_1 may be calculated.

In the form shown in Fig. 3.1 the rarified gas enters the bulb through the large tube D when the mercury is in the reservoir E. By opening the three-way cock F to the atmosphere the mercury is raised through the large capillary, and as it passes J it seals off the gas in bulb A. As the mercury continues to rise the gas confined in A is compressed more and more until it is entirely within the small capillary C. Another section of the capillary cut from the same piece of stock (to cancel the effects of capillary depression) is included in the apparatus at G. Since the pressure of the rarified gas above the mercury in G is of the order of 0.001 mm Hg it may be neglected, and the difference in levels of mercury in the two capillaries is, directly, the pressure in millimeters of mercury of the gas confined in C. By knowing the volume per unit of length of the capillary C it is possible to compute V_2, the final volume. The initial gas volume V_1 is found by measuring the volume of bulb A during the construction of the gauge. Hence all the data are available for a Boyle's law calculation of the initial pressure.

In practice the mercury is brought either to a fixed level in C or to a fixed level even with the top of the capillary C, in G. In the former case V_2 is fixed, and all that needs to be determined is the hydrostatic pressure P_2. In the latter method the difference in levels is a measure of both the final pressure and the final volume.

Suppose the capillary constant k is measured in cubic centimeters per millimeter of length. Then in the former method

$$P_1V_1 = V_2 \, \Delta h$$

or

$$P_1 = \frac{V_2}{V_1} \Delta h$$

and

$$V_2 = k \, \Delta h_0$$

where Δh_0 is the length of the capillary C, as measured from the mark to which the mercury is always brought to the end of the capillary. Since V_2/V_1 is a constant, this method allows a linear scale to be mounted behind the capillaries.

In the second method

$$P_1V_1 = \Delta h \cdot \Delta h \, k$$

hence

$$P_1 = \frac{k}{V_1} (\Delta h)^2$$

This method yields a quadratic scale. It has the virtue of being expanded at the low-pressure end where measurement is most difficult.

In any McLeod gauge the pressure is amplified in the ratio V_1/V_2. The value of V_1 is usually of the order of 100 cc; 200 cc is quite practical, but 1,000 cc of mercury is awkward to work with. The value of V_2 depends on the diameter of the capillary. If the capillary is made less than 0.5 mm in diameter, extreme care and cleanliness must be exercised in the construction and operation of the gauge, or the mercury will stick in the capillary. One millimeter in diameter is quite satisfactory. The sticking of the mercury has two detrimental effects: First, it leads to erroneous values of the final pressure P_2; the error may amount to several millimeters. This trouble may be somewhat tediously overcome by tapping the capillaries with a finger or pencil. Second, the sticking may lead to a breaking of the mercury thread, leaving a portion very firmly lodged in the capillary. This piece is usually brought down by repeated tapping. If this method fails, warming the glass with a soft flame usually works. Owing to these two limitations of weight and sticking, amplifications of more than 100,000 fold are difficult to work with.

Several methods are utilized in raising the mercury in the McLeod gauge. In one method a reservoir is connected by a rubber tube to the McLeod. In another a plunger is used. The method of Fig. 3.1 is more convenient where a rough vacuum is available. This model, introduced at the University of California Radiation Laboratory by S. M. Duke, has two refinements that are worth the slight extra complication. The large capillary connecting the reservoir and the bulb prevents a too rapid surge of mercury upward into the bulb and capillary when the reservoir is opened to the atmosphere. Such surging may break the gauge and frequently is a cause of a small thread of mercury becoming separated from the rest of the capillary. Too rapid a dropping of the mercury is also avoided. The second refinement is the constriction at the bottom of the reservoir and the expanded area at B. By making the area of B large compared to the area of the annulus between the large capillary and the reservoir the greater part of any change in barometric height can take place in the reservoir. Thus when the right amount of mercury has been put in the gauge the level will come up to the proper point in B, and hence in G, when the reservoir is opened to the atmosphere. A large number of designs of mercury McLeod gauges have been described in the literature. Some of the references are included at the end of this chapter.[9-13]

In the tilting McLeod gauge, originally described by Reiff,[14] the reservoir is always in communication with the vacuum being measured and is run into the bulb by tilting. Because of its compactness this type of gauge is very convenient. Many of them have been used at the Radiation Laboratory for the measurement of fore-vacuum pressures (most of these gauges were manufactured by the F. J. Stokes Machine Co.).

The pressure range of the mercury McLeod is from 10^{-6} up to 1 mm Hg for an extremely large bulb and fine capillary. The range of any one gauge is, however, much less. The lowest pressure that can be accurately and conveniently read with a 200-cc bulb and a 1-mm capillary is perhaps 10^{-4} mm Hg.

(b) Oil McLeod Gauge. From time to time, attempts have been made to use some other fluid, e.g., an oil, instead of mercury in a McLeod gauge. With so light a fluid a barometric column would be over 30 ft high; it is therefore necessary to have the fluid under vacuum on both sides. A very sensitive oil McLeod gauge described by Bannon[15] accomplished the raising and lowering of the oil by means of a magnetically operated glass plunger. Kirby[16] at the Radiation Laboratory developed, for use with an oil, a tilting McLeod gauge that accomplished the raising and lowering quite simply. A diagram of the gauge is shown in Fig. 3.2. It differs from the usual mercury tilting McLeod gauge in that the rotation is only 45 deg in order that the capillary will be steep enough to allow the oil to drain from it quickly. Butyl phthalate, butyl sebacate, and Litton Molecular C oil were tried. Butyl sebacate drained from the capillary most satisfactorily. Some of the new silicone oils should be even better. This gauge has two principal disadvantages: First, gas is absorbed in the oil used. It must be driven out by prolonged heating under vacuum. In practice the oil in the reservoir was heated with a bunsen burner until bubbling ceased, and then the gauge was left under vacuum for several hours before use. A valve in the vacuum line was used to keep the gauge under vacuum at all times. The second disadvantage is that the fluid had a tendency to stick in the capillary at the point where the capillary joined the bulb. A cylindrical heater, made of a thin tube of nichrome, slipped over the capillary was used to free the oil when it stuck.

The advantages of the gauge were that the sensitivity was increased about fourfold over that of the same gauge using mercury (the square root of the ratio of the densities, $\sqrt{13.6/0.92}$ in the case of butyl sebacate), that the oil had no tendency to "stick" in the fashion of mercury, and that the gauge was light in weight. Of these advantages the greatest is the absence of sticking. Readings could be repeated, and by different observers, as closely as the scale could be read. Readings have been made between 10^{-6} and 10^{-3} mm Hg. No absorption of rarified gas was observed. The oil McLeod gauge proved to be a useful research instrument.

The McLeod gauge was the first successful high-vacuum gauge, and it remains today the only satisfactory "absolute" gauge, i.e., a gauge whose calibration can be determined from measurements of the dimensions of the gauge. Although it is possible to calibrate other

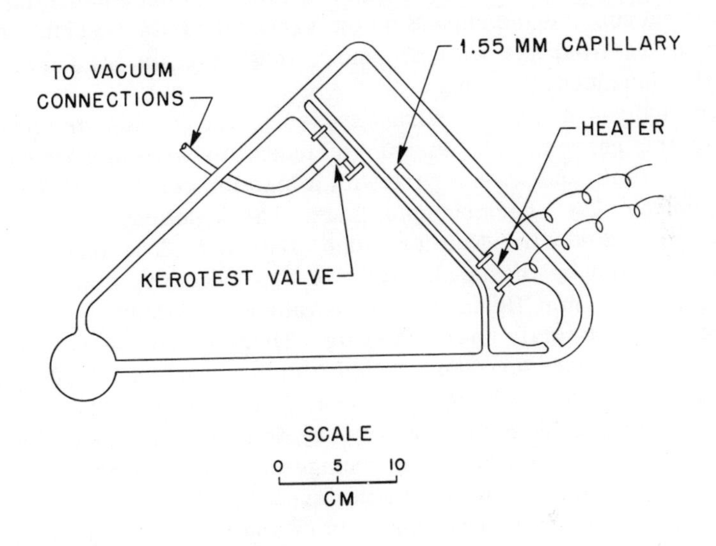

Fig. 3.2—Tilting oil McLeod gauge.

gauges by admitting a known mass of gas into a known large volume, it is still more customary to calibrate other gauges against a McLeod gauge. It has, however, several serious disadvantages. It does not read the pressure of condensable vapors, or at least not reliably. As water vapor is the main constituent of the atmosphere in many large vacuum systems this is a serious score against the McLeod gauge. The gauge is inherently intermittent in its operation, and the practical frequency with which readings may be taken is not much over once a minute. This fact makes it a poor device to use as a leak detector. Further, the McLeod gauge does not lend itself to remote readings or automatic control of any process. In some applications the presence of mercury vapor is an objectionable contaminant. Although some very rugged McLeod gauges have been built for use on industrial systems, e.g., mercury-arc rectifiers, the more sensitive McLeod gauges are fragile and bulky; on many large industrial types of vacuum systems fragility is a danger not only to the gauge but to the whole system. Moreover, the fact that the gauge reads the pressure of the gas independently of the nature of the gas is, as will be shown, a disadvantage in many modern systems. Nevertheless, the McLeod gauge's simplicity, reliability, and cheapness preserve for it a firm place in laboratory work and, in the range from 1 μ to several millimeters of mercury, in industrial plants.

3.4 Thermal-conductivity Gauges. Two common and useful varieties of vacuum gauges depend on the variation of the thermal conductivity of rarified gas with pressure; these two are the Pirani gauge and the thermocouple gauge.

Both gauges use a fine wire exposed to the vacuum and heated by an electric current. The Pirani[17] includes this wire in a Wheatstone-bridge circuit and uses a wire with a high temperature coefficient of resistance. The thermocouple gauge has a delicate thermocouple fixed to a heated wire. Neither gauge is absolute. The upper pressure range is fixed by the conductivity of gas, becoming almost constant above about 1 mm Hg pressure. Pirani gauges have been made to operate satisfactorily up to 3 mm Hg. There is no theoretical lower limit. In practice, however, it is difficult to work below 10^{-3} mm Hg with these gauges. There are several reasons for this difficulty. Heat is carried from the hot wire by the gas, by conduction to the supports, and by radiation. Any change in the heat conductivity of the joints between the fine wire and the support will change the calibration. As the pressure is lowered more and more, the loss of heat by molecular transfer goes down, while the loss of heat by radiation stays approximately constant (see Sec. 1.7, Chap. 1). DuMond and Pickels[18] have calculated that, for a typical wire and for a pressure of 3×10^{-5} mm Hg, the loss by gaseous transfer is only 1 per cent of the loss by radiation for moderate temperature rises. At pressures between this value and about ten times this value the calibration will be greatly upset by any change in the emissivity of the wire surface and the bulb surface. Such changes may occur because of the presence of oil vapor or any other contaminant found in a dirty vacuum system. Furthermore, the heat transferred by the molecules of gas may itself change owing to a change in the character of the surface of the hot wire, for a change in the surface will, in general, produce a change in the accommodation coefficient, i.e., the gas molecules will come closer than before to approaching the temperature of the hot wire when they strike it. The accommodation coefficient is also different for different gases on the same surface. This is one reason for doubting that a transfer from a calibration for one gas to a calibration for another can be safely made.

Once at the Radiation Laboratory, when the problem of finding a substitute for triode ionization gauges had become acute, an attempt was made to use a Pirani gauge at low pressure. It was not found possible to hold the zero setting well enough to use the gauge even at 10^{-4} mm Hg, whereas it was necessary to have a gauge reading below 10^{-5} mm Hg. In general, the experience was that Pirani calibrations in the 1- to 100-μ Hg range were fairly stable but that the zero point shifted.

The sensitivity of a Pirani gauge decreases rapidly as the pressure is increased, owing to the fact that collisions between molecules become more frequent and that the thermal conductivity tends to become independent of the pressure (see Sec. 1.7). A gain in sensitivity can be obtained by employing a small wire-to-wall distance. Rittner[19] has described a gauge consisting essentially of a 1-mil tungsten wire mounted in a 2-mm pyrex capillary tube, which it is claimed will measure pressures of 15 mm Hg with an accuracy of ±2.5 per cent.

In the usual Pirani gauge a dummy tube just like the one connected to the vacuum is used for one arm of the bridge. This tube is highly exhausted and sealed off. The two tubes are mounted together so that they will have the same ambient temperature. The bridge is balanced while the gauge tube is under high vacuum. The unbalanced current of the bridge is then taken as an index of the pressure. The bridge is frequently operated with a fixed voltage across it, although fixed current could be used.

In another commercial type of gauge two dummy tubes in opposite arms of the bridge balance against two gauge tubes in opposite arms. The sensitivity is doubled by this device. Also the dummy tubes are open to the atmosphere, and the bridge is balanced when the pressure to be read is high rather than zero. These gauges have proved very stable. The meter is adjusted to read full scale at zero pressure. A large number of designs of Pirani gauges and associated circuits have been described in the literature. Several references are included at the end of this chapter.[20-23]

A typical thermocouple-gauge circuit is shown in Fig. 3.3. The heater current may be alternating or direct. The gauge is usually operated with a constant current in the heater.[24] The cold junction of the thermocouple is, effectively, at the heavy leads to the thermocouple and hence at the temperature of the meter case. As the temperature difference between the case and the hot wire is unaffected by small changes in the temperature of the case, no temperature control or dummy tube is required in the use of the thermocouple gauge. The thermocouple gauge has the virtue of simplicity and the disadvantage of having an extremely nonlinear scale. It is very useful in fore-vacuum systems where great accuracy is not required. The calibration may be changed by changing the heater current. A low value of heater current and a sensitive meter in the thermocouple

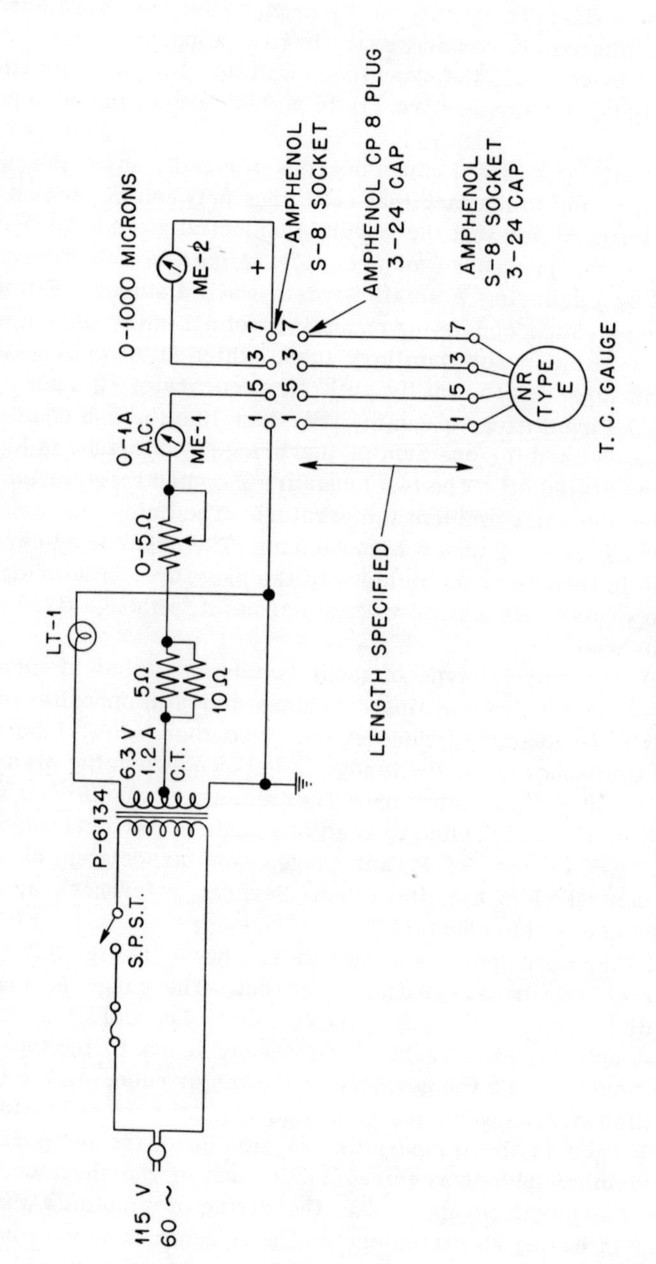

Fig. 3.3 — Thermocouple-gauge electrical circuit.

circuit spread the scale at low pressure, and a high current and a less sensitive meter spread it at higher pressures. Amdur and Pearlman[25] have described a thermocouple gauge claimed to be capable of measuring pressures down to 10^{-4} mm Hg. Pirani and thermocouple gauges compete with McLeod gauges and with the Alphatron gauge. Their advantages over McLeod gauges for industrial application are numerous. They respond to vapors, read continuously and remotely, need not be fragile or bulky, and may be used in an automatic control system. Their selective response to hydrogen and helium makes them useful for leak hunting. No damage is done to these gauges if the vacuum system is let down to atmospheric pressure while they are on.

3.5 Viscosity Gauges. Two principal varieties of viscosity gauges are described in the literature.[26-28] In the simplest[26] form a quartz fiber or strip is set into vibration, and the time for the vibration to drop to one-half amplitude is taken as a measure of the pressure. In the more complicated form[27] a disk supported by a fine fiber is rotated in the gas through an angle by a parallel rotating disk, the angle of twist depending on the gas pressure. The simple form has found some use because of its ease of construction and because it is well adapted to use with chemically active vapors.

3.6 The Knudsen Gauge. The Knudsen gauge[18,29-31] consists of a light vane suspended by a fine wire between two heaters (see Fig. 3.4). The gas molecules that gain momentum at the heaters bombard the vane more than do those molecules that hit the opposite side of the vane. The force of repulsion in dynes per square centimeter between heater and vane is

$$K = \frac{P}{4} \cdot \frac{T_1 - T}{T}$$

where P is the pressure in dynes per square centimeter, T is the temperature of the vane (and case), and T_1 is the temperature of the heater. The necessary conditions are that the separation between repelling surfaces be small compared to the mean path of the molecules and that, for this formula to hold, $(T_1 - T) \ll T$. When the first condition is not satisfied, convection currents arise causing erratic behavior of the vane. A mirror, light, and scale are used to measure deflection.

As may be seen from the formula the action is independent of the kind of gas in the gauge, and the pressure of those vapors that do not condense at the temperature of the gauge may be read. No other high-vacuum gauge has this property. Other virtues of the Knudsen gauge are that it is very nearly linear, that it involves no medium such as mercury with an undesirable vapor, that its use involves no expensive electrical measuring instruments, that there is no cracking of vapors, that there is very little likelihood of its calibration changing, as it is quite stable, and that there is no filament to burn out. With care this type of gauge can be used to measure pressures as low as 5×10^{-9} mm Hg. These merits have won it an increasing place in vacuum work.

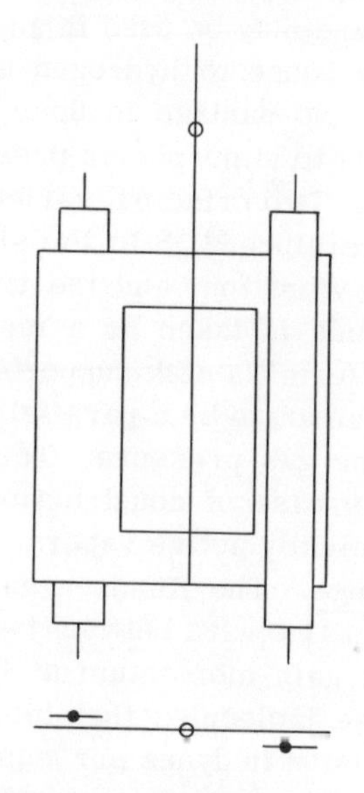

Fig. 3.4—Knudsen gauge.

There must be balanced against these virtues some very serious defects, particularly for industrial use. The first of these is its delicacy. A very firm vibration-free support is required, and the vacuum connection to the test vessel must be flexible if the test vessel vibrates because of the mechanical pumps (the usual case). The period is long (e.g., 10 sec), and since there is no air damping of the vane it must be of metal; a strong permanent magnet must be used for damping. The gauge must be let down to atmospheric pressure slowly, or the vane and suspending wire will be blown around so violently that they will be damaged. It would probably be easier to protect an ionization-gauge filament from this damage than to protect the suspension of a Knudsen gauge. Often a serious disadvantage in industrial use results from the fact that the gauge is not adapted to remote reading. The range may be increased by changing the heater temperature. Even so, the range is narrower than for an ionization gauge, and the change cannot be made so quickly as by a change of amplification.

A Knudsen gauge was constructed at the Radiation Laboratory following the design of DuMond and Pickels.[18] Platinum-foil strip heaters, having less heat capacity and more radiating surface, allowed a much more rapid check of the cold zero of the instrument than did the coiled-nichrome-wire heaters described by them. The gauge had ample sensitivity but was difficult to outgas. Moreover, in a laboratory where there is much magnetic dust it appears difficult to prepare a vane that will not exhibit marked magnetic properties. The problem of damping a gauge of this sort has been solved in the case of one variety by the use of a foil strip suspended from one edge instead of by a torsion wire. Such a device requires the use of a microscope to read the position of the foil.

It should be mentioned that Knudsen gauges are now commercially available and that they were successfully used on lens-coating systems during the war. The objections to this gauge appear to be the sort that can be overcome by technical advances, whereas difficulties that are characteristic of the McLeod gauge, the Pirani gauge, or the thermocouple gauge appear to be fundamental.

3.7 Ionization Gauges. Of the several types of ionization gauges, all have the common feature of measuring an ionization current that is proportional, for any one gas, to the molecular concentration. Inasmuch as the probability of a molecule being ionized by bombardment by a charged particle is almost independent of the thermal velocity of the molecule, the gauge may be more properly said to measure the molecular concentration in its electrode region rather than the pressure there. The different types of gauges vary in the manner of forming positive ions and in the manner of collecting them. All require calibration, although variation in sensitivity among examples of the same model is no greater than, for example, variation among specimens of a given amplifier tube.

Three main classes of ionization gauges are as follows: (1) thermionic ionization gauges, (2) the Philips ionization gauge, cold cathode, and (3) the Alphatron, a radioactive source of ionization.[32-35]

3.8 Thermionic Ionization Gauges. These gauges all employ a hot cathode for supplying electrons, a filament being used in all commercial types. These electrons are accelerated by a potential of from 100 to 300 volts and ionize gas molecules, which are collected on a negative electrode.

The type of gauge most frequently encountered is a triode,[36-38] the physical arrangement of which is somewhat as shown in Fig. 3.5. The usual method of operation is as follows: The filament is heated by an alternating current[39] that is automatically controlled so as to give a constant electron current to the positive grid of, for example, between 1 and 20 ma. With a fixed supply of electrons, accelerated by a given electrode of fixed potential, the rate of ion formation will be proportional to the molecular concentration, and these positive ions will be collected on the negative plate. The current in the plate circuit is found to be proportional to the molecular concentration, for a given gas, over a wide range of pressures, from the lowest that can be obtained, about 10^{-8} to 10^{-3} or even 10^{-2} mm Hg. The upper limit of usefulness is fixed by filament life rather than departure from linearity.

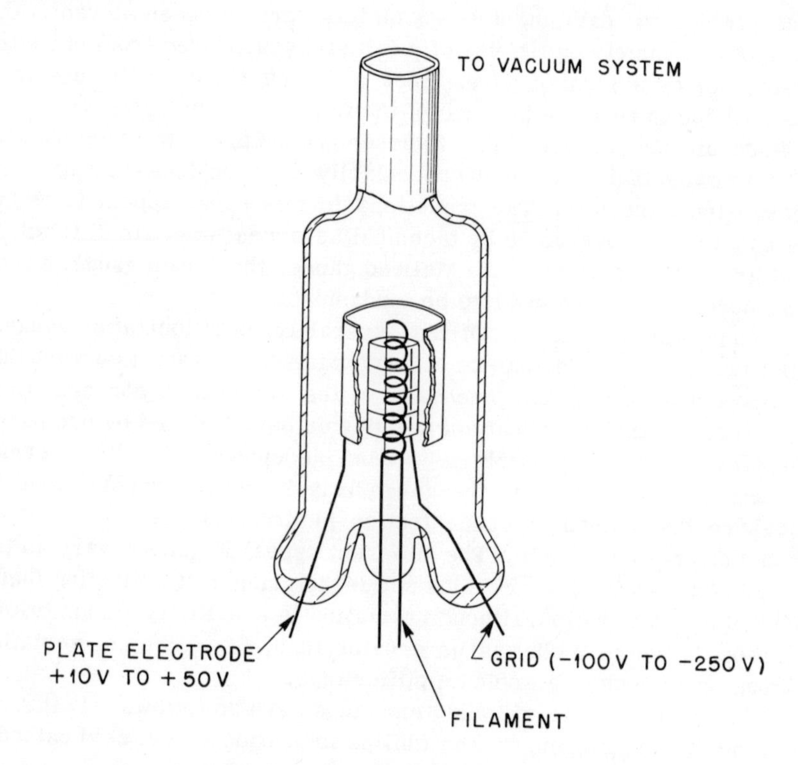

Fig. 3.5 — Triode ionization gauge.

The sensitivity of an ionization gauge for a given gas is usually stated in microamperes of positive-ion current per micron of mercury pressure (in the test vessel at room temperature). The sensitivity thus defined depends so linearly on the emission that it is possible to define a sensitivity per milliampere of emission which will provide a better figure of merit for use in the comparison of gauges. Experience at the Radiation Laboratory indicates that the various available commercial gauges do not differ by more than a factor of 6 in sensitivity under the same operating conditions. Qualitative evidence indicates that those gauges with large grid-to-plate spacing have high sensitivity. It is not difficult to predict the sensitivity of a conventional triode gauge to within a factor of 2 or 3. Commercial gauges agree among themselves so well that only very accurate work would justify individual calibration. Such calibration should be regarded as a calibration of the power supply plus the gauge. Most shifts in calibration have been traced to the supply rather than to the triode. A ± 5 per cent variation would probably be a fair estimate of the outside limits for commercial gauge calibrations.

A large number of circuits have been devised for use with triode thermionic ionization gauges.[40,41] Of several built and used at the Radiation Laboratory the one that proved most satisfactory and was also judged more satisfactory than several commercial ones that were tried is described later in this chapter. In use the gauge presents a number of problems, whatever circuit is used for supplying voltages and indicating currents, and these will now be considered under three main headings: (1) outgassing problems, (2) filament problems, and (3) leakage problems.

The first of these problems is, to be sure, not peculiar to the ionization gauge. Outgassing is troublesome in the ionization gauge because this device is being used to measure low pressures. The effect of outgassing is to add a Δp to the pressure in the vessel, a Δp that is proportional to the rate of outgassing and to the impedance of the line connecting the tube to the vessel. The rate of outgassing at constant temperature falls off gradually and may be negligible in a few hours even if the impedance is high. The outgassing can be made much more rapid by increasing the temperature. The glass envelope may be flamed with a soft flame, or the metal electrodes may be heated in a variety of ways. In the Distillation Products, Inc., VGIA gauge the plate is a thin metal film deposited on the inside of the glass envelope and is heated by flaming the glass. The grid may be heated by passing current through it since it is constructed in the form of a continuous spiral. An induction heater was devised at the Radiation Laboratory for heating the plate of the Eimac 35T. The hot plate heated the grid and also the envelope by radiation. The method that has persisted, although it has faults, is that of electron bombardment. It is easy to arrange the supply circuit so that by pressing a switch a high supply of electrons can be accelerated to plate and grid, at, for example, 150 to 200 volts. The bombardment heats the metals and thus increases the outgassing, but the increase is much greater than would be obtained by equal heating by other methods. This bombardment method has been combined with an increase in tubulation size. The Western Electric ionization gauge that is commonly used in the Radiation Laboratory is normally retubulated, the 12-mm tube with which it comes being replaced by a 20- or 22-mm tube. This change alone cuts the error due to outgassing by a factor of 10. The Distillation Products, Inc., VGIA gauge comes equipped with adequate tubulation. One-inch valves are now generally used instead of the small refrigerator valves previously used. With these, the large pumping speeds out of the gauge make it appear likely that the superiority of one electrode metal over another in respect to outgassing becomes unimportant where measurement of the pressures in large metal systems is concerned. It has occasionally been possible to hang the electrodes within the vacuum vessel. In such cases no heating is necessary. The very small impedance from the interior of the plate system to the tank cuts the Δp to a negligible quantity.

(a) Filaments. No hot cathode that will last for more than a few thousand hours even in a highly evacuated sealed tube has yet been devised. With careful use, on a clean dry system, under high-vacuum conditions, an ionization-gauge filament sometimes lasts for more than 1,000 hr. In a vacuum system containing oil, halogens, and water, a few hour's use may cause it to be hopelessly poisoned or broken.

The filament may be protected by the use of a liquid-air trap between the gauge and vacuum system; however, this prevents the gauge from indicating the line pressure in the system.

The problems characteristic of ionization gauges are of considerable importance when dealing with large-scale vacuum equipment. The principal problem is concerned with the characteristics of filaments in conventional triodes. The commonly used hot cathodes are pure tungsten wire, thoriated tungsten with or without carburetion, directly heated oxide-coated filaments, and oxide-coated cylinders heated by a separate heater. Indirectly heated cathodes were not tried to any extent at the Radiation Laboratory. They seemed likely to give trouble, and no tubes so equipped that were not otherwise undesirable could be found. The other varieties of cathodes listed above are all used by various manufacturers of ionization gauges.

The oxide-coated filament has the virtue of requiring very little power for a given emission. Under good vacuum conditions it may be just faintly red. However, it can be badly poisoned by oil vapor or water vapor, in which case several times as much power is necessary, or it may be impossible to reactivate the oxide at all. Sputtering at high pressures is very damaging to the oxide coating, tending to remove it mechanically.

Thoriated tungsten required higher temperatures and more power than oxide-coated filaments but is less subject to poisoning by water vapor. The filament of the Eimac 35T tube appeared to stand poisoning less effectively than some other, perhaps more liberally thoriated, filaments. It was felt that there would be no loss in using a thoriated-tungsten filament, as it could not become worse than a pure-tungsten filament. However, the change in power required when the filament becomes poisoned is very great, and this fact puts severe requirements on the power supply and regulator and may cause a change in calibration.

Pure tungsten has the virtue of being fairly predictable in behavior and of being impossible to poison permanently. Power requirements are high but do not change suddenly or erratically. They change owing to conduction of heat by gas at high pressures and owing to change in diameter of the wire with use. The great fault of tungsten is that it wears rapidly in the presence of water vapor.

At the Radiation Laboratory it was believed that operating the filaments hot shortened their lives. This belief was based on the effect of positive-ion bombardment of the filament, the effect of evaporation, and the effect of chemical attack on the filament. This view was tested by Bush[43] for the case of tungsten and tantalum in water vapor and air.

Four triode gauges were constructed, three having 10-mil tungsten filaments and the fourth having a 15-mil tungsten filament. The three 10-mil filaments were run at emissions of 0.010, 0.50, and 5.0 ma, respectively. The filaments wore away at essentially the same rate in an atmosphere of air at a pressure of 1 μ Hg with water vapor at 1 μ Hg pressure. The 15-mil filament at 0.50 ma emission lasted longer than the other filaments, in proportion to its diameter. The filament emitting 5.0 ma must have been subjected to 500 times as much positive-ion bombardment as the one emitting 0.010 ma, and yet it actually lasted longer.

The results, shown in Fig. 3.6, demonstrate that nothing is gained by operating these filaments at low emission in an atmosphere of water vapor. They also appear to show that positive-ion bombardment is of small importance compared to the chemical action of water. Further, it appears evident that longer life can be obtained by increasing the diameter of filament wire and that the rate of chemical transfer of tungsten is not greatly different over the range of temperature from 1300 to 2400°C. In all tests, in fact, the higher temperature gave longer life, although not conclusively so. Power requirements increase rapidly with increase in filament diameter, and, in particular, current must be increased, which means heavy lead wires. It is evident that evaporation was never a serious problem in the Radiation Laboratory use of filaments.

The above tests also terminated any interest in a novel method of operating gauges that had attracted some interest at the Radiation

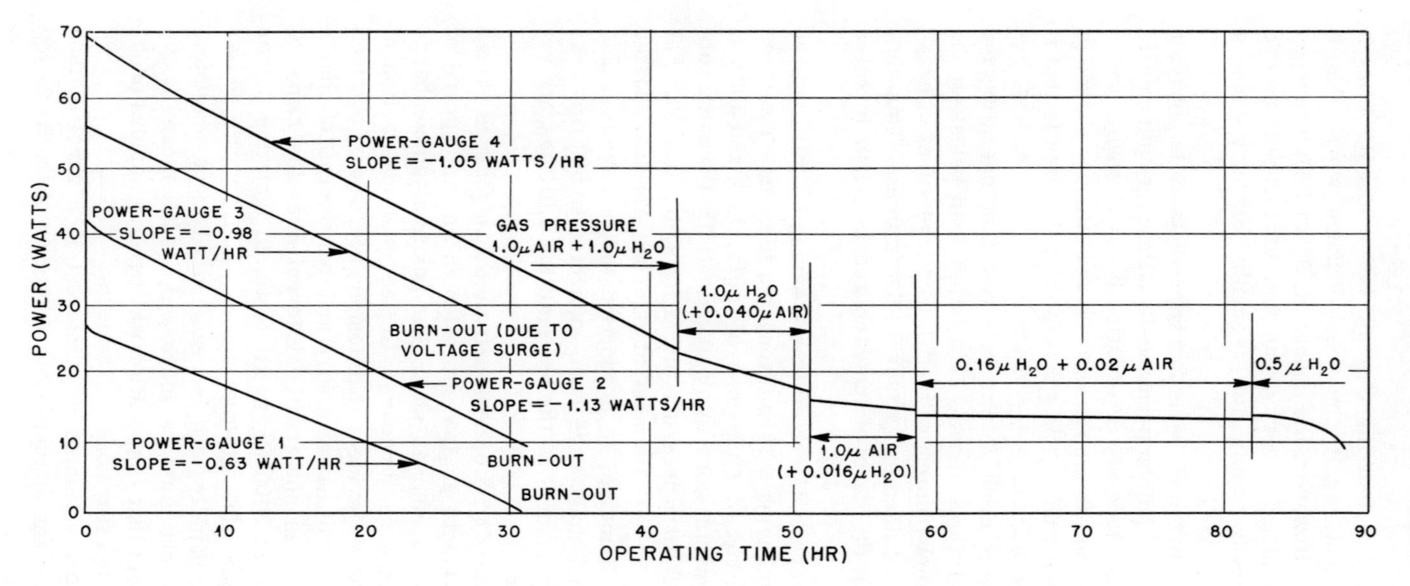

Fig. 3.6—Behavior of tungsten filaments in air and in water vapor. Filament specifications: length, 10 cm; form, eight-turn coil; size, Nos. 1, 2, and 3, 10 mils; No. 4, 15 mils. Operation characteristics were as follows:

Size	Emission, ma	E_p, volts	E_g, volts
1	0.010	−22	128
2	0.50	−22	128
3	5.00	−22	128
4	0.50	−22	128

Laboratory. The method was to hold the positive-ion current to the plate constant at some fixed value, e.g., 1 μa, by automatic change of filament current and to take the emission current necessary to produce this amount of ionization as a measure of the vacuum. Such power supplies have been developed. It has not been proved that this method would not be of some use where dry gases at high pressure were generally encountered, but it was quite certain that in many cases high water-vapor pressures had to be dealt with. One virtue of an ionization gauge has been pointed out by Perrot, namely, that it may be calibrated to read directly in mean free path (m.f.p.) at a given temperature, a quantity perhaps more directly relevant than is pressure in most high-vacuum work.

A few more points worth noting in connection with filaments follow:

1. The centering of a filament within the grid structure does not appear to affect the calibration seriously. Centering by eye is adequate.

2. The reading of vapor pressures of organic compounds is probably impossible owing to cracking on the hot filament.

3. There is some evidence that a change of calibration, and always a reduction in sensitivity, accompanies the sudden poisoning of a filament. This effect has been most noticeable in the case of Eimac 35T gauges. Spotty emission and high plate temperature are the two explanations considered.

4. Burning out filaments by operating at atmospheric pressure can be controlled by suitable overload relay devices. These were not used at the Radiation Laboratory.

(b) Leakage Problems. Electrical leakage between electrodes, cable wires, and some elements of the power supplies is a serious source of trouble with thermionic gauges. Tubes that would give no leakage troubles in ordinary sealed-off usage develop leakage due to sputtering and the chemical transfer of tungsten to the walls, when used as ion gauges, where pressures are often high. In the Radiation Laboratory applications plate currents as low as 10^{-8} amp had to be measured. For these low currents the input resistance of the amplifier was 1 megohm.

Electrical leakage has two main effects: First, the grid current is supposed to be entirely electron emission from the filament, yet neither the meter nor the regulating circuit distinguishes emission current from leakage current. Referring to Fig. 3.7, the main leakage paths are from grid leads to filament leads LR 1 and from grid lead to ground LR 2. These leakage resistances are across voltages of 125 and 150 volts, respectively. With the gauge operating at 1.0 ma emission, these resistances must be large compared to 150,000 ohms, say 15 megohms for 1 per cent leakage. If this leakage is not detected the gauge will give readings that are too low. A common way of detecting such leakage is to turn down the emission, i.e., turn down the grid-current regulating control until the positive-ion current has dropped to zero. The remaining grid current is leakage. In some circuits the grid voltage is still applied with the filament heating

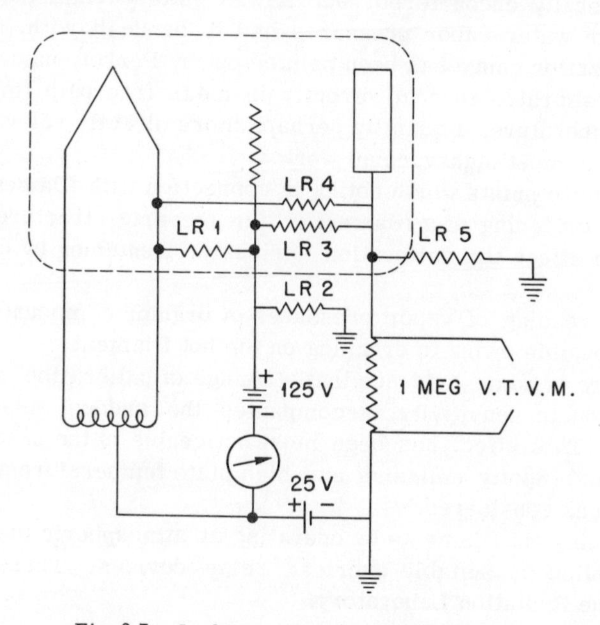

Fig. 3.7—Leakage paths in ionization gauge.

power turned off. The leakage is usually sufficiently independent of temperature for this method to be used in checking. In any case the leakage is not a function of the emission, and one way of diminishing the importance of grid leakage would be to operate at higher emission. The usual method of reducing this leakage is by shielding the press seal from direct sputtering by means of a mechanical guard. Taking the grid out of the side of the tube is also effective.

The other main kind of leakage may be called "plate leakage." The three principal paths are plate to grid LR 3, plate to filament LR 4 (these may be inside the tube or outside it), and plate to ground (usually in the cable). The first two of these are of the same type, across fixed voltages of 150 and 25, respectively. The leakage current must be kept to 10^{-8} amp, and hence leakage resistances of 15,000 megohms are required. This resistance is obtained in the tube by protecting the press seal where the plate lead leaves the tube or, better, by locating the plate lead far from the others. Within the cable it is customary to shield the plate leads with a grounded shield. The leakage resistance to ground is in parallel with a 1-megohm resistor, and the drop across it is read with an electronic voltmeter. Hence a 100-megohm leakage resistance will give a 1 per cent error at any positive-ion current below 1 μa (1 volt full scale on voltmeter). The internal plate leakages depend on fixed voltages and hence are independent of the positive-ion current. The plate-to-ground leakage divides any current to the plate, whether positive-ion or leakage current from grid or filament, into a metered and an unmetered path.

The usual way of testing for plate leakage is to cut the emission to zero, while maintaining grid and plate voltages, and thus cut the positive-ion current to zero. Any remaining current in the plate circuit indicated filament or grid-to-plate leakage. Plate-to-ground leakage may be tested with a Megger. It is much less serious than the other types of leakage.

(c) Ionization-gauge Power Supplies. The usual method of operating a triode ionization gauge is greatly facilitated by the use of an electronic power supply and metering system. Such a supply has, typically, a variable source of voltage for the filament; fixed voltages for the grid and plate; a method of varying, reading, and regulating the emission; and a method of reading the positive-ion current.

Electrons whose energy is about 125 volts are the most efficient ionizers of oxygen and nitrogen, and this might be expected to be the ideal grid potential. The electrode arrangement is such, however, that the extra path length of the electrons with greater energy more than compensates for reduced ionizing efficiency so that there is a gain, though a diminishing one, in going to higher voltages. In the early power supplies designed at Berkeley, the grid voltage was kept low, e.g., at 125 volts, to avoid strong bombardment of the filament by the ions formed in the space between the grid and the filament. Whether this was a good reason or not, the eventual reason was mere circuit convenience. Better regulation of the grid voltage is required at the lower voltages; a 2 per cent variation in E_g caused about a 1 per cent variation in gauge sensitivity in the case of the Western Electric ionization-gauge tube and the Radiation Laboratory circuit. The plate-collecting voltage is not critical, -20 to -30 volts being typical. These voltages are easy to obtain and hold constant.

The chief problems in circuits for ionization gauges arise in connection with the regulation of emission[44] and the amplifying of the small positive-ion current. An individual ionization-gauge tube may require, owing to poisoning of the filament or gas cooling, as much as a fivefold power change to produce the same emission during even

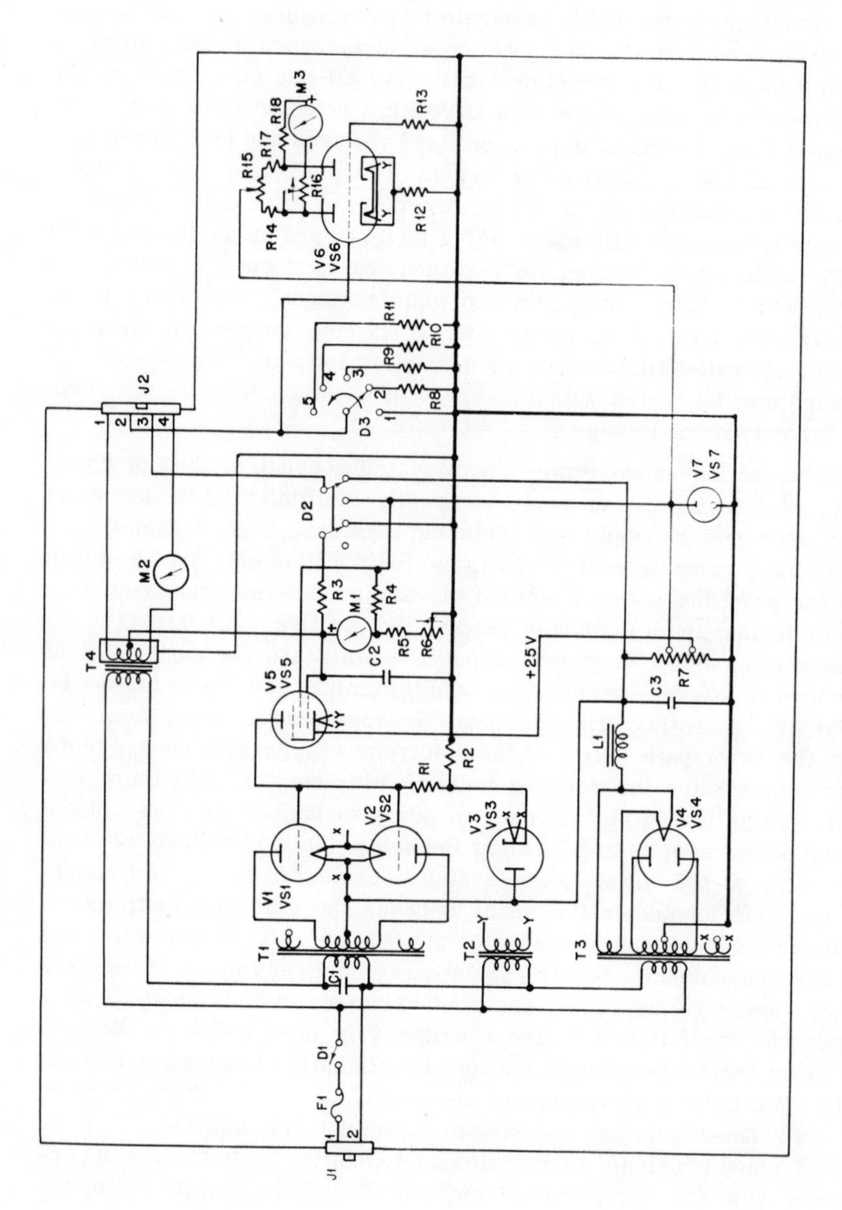

Fig. 3.8—See facing page for legend.

short periods of operation. Automatic devices control the filament current so as to hold the emission steady. For accurate reading of the positive-ion current it is considered good practice to use a rather large emission current, e.g., 5 to 20 ma, and to read the ion current directly with a good microammeter. For other use, however, an amplifier and 200-ma meter have proved satisfactory.

There are in the literature many accounts of ionization-gauge circuits,[45-47] several of which were developed at the Radiation Laboratory. The diagram of one of these circuits is included (Fig. 3.8) because it has given very satisfactory service on a variety of gauges and on widely differing systems. About thirty examples of the circuit of Fig. 3.8 have been in use for three years. Among its special features are the following:

1. An outgassing switch for bombarding the grid by electrons.
2. A booster filament transformer to permit the use of heavy filament gauges.
3. A test jack for checking the calibration of the vacuum-tube voltmeter calibration with the aid of a standard cell.
4. A filament-current meter used to give an index of the state of the filament. This meter would be quite unnecessary for ordinary purposes.

At one time it appeared that the way to make ionization gauges last a reasonable time was to make the filaments of heavy tungsten. The filament currents would then be 20 amp or more, and the problem of

---

Fig. 3.8 — Radiation Laboratory ionization-gauge circuit.

Symbol	Description	Symbol	Description
C1	1-μf 600-volt capacitor	R13	500K-ohm ½-watt resistor
C2	0.05-μf 600-volt capacitor	R14,17	7500-ohm 2-watt resistor
C3	8-μf 450-volt capacitor	R15	5K-ohm potentiometer
M1	5-ma d-c meter	R16	20K-ohm potentiometer
M2	5-amp a-c meter	R18	15K-ohm ½-watt resistor
M3	200-μa d-c meter	T1	Thordarsen T-13R14 transformer
R1,2,4	250K-ohm 2-watt resistor	T2	Thordarsen T-19F80 transformer
R3	150-ohm 10-watt resistor	T3	Thordarsen T-13R12 transformer
R5	3K-ohm 10-watt resistor	T4	Gardner 10-volt 5-amp transformer
R6	25K-ohm 10-watt resistor	V1,2	6A3 tube
R7	5K-ohm 50-watt resistor (tapped)	V3	1-volt tube
R8	10K-ohm ½-watt resistor (1 %)	V4	5Z3 tube
R9	50K-ohm ½-watt resistor (1 %)	V5	6SH7 tube
R10	200K-ohm ½-watt resistor (1 %)	V6	6AC7 tube
R11	1-megohm ½-watt resistor (1 %)	V7	VR150/30 tube
R12	2K-ohm 1-watt resistor		

controlling this current with cheap electronic devices seemed too formidable. To avoid this, a second grid was used to control the electronic flow, the voltage of this grid being controlled by the electron current to the outer grid. Such a power supply and tetrode gauge were built and might have been used but for the difficulty of getting a suitable tetrode into production and because a better solution of the entire problem was found.

The calibration data available for ionization gauges that were used in the Radiation Laboratory are not too reliable. Nevertheless, it may be worth while to include some fairly typical curves for a number of gases. Foote[48] has reported data obtained with a Distillation Products, Inc., ionization gauge in connection with some work on Philips ionization gauges. Compressed bottles of gas were used to supply nitrogen, oxygen, helium, and hydrogen through a variable leak. Atmospheric air and water vapor were also used. The ionization gauge, and the oil McLeod gauge that was used as a standard, were connected to the vacuum chamber through liquid-nitrogen traps. In the case of the water vapor these traps were blown dry. The data obtained are shown in the curves of Fig. 3.9. An examination of these curves shows a factor of about 5 for the ratio of the responses for air and helium, which is of interest in leak-hunting procedures (see Chap. 5).

3.9 Philips Ionization Gauge. In 1937 Penning described a vacuum gauge based on a cold discharge in a magnetic field. For some reason this gauge did not become generally known in this country before the war, although commercial models were in use in England.

Penning's gauge as described by him and manufactured by Philips consists of two small rectangular plates forming a cathode system and, between them, a larger rectangular loop of wire forming the anode (Fig. 3.10). These elements are enclosed in a glass envelope, and outside the glass a permanent magnet is fixed with its field normal to the cathode plates. A half-wave rectifier supplies about 2,000 volts to the gauge, and a milliammeter in series with a ballast resistance reads the current. The elementary explanation is that an ordinary Geissler discharge fails at pressures of a few microns or less because the m.f.p. of the ionizing electron becomes larger than the path of the electrons between the electrodes. Suppose now that an anode and a double cathode are arranged with a magnetic field as shown in Fig. 3.10. An electron that happens to be near the upper plate is accelerated downward. Instead of traveling to the ring, however, it continues through the ring, moving in a tight helix whose axis is parallel to the direction of the magnetic field. As it approaches the lower cathode its direction is reversed, it returns to the upper one,

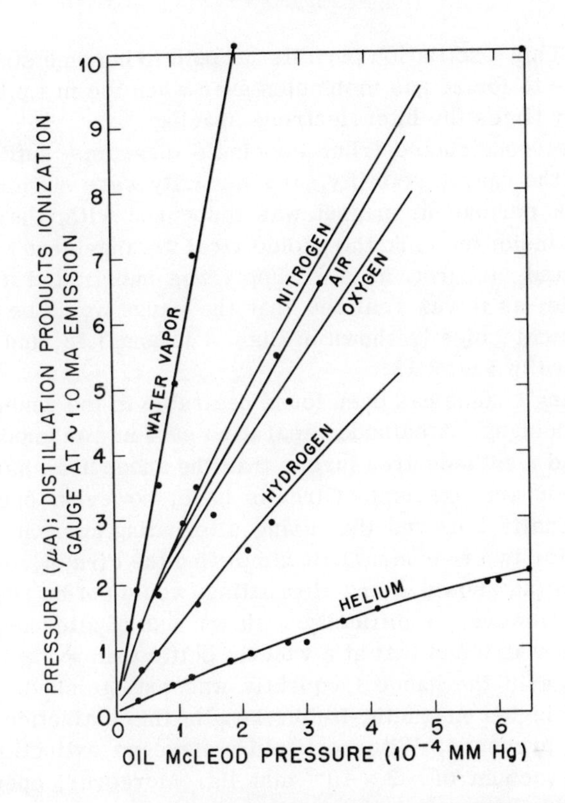

Fig. 3.9—Response of ionization gauge to various gases.

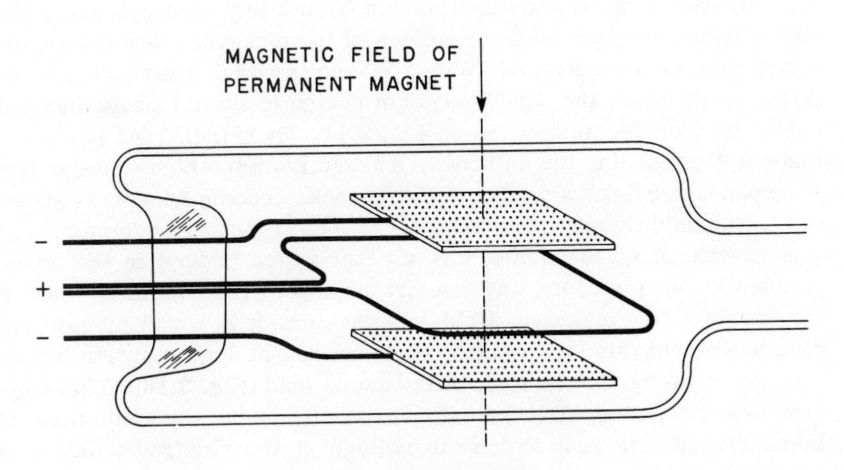

Fig. 3.10—Penning's gauge.

and so on. This oscillation permits its path to become so long that it has a chance to ionize gas molecules even when the m.f.p. of an electron is many times the interelectrode spacing.

The model constructed from Penning's diagrams sufficed to establish that the range, stability, and linearity were sufficient for our purposes. A permanent magnet was dispensed with, the electrodes were placed inside the tank, the geometrical arrangement was changed somewhat, and, at first, an a-c supply was substituted for the half-wave rectifier as it was realized that the gauge would be self-rectifying. A typical gauge is shown in Figs. 3.11 and 3.12, and the circuit used is shown in Fig. 3.13.

Little if any change has been found desirable in the general cathode and anode designs. A cathode separation of ½ in., an anode diameter of 1 in., and a cathode area larger than the anode area have been the most common arrangement. Circuits have, however, been changed. It was originally believed that using alternating current was an improvement, for two reasons: (1) it simplified the circuit, and (2) leakage currents (as shown), being alternating, would not be registered by the meter. However, a difficulty with the use of alternating current developed. It was found that at a vacuum better than $\approx 2 \times 10^{-5}$ mm Hg the discharge in the gauge frequently was extinguished. Also when operating at higher magnetic-field strengths this extinction took place at a higher pressure. With rectified voltage no extinction was observed at a vacuum of $\approx 2 \times 10^{-6}$ mm Hg. Moreover, operation was steadier at low pressures than in the case of a-c operation. For use below 1×10^{-4} mm Hg, a d-c source appears definitely desirable.

(a) Leakage Problems. Some care must be taken to avoid electrical leakage. Typical sensitivities run from 1 to 3 amp/mm Hg in the high-vacuum region. Hence readings of the order of a few microamperes may be encountered. With 2,000 volts on the electrodes, insulation must be in the 1,000-megohm region to avoid leakage current being read on the meter, as in Fig. 3.14. By bringing out two leads instead of grounding the cathodes, leakage from the high-voltage side to ground is by-passed (Fig. 3.15). It does become necessary, however, to shield the cathodes from stray ions if they are common.

A discharge of the same sort as that which occurs in the gauge frequently occurs along any lead at high positive potential when it lies normal to a magnetic field in a vacuum. It is sometimes desirable to prevent this by operating the cathodes at high negative potential and reading the current in the anode lead (Fig. 3.16). This system has the virtue that the cathodes need not be shielded. None of these circuits prevent a drop in voltage at the electrodes due to a potential drop occurring across the high ballast resistance when there are leakage currents of considerable magnitude. As a check on

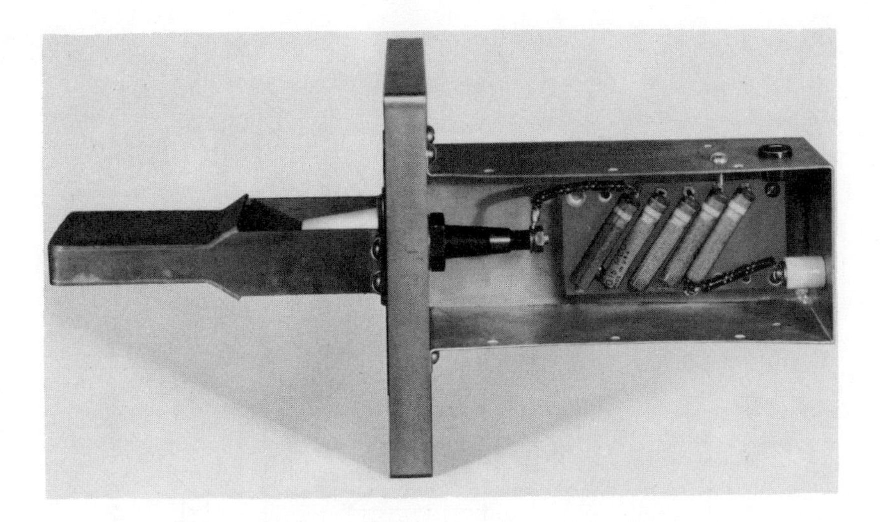

Fig. 3.11 — A standard Radiation Laboratory Philips ionization gauge.

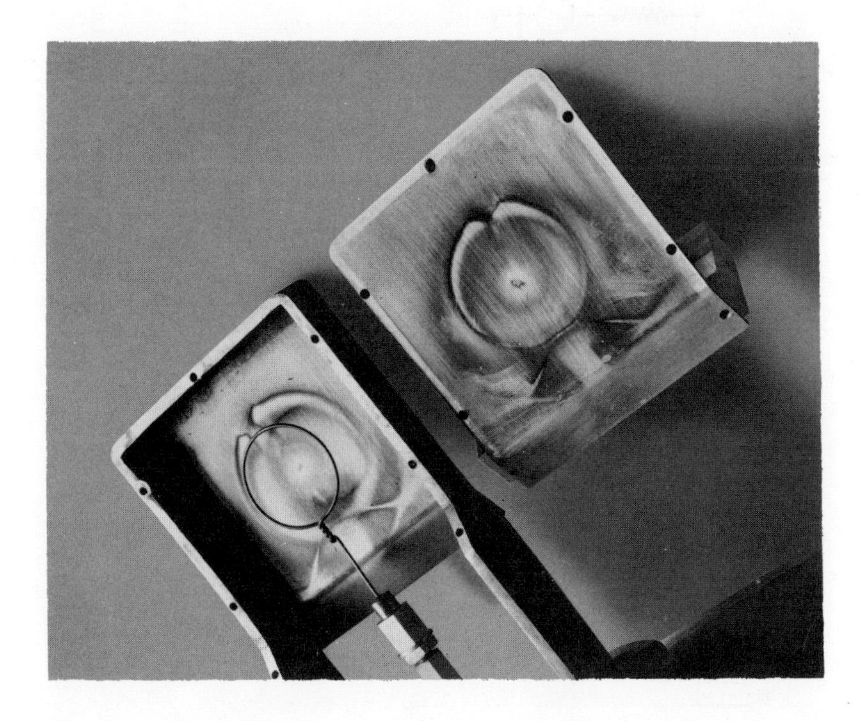

Fig. 3.12 — View of Radiation Laboratory Philips ionization gauge with one of the copper cathode plates removed.

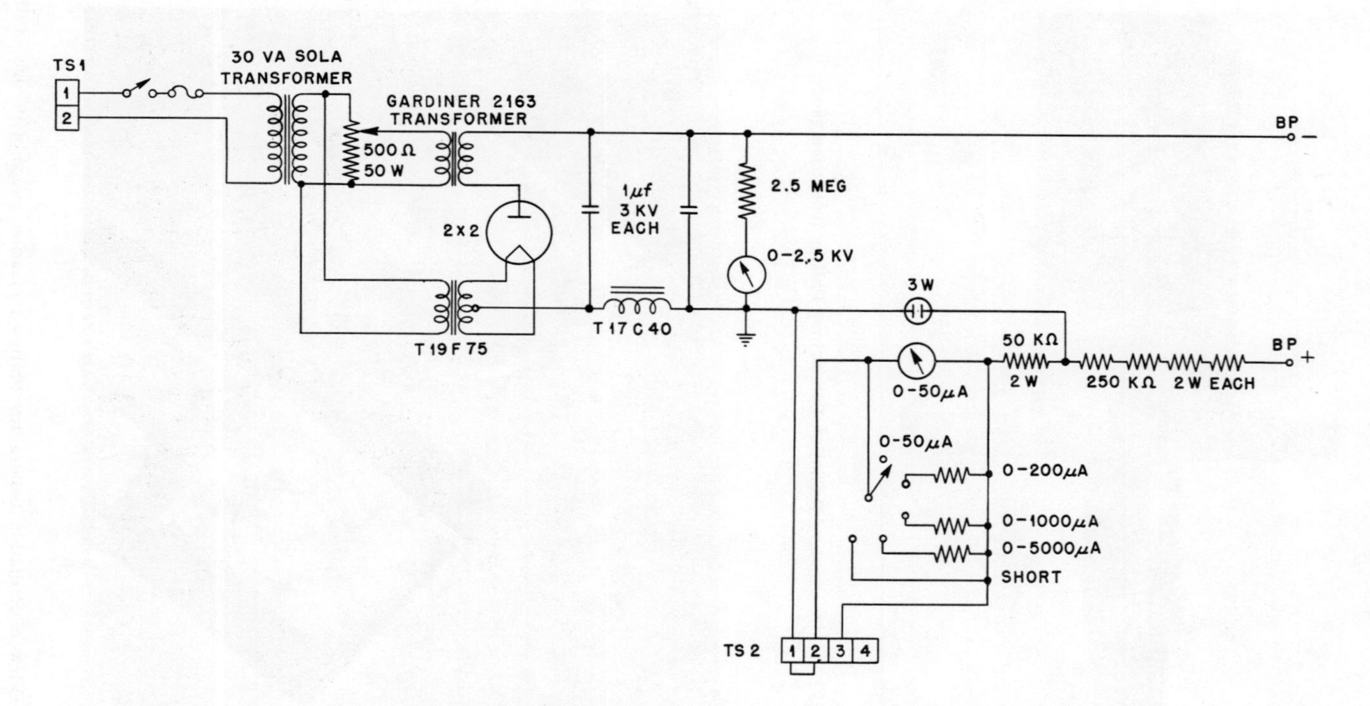

Fig. 3.13—Electrical circuit for Radiation Laboratory Philips ionization gauge.

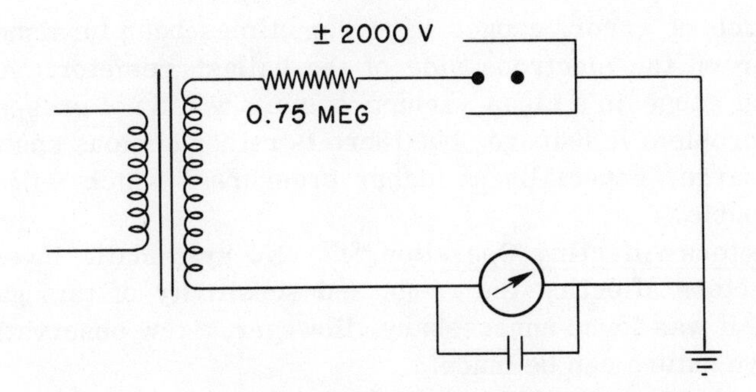

Fig. 3.14 — Leakage paths in Philips ionization gauge (I).

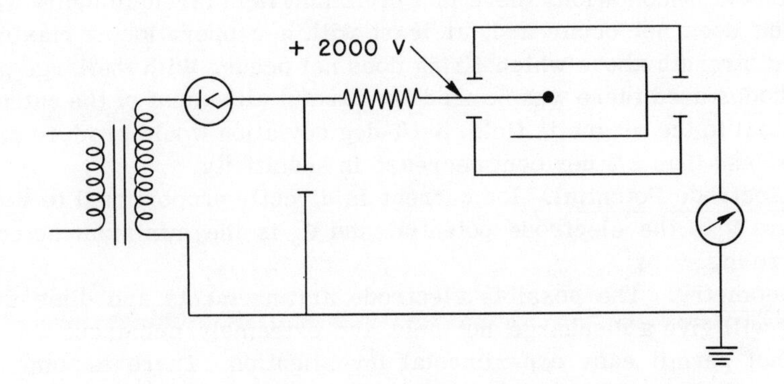

Fig. 3.15 — Leakage paths in Philips ionization gauge (II).

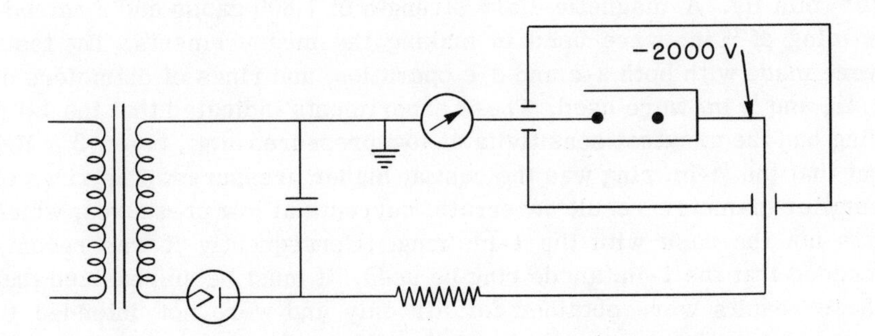

Fig. 3.16 — Leakage paths in Philips ionization gauge (III).

this source of error, gauges have sometimes been furnished with a voltmeter on the electrode side of the ballast resistor. A Philips ionization gauge in a clean vacuum system would not present a very serious problem in leakage, but there is rather copious sputtering in the discharge, especially at higher pressures, which will in time cause trouble.

(b) Factors Affecting Operation.[48,50] No systematic investigation of the factors affecting the range and sensitivity of this gauge was made, as it was found unnecessary. However, a few observations of a qualitative nature can be made.

Effect of Magnetic-field Strength. Magnetic-field strengths of from 300 to 8,000 oersteds have been used. With all other conditions constant, then, as the field strength increases, the sensitivity increases to a maximum quite rapidly and then falls off slowly. For a given set of conditions there is a minimum field strength below which firing does not occur and, at least with a-c operation, a maximum field strength above which firing does not occur. With the large plate cathodes used there was no need for careful alignment of the cathodes normal to the magnetic field. A 10-deg deviation would produce probably less than a 3 per cent decrease in sensitivity.

Electrode Potential. Ion current is directly proportional to $V - V_0$ where V is the electrode potential and V_0 is the minimum potential for firing.

Geometry. The possible electrode arrangements and dimensions that will give a discharge not only are extremely numerous but also do not permit easy experimental investigation. There is some evidence that sensitivity increases with plate separation in the type of gauge used here and that the size of the anode ring has less effect on sensitivity.

Dole[52] has reported some studies made of the effect of ring size on the performance of a Philips ionization gauge up to pressures of 10^{-2} mm Hg. A magnetic-field strength of 1,800 gauss and a cathode spacing of ½ in. were used in making the measurements. The tests were made with both a-c and d-c operation, and rings of diameters of 1, ½, and ¼ in. were used. These experiments indicated that the 1-in. ring had the greatest sensitivity at low pressures (e.g., below 2 μ Hg) but that the ¼-in. ring was the best at higher pressures. The rings of smaller diameter result in erratic currents at low pressures, which was not the case with the 1-in. ring. Consequently it was recommended that the 1-in. anode ring be used. It must be emphasized that these results were obtained for air only and were not intended to represent a systematic study of the effect of geometrical form on gauge performance.

Cathode Material. No change in sensitivity with the use of different cathode materials was observed. Graphite, molybdenum, copper, brass, and nickel were used in gauges sufficiently similar to indicate that there is no great variation with material. Experiments show the discharge to be independent of secondary electrons from the cathodes.

Alternating vs. Direct Current.[54] Filtered half-wave rectified d-c power gives the gauge about 2½ times the sensitivity obtainable with a-c power. With d-c power the gauge stays on all the time. With a-c power the gauge fires when the anode becomes sufficiently positive, e.g., at about +800 volts, and goes out when it reaches the extinction potential, about +400 volts. It therefore does not fire for an entire half cycle.

Kind of Gas. The data on the comparative sensitivities of the gauge for different gases are not too reliable. However, the common gases appear to stand in the same order as regards sensitivity of the Philips ionization gauge as they do for a triode ionization gauge. This fact is fairly evident from experiments made by Foote.[48] Air, nitrogen, oxygen, helium, and water vapor were tested. An oil McLeod gauge that had been calibrated against a mercury McLeod gauge was used as a standard. Two Philips ionization gauges of different geometrical form were used to make the tests. Although the absolute readings for these gauges differed considerably, they stood in the same relationship with respect to the gas being used. Consequently data for only one of these gauges are given here. This gauge had a ½-in. cathode spacing and a wire-ring anode 1 in. in diameter. Voltage was obtained from a half-wave rectifier and was maintained at 2.0 kv, with a 1-megohm series resistor. Bottles of compressed gas supplied the nitrogen, helium, hydrogen, and oxygen, and the air was drawn from the atmosphere. All gauges used were attached to the vacuum chamber through liquid-nitrogen traps. These traps were blown dry for the water-vapor measurements. Some of the data obtained are shown in Fig. 3.17. A comparison of these results with calibration curves for a Distillation Products, Inc., ionization gauge, which were obtained in the same experimental arrangement (Fig. 3.9), indicates that the relative effects of the gases tested are in the same order for the two types of gauges. A good deal of difficulty was experienced in getting consistent results on the same gas with the Philips ionization gauge. The data for the curves shown were checked as closely as possible, and it is believed that at least the relative effects of these gases are in the correct order.

(c) Factors Affecting the Range. The d-c gauges in use have a range of from below 2×10^{-6} to about 5×10^{-4} mm Hg. The upper limit may be pushed higher for the same gauge by decreasing the ballast resistance, but no very great extension can be achieved in this way. The gauge has, at high pressure, effectively zero resistance.

The large dimensions and high voltage of this gauge appear best for very low pressures. For higher pressures, in the range of from 1 to 20 μ Hg, low voltage (below 1,000 volts) and small spacings should be used.

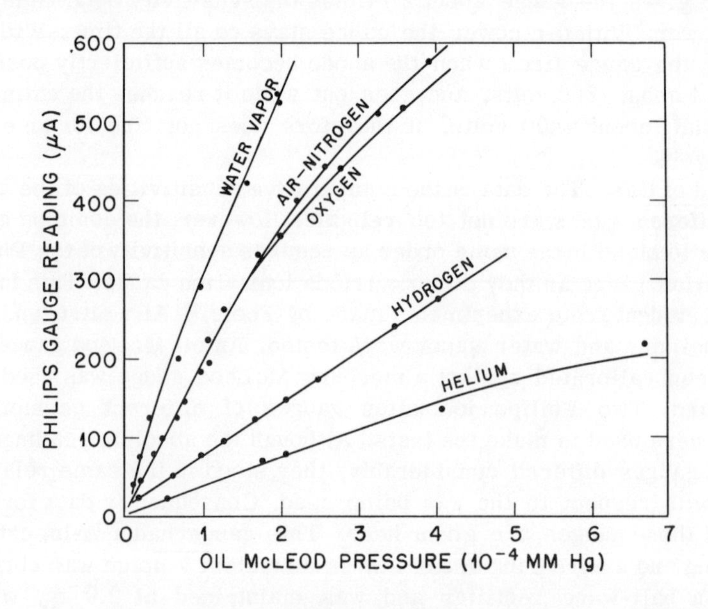

Fig. 3.17—Response of Philips ionization gauge to various gases.

The lower limit of operation is governed by the failure of a discharge to take place. For a given gauge, voltage, and magnetic field there appears to be a lower limit to pressure at which the Philips ionization gauge will fire. Some tests at fixed pressure indicate that the firing potential is several hundred volts higher than the extinction potential. When the potential is just barely in the firing range a lag of a minute or more is frequently observed between the application of the potential and the firing. It is clear that a-c potentials would be useless in this region.

Increasing the magnetic-field strength has the effect of raising the pressure at which extinction takes place, provided that field is already higher. The effect has not been investigated at the low field strengths common to permanent-magnet gauges.

(d) Consistency of Operation. Two sample gauges were constructed having dimensional agreement within 2 or 3 per cent. When these were run in parallel in the same chamber and magnetic field the response to pressure change was found to be the same within experimental limits—about 2 or 3 per cent. An insulating varnish that forms on the cathodes does not seem to affect the calibration. The theoretical understanding of this discharge and especially the conditions governing its stability are not sufficient to warrant great confidence in the reproducibility of observations. Any confidence at present must rest on experiment. The experimental evidence does not appear to warrant faith in much better than 10 per cent consistency in the results for gauges of apparent identity of construction or for the same gauge when new and after operation for an extended period. However, this is better agreement than is required for most vacuum work.

It has been established that the discharge is oscillatory and that the frequency of the oscillations is proportional to the pressure.[56] Besides the use of this sort of discharge as a gauge, by use of a slightly different anode it becomes a useful source of ions. Such sources are used in the vacuum analyzer and the helium leak detector described in Chap. 5.

There has been very little employment of permanent-magnet gauges at the Radiation Laboratory. However, judging from the evidence available it would appear desirable to provide a high enough field to put operation into the region where sensitivity is nearly independent of field strength.

(e) Calibration of the Philips Ionization Gauge. No systematic studies on the calibration of this type of gauge for air have been carried out at the Radiation Laboratory. However, some data reported[55] may be of interest in this connection.

The gauges used anode rings 1 in. in diameter and two copper cathodes 2½ in. square with a separation of ½ in. The Distillation Products Company triode-type ionization gauge used was very carefully calibrated against a number of Distillation Products and Western Electric ionization gauges.

The data obtained are shown in Fig. 3.18. From Fig. 3.18 it is seen that in the pressure range of 0.2×10^{-4} to 5×10^{-4} mm Hg the glow discharge current of the Philips ionization gauge is a substantially linear function of the pressure. Above the latter pressure, in the region of 5×10^{-4} to 20×10^{-4} mm Hg, an appreciable curvature becomes manifest. Good correlation between data obtained on successive days was observed.

3.10 The Alphatron. Since the war an ionization gauge employing alpha particles from radium as the ionizing source has been reported in the literature[57] and put on the market. The radium is prepared and mounted in such a way that the alpha activity remains substantially constant for a long period. This source of ions requires no power supply and gives perfect regulation without benefit of electronics. The gauge consists of a simple ionization chamber with a well-insulated

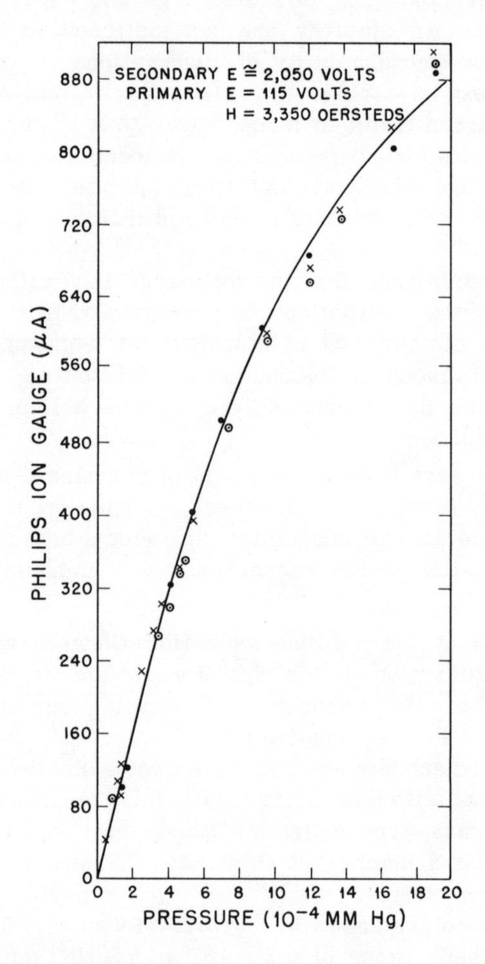

Fig. 3.18—Response of Philips ionization gauge to air (I). The dots represent data recorded Mar. 21, 1944; the crosses, data recorded Mar. 18, 1944; and the circled dots, data recorded Mar. 17, 1944.

collector plate plus the radium source. Very high amplification is required. The lower limit of pressure at present is about 10^{-4} mm Hg, at which pressure the collector current approaches the grid current of the first-stage amplifier tube in magnitude. The linearity of response of the gauge extends from 1 μ Hg to 25 or 40 mm Hg. The relative sensitivity for various gases is reported in Table 3.1.

These ratios are in good agreement with the ratios found for triodes and Philips ionization gauges for the noble gases but are off by as much as a factor of 2 in the cases of water vapor and hydrogen.

The advantages of such a gauge in all but very-high-vacuum work are so great that it must be supposed that only high cost would prevent its general use. It is to be hoped that eventually the gauge will be improved to read down to 10^{-6} mm Hg.

Table 3.1

Acetone	2.5	H_2O	0.88
CO_2	1.5	Ne	0.5
A	1.2	H_2	0.230
Air	1.0	He	0.208

3.11 Discharge Tubes. If two electrodes are sealed into a glass tube and a high potential is applied between them, a discharge occurs when the pressure in the tube reaches a value of a few millimeters of mercury. At this relatively high pressure the discharge consists of a streamer between the two electrodes. As the pressure is reduced the streamer widens until it fills the entire tube. For pressures somewhat less than 1 mm Hg the discharge takes on the appearance of a glow discharge with well-defined cathode dark space, cathode glow, and positive column. At pressures below 10^{-2} mm Hg (high potential less than 10,000 volts/cm) the discharge disappears ("black" discharge).

The physical characteristics of the discharge, such as the light emitted and the width of the cathode dark space, will depend on the gas being used, on the pressure, on the high voltage, and on the geometrical arrangement of the discharge tube. A good indication of the order of the pressure in a vacuum system can be obtained by the use of such a discharge tube attached to the system. The color of the light emitted or of the width of the cathode dark space can be used as a pressure indication. Somewhat more quantitative results can be obtained by viewing the emitted light with a spectroscope. Some indication of the colors of the various parts of a discharge for a number of gases is given in Table 3.2.

Since carbon dioxide has an appreciably higher molecular weight than oxygen or nitrogen, at the lower pressures it diffuses more slowly to the pump. This accounts for the bluish color of the positive column in air at low pressures. The width of the cathode dark space can be used as an indication of the pressure since it is roughly proportional to the reciprocal of the pressure.[58] Of course, this method does not permit of great accuracy, but it is satisfactory for many purposes.

The discharge tube as a pressure-indicating device is essentially a qualitative instrument. However, it is useful in giving the order of magnitude of the pressure in a vacuum system. For instance, if a

Table 3.2

Gas	Cathode glow	Negative glow	Positive column
Air	Rose	Blue-pink	Pink at higher pressures, blue at lower pressures
Oxygen	Red	Violet	Yellow with reddish core
Nitrogen	Red-pink	Blue or violet	Orange or yellow red
Helium	Rose	Pale green	Violet-red to yellow-pink
Hydrogen	Brown-pink	Light blue	Reddish-pink or orange
Water vapor	White-blue	Blue	White-blue
Carbon monoxide			White
Carbon dioxide			Bluish-green
Argon	Rose		Violet
Neon	Yellow	Dark red	Blood red
Mercury vapor	White-blue	Blue	White-blue
Ammonia	Blue	Green-yellow	Blue

discharge tube of known dimensions is used with a known high voltage, it is possible to indicate an adequate pressure in certain processes by a black discharge. If an adjustable high-voltage supply is used, then the higher the voltage required to obtain a black discharge, the lower the pressure. This type of tube can also be used to indicate the presence of condensable vapors in the vacuum system, from the color of the discharge. In so far as the construction of the tube is concerned, the outside envelope should be of pyrex glass. The electrodes should be of sufficient size to avoid excessive temperature rise and are usually constructed of nickel, stainless steel, or platinum.

A spark coil, such as a Tesla coil, can also be used to give a rough indication of the pressure in a vacuum system. The color of the gas discharge produced in the portion of the vacuum system to which the spark coil is applied indicates the pressure, as in the case of the discharge tube. The most important application of the device is in leak hunting in a glass system, as described in Chap. 5. Also, a Tesla coil is often used to indicate the point at which the pressure has reached a sufficiently low value for the diffusion pump to be turned on. This is usually taken as the point at which the coil will not produce a gas discharge in the system and at which the glass envelope shows a green fluorescence.

3.12 What Is Measured by Vacuum Gauges? Historically, vacuum measurement began with the use of hydrostatic gauges, which, it is clear, measure pressure. Moreover, it is still customary to calibrate other types of gauges against a McLeod gauge, which measures pressure. It is not surprising, then, that all vacuum gauges are called "pressure gauges" and that the common question asked is, what is the pressure in the vacuum vessel? However, in high-vacuum practice it is seldom the important variable. Perhaps it is in the case of pump-speed measurement, but more often a m.f.p. is the relevant characteristic, i.e., a molecular m.f.p. in the case of distillation and an ionic m.f.p. in the case of electronic tubes, cyclotrons, mass spectrometers, and other electronic vacuum devices. At the Radiation Laboratory it was customary to take high-vacuum measurements with a Western Electric ionization gauge and, using standard power supplies and metering systems, to refer to a pressure of, for example, 0.5 μa, this being the positive-ion current in the gauge. The author and associates were always apologetic about this usage, but it gradually came to be realized that the ionization current was a better index of the important characteristics of the atmosphere in the cyclotron than its pressure would have been. The processes of electrical breakdown, plasma formation, and scattering are all independent of temperature and dependent on the kind of gas. It turned out that the ionization processes involved were sufficiently similar to those in a triode ionization gauge or a Philips ionization gauge for the positive-ion current in such a gauge to be a good index of the proper state of the vacuum even when the kind of gas was varied. A gauge that really read pressure would have been out of place. In general, vacuum measurements of even 10 per cent accuracy have not been needed, and hence it has usually been unnecessary to make temperature corrections. In the following sections on what several varieties of vacuum gauges measure, the methods of making temperature corrections are indicated for the sake of completeness and because the method, under high-vacuum conditions, is perhaps not obvious.

If, as is usually the case, the various gauges that have been considered are self-contained units connected to a vacuum vessel by tubes, then the question is, what property of the gas in the gauge is used to give the measured response?

Hydrostatic gauges respond directly to pressure. Temperature and molecular concentration may vary without altering the reading so long as their product is constant. The pressure read is independent of the kind of gas present. For the McLeod gauge the pressure is the pressure in the large bulb.

The readings of all types of ionization gauges depend on the molecular concentration in the region where ionization takes place and on the kind of gas. The rate of ionization is independent of the gas temperature.

Dushman gives the following formula for the radiometer effect in a Knudsen gauge

$$K = \frac{1}{4}\frac{P}{T}\Delta T$$

where K is the force of repulsion between vanes, T is the temperature of the case, ΔT is the heater temperature minus case temperature, and P is the pressure. Since ΔT must be independent of T to a first approximation and since n, the molecular concentration, is proportional to P/T, this gauge responds to molecular concentration, independently of the kind of gas. As the temperature of the case varies only slightly the gauge may be said to read the pressure in the case.

When an inference from the condition of the gas in the gauge to that of the gas in the test vessel is to be made there are two extreme situations to be considered. It is assumed that the same kind of gas is contained in the gauge and in the test vessel. First, under high-vacuum conditions, where the m.f.p. of the molecules is long compared to the diameter of the connecting tube, the phenomenon of thermal transpiration occurs, and $n_1/n_2 = \sqrt{T_2/T_1}$ or $P_1/P_2 = \sqrt{T_1/T_2}$ (Eq. 69 in Chap. 1) where the subscript 1 refers to the test vessel and the subscript 2 refers to the gauge. The quantities n_1 and n_2 refer to the number of molecules per cubic centimeter in the test vessel and gauge, respectively. Second, at higher pressures, where the m.f.p. is much smaller than the tube diameter, the pressure throughout the system equalizes, and $P_1 = P_2$, $n_1/n_2 = T_2/T_1$.[59] From these equations and the relation $n = NP/RT$, where N is Avogadro's number and R is the gas constant,

Low Pressure	High Pressure
$P_1 = \sqrt{\frac{T_1}{T_2}}\, P_2$	$P_1 = P_2$
$n_1 = \frac{N}{R}\frac{1}{\sqrt{T_1 T_2}} P_2$	$n_1 = \frac{N}{R}\frac{1}{T_1} P_2$

$$P_1 = \frac{R}{N} \sqrt{T_1 T_2}\, n_2 \qquad P_1 = \frac{R}{N} T_2 n_2$$

$$n_1 = \sqrt{\frac{T_2}{T_1}}\, n_2 \qquad N_1 = \frac{T_2}{T_1} n_2$$

Some illustrative conclusions to be drawn from the analyses of what these gauges respond to directly and how the gauge vacuum is related to the test-vessel vacuum follow:

1. A cold trap may be interposed between a gauge and the vessel without affecting the reading for permanent gases.

2. So long as a high-vacuum ionization gauge stays at constant temperature its reading is proportional to $n\sqrt{T}$ or $P/\sqrt{T}$, where these quantities are measured in the test vessel. If the gauge's temperature increases, the reading will decrease by the factor $\sqrt{T_{original}/T_{new}}$. On a number of occasions a drop in sensitivity due to filament poisoning in the Eimac 35T has been observed to accompany an increase in filament power.

3. For a high-pressure ionization gauge the reading would be proportional to P_1 or n_1T_1, provided the gauge temperature remained constant.

4. A McLeod gauge at high pressures also responds to P_1 or n_1T_1, and its reading is independent of its own temperature.

5. With the Philips ionization gauge immersed in the vacuum vessel or with the super ion gauge, an immersed triode gauge, there could hardly be a variation in vacuum-tank temperature while the gauge temperature remained constant, or vice versa. Hence the readings of these gauges should vary with n_1 and be independent of T_1.

At the end of this chapter are listed a number of references in which the various types of pressure-measuring gauges considered here are discussed. Most of these references are concerned with particular types of gauges and the circuits associated with them. However, a few references treating the general problem of measuring low pressure are included.[60-62]

REFERENCES

1. H. Lifschutz, Rev. Sci. Instruments, 10: 27 (1939).
2. William Hurst, Rev. Sci. Instruments, 12: 265 (1941).
3. K. C. D. Hickman, Rev. Sci. Instruments, 5: 161 (1934).
4. K. C. D. Hickman and W. J. Weyerts, J. Am. Chem. Soc., 52: 4714 (1930).
5. C. G. Malmberg and W. W. Nicholas, Rev. Sci. Instruments, 3: 440 (1932).

6. O. Beeck, Rev. Sci. Instruments, 6: 399 (1935).
7. Hiromu Wakesima, Proc. Phys. Math. Soc. Japan, 22: 526 (1940).
8. T. P. Kozlyakooskaya, J. Tech. Phys. U.S.S.R., 8: 1850 (1938).
9. Paul Rosenberg, Rev. Sci. Instruments, 10: 131 (1939).
10. W. Gaede, Ann. Physik., 41: 289 (1913).
11. K. C. D. Hickman, J. Optical Soc. Am., 18: 305 (1929).
12. A. H. Pfund, Phys. Rev., 18: 78 (1921).
13. Guenther Hasse, Z. tech. Physik, 24: 27 (1943).
14. H. J. Reiff, Z. Instrumentenk., 34: 97 (1914).
15. J. Bannon, Rev. Sci. Instruments, 14: 6 (1943).
16. Frank Kirby, University of California Radiation Laboratory Report RL 20.6.13, Nov. 6, 1943.
17. M. von Pirani, Verhandl. deut. physik. Ges., 8: 24 (1906).
18. J. W. M. DuMond and W. M. Pickels, Jr., Rev. Sci. Instruments, 6: 362 (1935).
19. E. S. Rittner, Rev. Sci. Instruments, 17: 113 (1946).
20. E. J. Scott, Rev. Sci. Instruments, 10: 349 (1939).
21. C. F. Hale, Trans. Am. Electrochem. Soc., 20: 243 (1911).
22. A. M. Skellett, J. Optical Soc. Am., 15: 56 (1927).
23. L. F. Stanley, Proc. Phys. Soc. London, 33: 287 (1921).
24. G. C. Dunlap and J. G. Trump, Rev. Sci. Instruments, 8: 37 (1937).
25. I. Amdur and H. Pearlman, Rev. Sci. Instruments, 10: 174 (1939).
26. I. Langmuir, J. Am. Chem. Soc., 35: 107 (1913).
27. F. Haber and F. Kerschbaum, Z. Elektrochem., 20: 296 (1914).
28. Arnold O. Beckman, J. Optical Soc. Am., 16: 276 (1928).
29. M. Knudsen, Ann. Physik., 28: 75 (1909).
30. A. L. Hughes, Rev. Sci. Instruments, 8: 394 (1937).
31. A. E. Lockenwitz, Rev. Sci. Instruments, 9: 417 (1938).
32. O. E. Buckley, Proc. Natl. Acad. Sci. U. S., 2: 683 (1916).
33. S. Dushman and C. G. Found, Phys. Rev., 17: 7 (1921).
34. E. K. Jaycox and H. W. Weinhart, Rev. Sci. Instruments, 2: 401 (1931).
35. H. Simon, Z. tech. Physik, 5: 221 (1924).
36. L. N. Ridenour and C. W. Lampson, Rev. Sci. Instruments, 8: 162 (1937).
37. R. S. Morse and R. M. Bowie, Rev. Sci. Instruments, 11: 91 (1940).
38. James Rainwater, Rev. Sci. Instruments, 13: 118 (1942).
39. J. B. H. Kuper, Rev. Sci. Instruments, 8: 394 (1937).
40. R. M. Bowie, Rev. Sci. Instruments, 11: 265 (1940).
41. C. G. Montgomery and D. D. Montgomery, Rev. Sci. Instruments, 9: 58 (1938).
42. F. Schmidt, University of California Radiation Laboratory Report RL 20.6.2, November, 1942.
43. William E. Bush, University of California Radiation Laboratory Report RL 20.6.17, Jan. 8, 1944.
44. R. B. Nelson and A. K. Wing, Jr., Rev. Sci. Instruments, 13: 215 (1942).
45. E. A. Hamacher, Rev. Sci. Instruments, 17: 281 (1946).
46. Louis N. Ridenour, Rev. Sci. Instruments, 12: 134 (1941).
47. W. E. Parkins, Jr., and W. A. Higinbotham, Rev. Sci. Instruments, 12: 366 (1941).
48. L. R. Foote, University of California Radiation Laboratory Report RL 20.6.25, June 17, 1944.
49. Z. M. Penning, Physica, 3: 873 (1936); 4: 71 (1937).
50. Louis Wouters, University of California Radiation Laboratory Report RL 20.6.18, Jan. 8, 1944.
51. K. M. Simpson, University of California Radiation Laboratory Report RL 20.6.19, Jan. 6, 1944.
52. Malcolm Dole, University of California Radiation Laboratory Report RL 20.6.29, Aug. 10, 1944.

53. J. R. Tolmie and K. M. Simpson, University of California Radiation Laboratory Report RL 20.6.22, May 3, 1944.
54. J. R. Tolmie, University of California Radiation Laboratory Report RL 20.6.20, Mar. 25, 1944.
55. W. H. Nelson, University of California Radiation Laboratory Report XL 7.6.801, Feb. 4, 1945.
56. J. R. Downing and Glenn Millen, Rev. Sci. Instruments, 17: 218 (1946).
57. F. W. Aston and H. E. Watson, Proc. Roy. Soc. London, 86: 168 (1911).
58. H. H. Zielinski, Electronics, 17: 112 (1944).
59. Swami Jnanananda, ''High Vacua,'' p. 70, D. Van Nostrand Company, Inc., New York, 1947.
60. J. Blears, Nature, 154: 20 (1944).
61. Edwin Weise, Z. tech. Physik, 24: 66 (1943).
62. A. Etzrodt, Chem. App., 25: 321 (1938).

Chapter 4

VACUUM MATERIALS AND EQUIPMENT

By William E. Bush

4.1 Vacuum Tanks, Seals, and Valves. Although the design of vacuum processing equipment is certainly to be governed primarily by the process requirements involved, the details of such design must include attention to the requirements of satisfactory vacuum operation itself. That certain features of design are necessary in tanks, seals, and valves when used in high-vacuum work is obvious. To outline these general features and to review current practice is the purpose of this chapter.

When large vacuum tanks (e.g., more than 100 cu ft in volume) are required for a process, the design is considerably guided by the mechanical forces involved. These forces are in general in two main categories: those due to atmospheric pressure and those due to temperature changes. Steel tanks have been used with satisfactory results, although it has been necessary to use wall thicknesses as great as 2 in. for flat surfaces in order to avoid excessive deformation.

The welding of steel walls must be such that any leaks resulting from faulty welding during manufacture or from later failure can be detected and repaired. A type of weld that has given satisfactory performance is shown in Fig. 4.1. The walls used are of single sheet. These are welded to the ends as illustrated, the inside and outside welds being made independently. Periodically a dam is established all the way across the space between the two welds. Between each dam the external weld is drilled and tapped and fitted with a plug. In testing, a tank failing to prove tight could be tested section by section, either by pumping out the interweld spaces one at a time until the leak rate was changed, or by noting soap films across the drilled holes. Or, by applying compressed air to the interweld space, leaks may be exactly located by soap films. In any event the inside weld must be gastight.

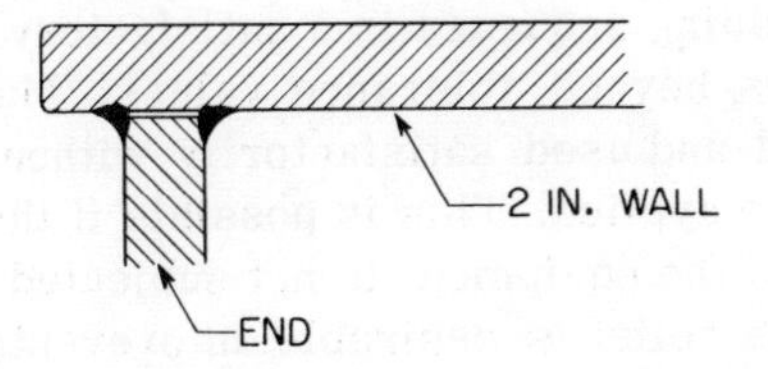

Fig. 4.1—Welded joint in vacuum-tank wall.

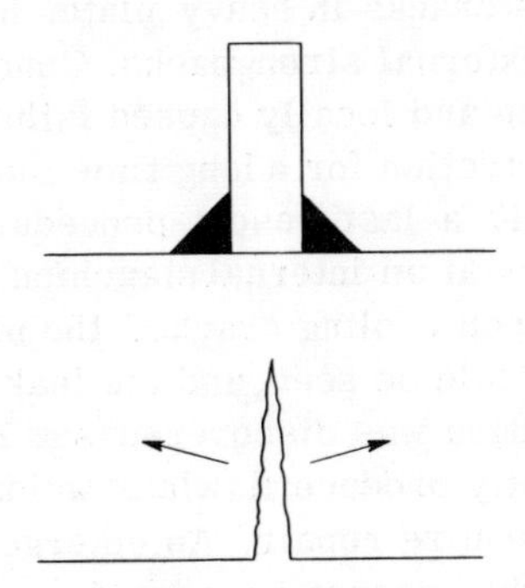

Fig. 4.2—Crack in vacuum wall resulting from improper welding of external strong-back.

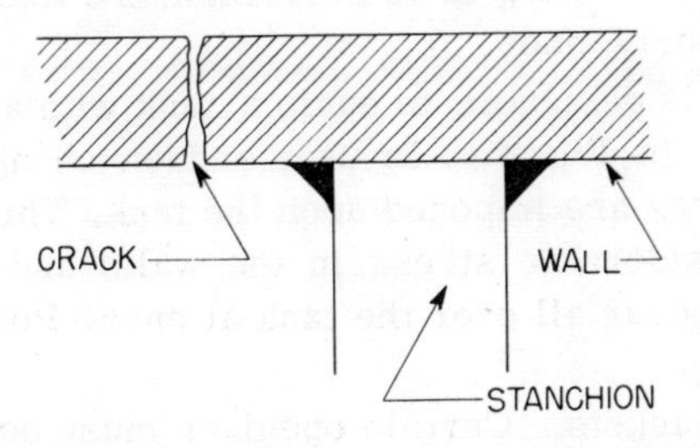

Fig. 4.3—Crack at internal stanchion due to contraction of welded region.

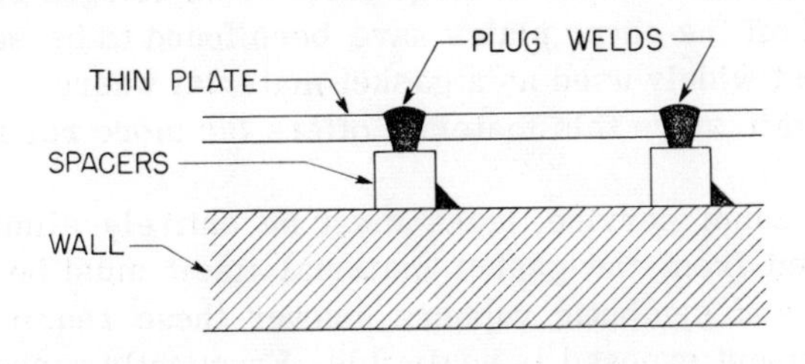

Fig. 4.4—Welded jacket in vacuum wall.

Care in the welding sequence is a satisfactory means of combating residual stresses beyond tolerance values. Many large tanks have been constructed and used satisfactorily without any form of stress relief having been applied. This is possible if the stresses applied in use are small and the equipment is not subjected to serious vibration. In general, stress relief is desirable in preventing cracking at some later time, although this procedure does add to the initial cost of the equipment.

In several instances cracks in heavy plates have resulted from the improper welding of external strongbacks. Continuous heavy welds on each side bent the plate and locally caused failure (see Fig. 4.2). Such leaks usually evade detection for a long time since leak hunting except along seams is usually a last-resort procedure. At least one case was reported of a crack at an internal stanchion where the contraction of the welded region upon cooling cracked the plate. In this instance, no external evidence could be seen, and the leak persisted for several months before its location was discovered (see Fig. 4.3). Experienced welders will consistently produce flawless welds, although occasional leaks will occur and require repair. An emergency method is to peen the leak closed, but this cannot be considered satisfactory. Actual welding over is certainly to be preferred. In some instances soft soldering over a small leak is satisfactory. Local stresses, usually due to local heating or cooling or to corrosion, are likely to open up a repair that was poorly made.

Sometimes it is desirable to equip a tank with a jacket outside the walls, as shown in Fig. 4.4. In use, sudden changes in circulating-fluid temperatures are imposed upon the tank. This heating and cooling causes considerable stress in the walls and welds since these changes do not occur all over the tank at once. Poor welds fail under such treatment.

4.2 Rubber Gaskets. Certain openings must be provided in a tank for the insertion and removal of equipment or materials for a given process. During operation these openings must be sealed vacuum tight by appropriate covers. In large steel tanks, flanges bearing gaskets that seal off the cover plates have been found to be satisfactory. Rubber is most widely used as a gasket material where temperatures and loads permit, since this material offers far more reliable sealing than any other.

For high-vacuum service, leaks must be entirely eliminated, and the gas evolved from the gasket material itself must be negligible. Both natural and synthetic rubbers answer these requirements, as long as the amount exposed is negligible. Frequently gaskets must be exposed to oil or other deteriorating substances, and sometimes rather high or low temperatures must be tolerated. In designing a gasket these factors must be considered, and specifications must be based on the requirements at hand. Another important requirement of gasketed joints is that it should be possible at all times to test the gasketed joint for leakage.

Rubbers, both synthetic and natural, have certain important qualities that must be considered before a gasket design is attempted, namely,

1. Rubber is essentially an incompressible material. Deformation in one direction must be suitably allowed for in other directions so that the total volume of the gasket may remain constant.
2. All rubbers experience a certain amount of permanent set resulting from flow when stressed over a period of time.
3. Permanent set increases rapidly as the temperature is raised.
4. A change of hardness occurs with age.

In actual practice, gasket materials do not usually have to be very closely specified to yield reasonable satisfaction if certain precautions are observed.

Much could be written concerning the areal loading of gaskets, but actually a gasketed joint is bolted together until an almost metal-to-metal contact brings a halt to the tightening of the flange bolts. This means that in the vicinity of the bolts the plates are frequently warped and that the rubber gasket is squeezed out of the joints. Figure 4.5 shows two types of gasket grooves used. Figures 4.5a and b show a square gasket in a satisfactorily designed groove. This is designed to allow for a 25 to 30 per cent compression. The corners of the groove are tapered off to provide room for the rubber. Permanent set in a gasket so used will resemble Fig. 4.5c. On the other hand, Figs. 4.5d and e show a rectangular groove in which no provision has been made for gradual strain of the rubber. When a gasket is compressed in this groove, permanent set (Fig. 4.5f) of drastic proportions is accompanied by cutting at the corners. A gasket so used will have to be replaced once it is removed.

Another consideration in bolting gasketed surfaces together is that an apparent softening of the rubber occurs in time. The effect is much more noticeable on lubricated surfaces than on nonlubricated surfaces, and this is due to surface slippage. The diagrams of Fig. 4.6 show that a gasket of square cross section held between two nonlubricated surfaces would remain with the contact surfaces in their initial position (Fig. 4.6a) and that the load required to cause additional deflection would be large. However, if the surfaces are lubricated, then, as the load is applied (Fig. 4.6b), the contact surfaces slide, and alteration of shape due to compression is less restricted.

This results in the frequently observed phenomenon of the loosening of flange bolts initially found to be tight. Actually the rubber has not softened, nor is permanent set the major cause. Such migration will not cause a leak, but subsequent retightening will finally ruin the gasket by tearing.

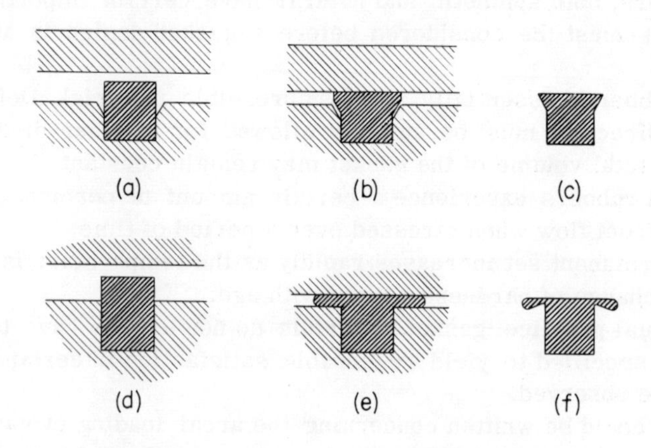

Fig. 4.5 — Effect of gasket groove on gasket.

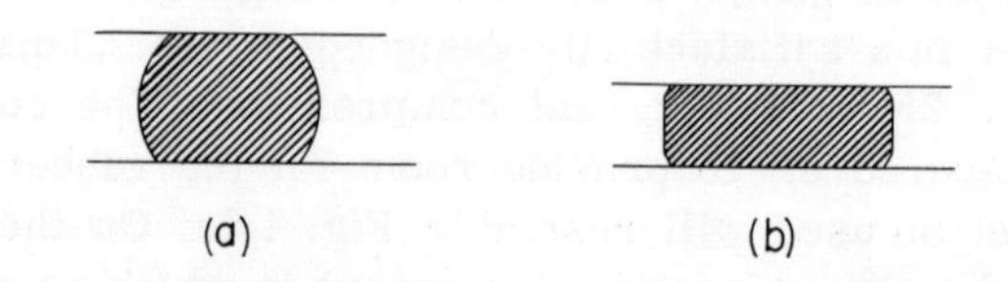

Fig. 4.6 — Gasket compressed between (a) nonlubricated surfaces and (b) lubricated surfaces.

In principle at least, gaskets should be designed for sealing purposes only and should not bear a mechanical load upon which an alignment is to be based. This means that stops should be provided so that when the flange bolts are pulled down a metal contact is established before the deformation of the gasket is so great that it is ruined for further use. It should be noted that the gasket groove and the part of the gasket therein have no sealing value in themselves but serve only to hold the useful (deflecting) portion of the gasket in place.

The foregoing remarks hold for all types of rubber gaskets. The effects of oil solvents and elevated temperatures vary according to the type of rubber used, so that only general statements can be made concerning these items. Specific behavior depends on the particular rubber compound used, and such behavior characteristics should be obtained from the manufacturers of rubbers being considered. However, general statements may be made as follows:

1. All rubber compounds flow at temperatures well under their so-called "melting points." Permanent set for a given time under a given deformation increases as the temperature increases.

2. Neoprene becomes useless at about 90 to 100°C because of permanent set, but both natural and most other rubbers can be used at somewhat higher temperatures, possibly up to 120 to 125°C.

3. Synthetic rubbers are not so subject to swelling caused by oil and most solvents as is natural rubber.

4. Tearing occurs more readily in synthetic rubbers than in natural rubbers.

5. All rubbers lose their elastic properties at low temperatures. They are brittle at liquid-air temperatures.

The proper hardness of a gasket rubber depends upon the load it is expected to bear and upon the deflection expected to be necessary for sealing. The actual load on a gasket also depends somewhat on its shape. However, these factors have proved to be very far from critical, and the examples of Table 4.1 may serve as a guide in design. These have been found to be good working ranges for rubbers having durometer hardnesses of from about 45 to 60. For use at elevated temperatures the loadings should be kept to the smaller values, since flow becomes more serious. The values suggested are for gaskets held in standard gasket grooves. Minimum loads for obtaining seals depend on evenness of the gasket and surfaces and the care with which they are installed. The choice of rubber to be specified for a given application depends on the combined qualities desired. In the case of rubbers generally used for the gaskets described, a wide range of characteristics is acceptable. Perhaps the most important single factor is that of allowable deflection under compression. This is a function of hardness and allowable permanent set. Permanent set as a function of constant deflection is tested at deflections dependent on the durometer hardness numbers. The values of Table 4.2 are listed as the test conditions for A.S.T.M. tests and represent feasible design specifications.[1] The table refers specifically to cylindrical test specimens 1.129 in. in diameter and ½ in. thick. It should be noted that the percentage deflection should be calculated only for the portion of the rubber unrestricted. Thus, if a square gasket is embedded in a groove half the depth of the gasket, only the protruding portion can be considered to be under the deflecting load.

Table 4.1

Size, in.	Shape	Load per linear inch, lb
1/8	Round	5–15
1/8	Square	10–30
1/4	Round	20–40
1/4	Square	20–50
3/8	Square	40–125

Table 4.2

A.S.T.M. hardness numbers	Approx. durometer hardness numbers	Limits of permissible original deflection, % of original thickness
>109	<41	35–40
109–80	41–50	30–25
79–60	51–60	25–40
59–45	61–70	25–35
44–30	71–80	20–30
<30	>80	17–25

Table 4.3—Effect of Temperature on Hardness and Permanent Set*

Substance	At 25°C	At 50°C	At 70°C	At 100°C
		Hardness, psi		
Butyl rubber	105	53	57	66
Natural rubber	115	54	61	69
GR-S	129	55	69	77
Neoprene GN	143	60	68	83
		Permanent set, %		
Butyl rubber	8	4	7	11
Natural rubber	14	14	11	40
GR-S	15	20	14	47
Neoprene GN	65	97	Fails	98

*From "Rubber in Engineering," Chemical Publishing Co., Inc., Brooklyn, N. Y. Reprinted by permission of the publisher.

The actual compression set resulting from either constant load or constant deflection varies considerably with both the composition and history of the rubber. Permanent set in rubber compounds loaded to a fixed deflection tends to reach a more or less constant value within a relatively short time (see Fig. 4.7). Thus the A.S.T.M. tests are

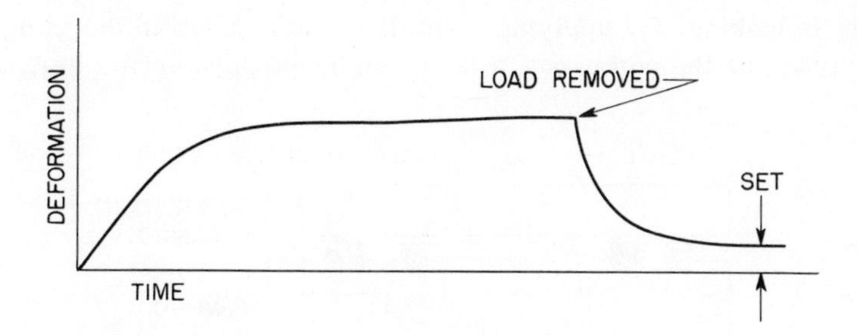

Fig. 4.7—Set in a gasket after it was subjected to a load.

based on a period of 22 hr. The stress set up in any real loading situation will continue to change indefinitely owing both to set (unrecoverable deflection) and to gradual load alterations caused by surface slippage and resulting altered local deflections. The over-all effect is called "creep," of which the set is the unrecoverable change of dimension in the direction of loading.

As already pointed out, creep can be greatly reduced by using rough surfaces and no lubrication. This situation permits high loading (up to 2,000 to 3,000 psi for thin sheet gaskets) and minimum stress decay. However, for many vacuum-service situations it is preferable to use smooth lubricated surfaces and light loadings (50 to 200 psi) in order to obtain sealing with minimum deflections. This is particularly true of gaskets for valves and other frequently moved parts.

Increasing temperatures greatly affect both hardness and permanent set. Table 4.3 illustrates a typical situation.[2] The samples were stretched 100 per cent and held for 22 hr. The set was measured after being unloaded for 30 min at 25°C.

Tests on samples of silicone rubber of an initial durometer hardness of about 50 indicate that relatively no set or hardness changes occur below 100°C, but at 150°C its performance is similar to that of butyl rubber at 100°C, except that it becomes softer rather than harder as do the rest.

Most flanges and cover plates that have been used on large steel tanks have been fitted with a double set of gaskets set in a pair of grooves on one of the faces. The face applied to these gaskets is then flat. Figure 4.8 shows a typical flange-and-plate arrangement. The inner gasket is the sealing gasket and is relied on at all times. The outer gasket, although also tight, simply provides a means of determining whether or not the inner one is holding. If it is not, the outer gasket provides an emergency means of preventing leakage of the seal. A soap film across the pump-out will be drawn in if the inner gasket is leaking. By applying a small vacuum pump to the pump-out or by plugging the pump-out, a leak can be stopped until a permanent

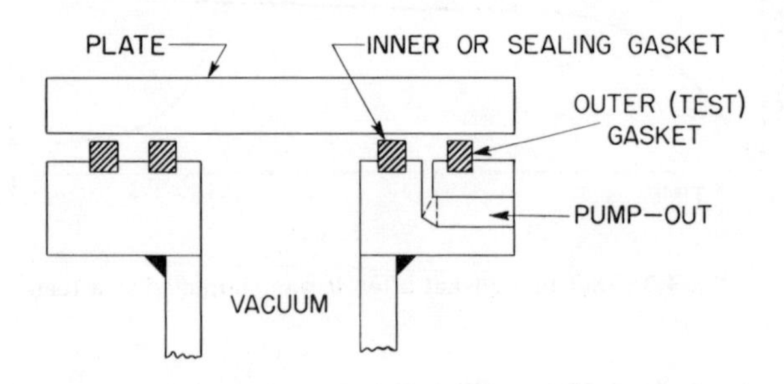

Fig. 4.8—Typical flange-and-plate arrangement.

repair can be made. Occasionally single gaskets are used, but these cannot be easily checked and should not be used in equipment that is subject to frequent disassembly.

Gaskets for installations similar to the above are made of extruded sections, or else they are molded to fit the particular piece of equipment. If a long extruded piece is used, the problem of cutting and joining the ends must be faced. Three methods are used: (1) bevel cutting and press fitting without cementing, (2) bevel cutting and cementing the ends together, and (3) vulcanizing the ends. Although all methods have been used, vulcanizing has proved to be the most satisfactory of these methods. However, special equipment is necessary. Some technicians develop sufficient skill at cutting and fitting the gasket material into the grooves so that an adequate end-to-end seal is obtained by beveling and laying the ends of the gasket together (Fig. 4.9). When compressed by the flange plate no cementing is required. This requires very careful cutting and fitting.

An improvement in this technique is to cement the ends together. Rubber cement is applied to each surface of natural-rubber gaskets, and after it has dried the surfaces are pressed together. Neoprene and Hycar require special cements obtainable from the makers of the rubbers. The rapidity of drying and subsequent curing of the cement is determined by the compounding of the cements. Manufacturers can furnish a wide range of cements.

Vulcanizing is accomplished by first cementing the ends together and then applying heat at a temperature appropriate for the material. A substantial and permanent bond is made in this manner. A heating element made to fit the gasket is required in this case.

No attempt will be made here to go into detail regarding the relative merits of the various types of natural and synthetic rubbers. A good deal of information can be obtained from "Rubber in Engineering" published by Chemical Publishing Co., Inc., Brooklyn, N. Y., and from other publications.

A satisfactory gasket material that has been developed has a Hycar (OR-15) base mixed with suitable compounding ingredients and cured to meet the physical specifications. In view of its widespread use some details of its composition follow:

Mechanical:	
Tensile strength	1,800 psi minimum
Elongation	300% minimum
Shore hardness	60 ± 5
Compression set	15% maximum
Thermal: max. service temp.	150 – 170°F
Chemical: oil resistance	±6% wt. change maximum (70 hr at 212°F)

A typical compounding to meet these specifications is as follows:

	Amount, parts by weight
Hycar OR-15	100
Zinc oxide	5
Tetramethyl thiuram disulfide	3
Benzothiazol disulfide	3
Gastex (carbon black)	85
P-25 Cumar	5
Dibutyl phthalate	10
Stearic acid	0.5
Plasticizer S.C.	15
	226.5

Cure 45 min at 310°F.

Prior to the use of the above gasket material, neoprene was used extensively owing to its oil-resistant characteristics.

4.3 Faceplate and Flange Gaskets. As previously mentioned, grooves cut in one member of a pair of flanges (Fig. 4.8) have been generally used to hold gaskets in place during assembly and during subsequent use. Since maximum pressures held by the gaskets are seldom more than 15 psi, cross sliding along the surfaces, even when lubricated, is almost never observed.

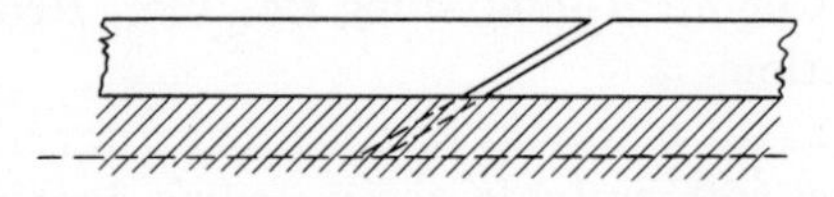

Fig. 4.9—Bevel cuts in gasket to effect sealing without use of cement.

Circular flanges offer little difficulty in the cutting of the grooves. Details of the grooves are shown in Figs. 4.10a, b, and c. The central V groove is cut as shown to ensure complete venting so that no section of the intergasket region may become isolated from the pumpout. The dimensions of standard gasket grooves that have been used with satisfactory results in the University of California Radiation Laboratory are shown in Figs. 4.10b and c.

In rectangular flanges the grooves must be milled, and the corners are always a troublesome detail both from the machining aspect and also in the matter of fitting gaskets around the corners. The method most commonly used is illustrated in Fig. 4.11a, in which a straight groove is cut through to the edge of the flange in each case. Fillets are then welded into the grooves to lend support to the gaskets. The surfaces are subsequently ground smooth. This must be well done so that leaks do not occur around the gaskets at this point. The gasket is forced into the grooves without shaping. A joint attempted at the corners almost always produces a leak. This type of groove is very satisfactory with molded gaskets made to fit the flange. For plates using very small gaskets and consequently where small compression distances are allowable (⅛-in. gaskets), rounded corner grooves are frequently required in order to avoid trouble in installation. This circular milling or routing is obviously a costly job.

Considerable progress has been made in the development of grooveless gaskets that not only are satisfactory but also eliminate the trouble and expense of the machined grooves. A design developed by Samuel[3] has been used with great success with standard pipe flanges

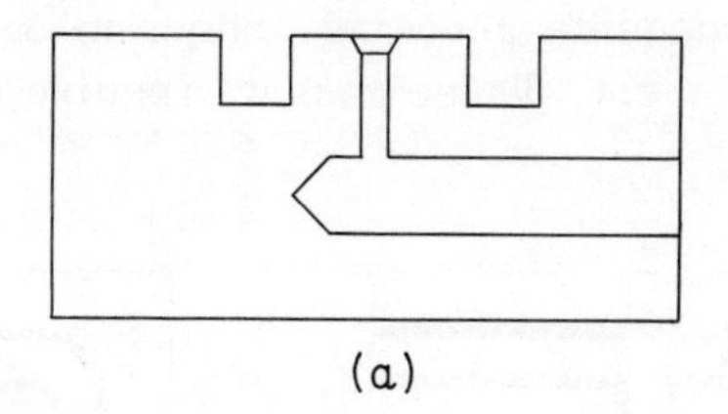

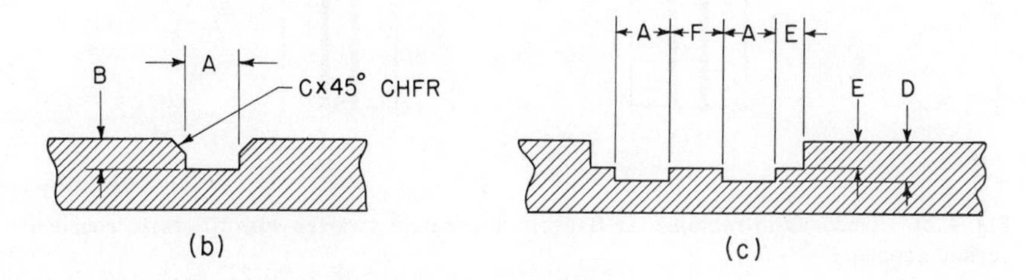

Fig. 4.10a—Grooves and pump-out in circular flange.

Fig. 4.10b—Regular standard gasket groove; ⅛-in. gaskets are to be used only where space will not permit use of larger sizes.

Fig. 4.10c—Metal-to-metal standard gasket grooves. This method provides 33 per cent compression of gasket, which requires a pressure of about 330 psi; ⅜- and ¼-in. sizes are being used.

Dimensions for Figs. 4.10b and c in Inches

Nominal square gasket size*	A	B	C	D	E	F
⅛	0.120 0.125	0.071 0.076	1/32 max.	0.089 0.094	1/16	⅛
3/16	0.182 0.187	0.108 0.113	3/64 ± 1/64	0.136 0.141	3/32	3/16
¼	0.245 0.250	0.146 0.151	1/16 ± 1/64	0.183 0.188	⅛	¼
⅜	0.370 0.375	0.221 0.226	3/32 ± 1/64	0.277 0.282	3/16	⅜

* 55 to 65 durometer Hycar

up to 6 in. in diameter. A drawing of this gasket is shown in Fig. 4.12. The rubber is vulcanized to both sides of a sheet-metal ring. Spacers mounted on the ring assume the mechanical load as the flange bolts are tightened. A hole drilled in one of the flanges into the intergasket space provides an adequate checking and pump-out device. The ears provide proper alignment. These gaskets require no alteration of the

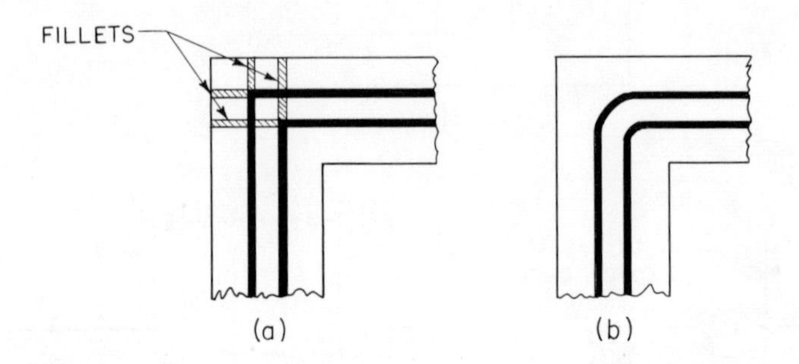

Fig. 4.11—Grooves in rectangular flanges: a, straight grooves with fillets; b, rounded corner grooves.

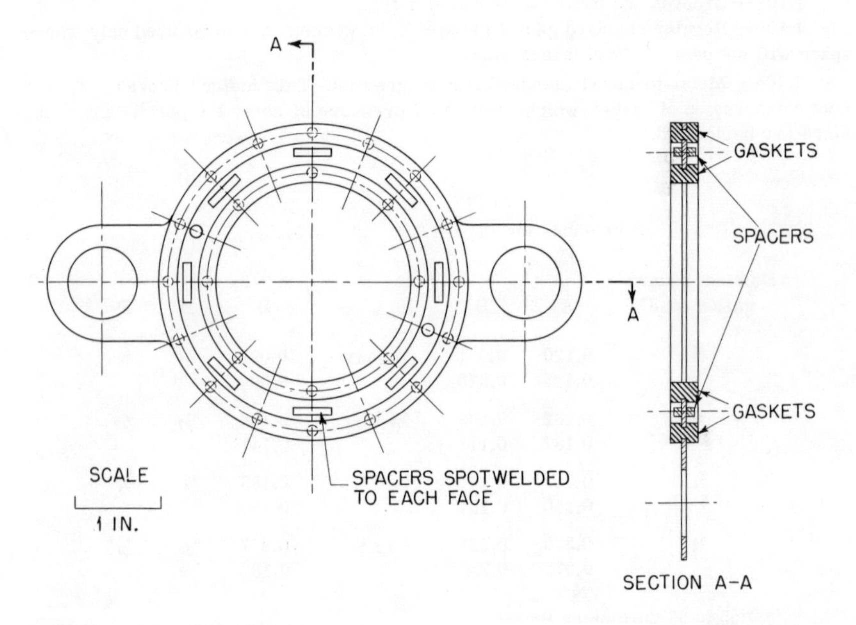

Fig. 4.12—Grooveless gasket for use on standard pipe flanges.

standard flanges. In many months of service, none have been known to fail.

Several amended designs have been suggested and used for large rectangular flanges. The same design fabricated for a particular flange could be used. However, it has been observed that when separators have been used on large plates and flanges there is frequent difficulty in getting a seal because these large flanges and plates seldom have flat surfaces to within tolerances that make uniformly small gasket deformation possible.

All rubber gaskets of the so-called "dumbbell" design of Fig. 4.13 can be used without grooves. The gasket is molded in the section shown, with a perforated web. At intervals of a foot or two a pin is put into the gasket and into loose-fitting holes in the cover plate in order to hold the gasket in place while being assembled.

As has been mentioned, the application of lubricants such as Lubriseal or silicone greases, although it ensures gas tightness, also reduces the ability of the gaskets to bear a load. Thus, if the loading is uncontrolled and smooth greased surfaces are used, it may be expected that excessive deformation of the gaskets will result and that early destruction of the gaskets will occur. In all cases the use of lubricants should be kept to a minimum so that the intergasket region does not become clogged, thereby preventing testing.

A rough surface flange is a partial solution to this problem. Even sandblasted surfaces have been noted to be highly satisfactory in this respect. Where flatness tolerances will allow, shims are, of course, the most reliable means of carrying the mechanical load and protecting the gasket.

In cases where the gasket loading must for one reason or another be kept at a minimum, a tongue left on the otherwise flat flange guarantees a seal without great deflection of the gasket (Fig. 4.14). A flange gasket used by Westinghouse in high-vacuum work consists of a sheet-metal ring formed into a V (Fig. 4.15). A soft molded- or cut-rubber ring gasket fits loosely into this V. When the flanges are drawn together, the rubber, while forming the seal, is almost completely eliminated from the vacuum side of the system. That in most cases this is important has not been shown.

4.4 Rubber in Compression Fittings. Rubber seals have frequently been used to seal wires and metal tubing and rods into a vacuum system. A few precautions make the practice in many cases quite permanent and satisfactory. Figure 4.16 illustrates the general features that must be incorporated in such a packing gland.

Of considerable importance is the matter of maintaining the clearances between the rod and wall and between the rod and the washer quite small (a loose sliding fit), since extrusion takes place as the compression is increased. A long unthreaded shoulder on the compression nut should fit into the unthreaded section of the cell so that rubber will not become chewed up in threads. It should be remem-

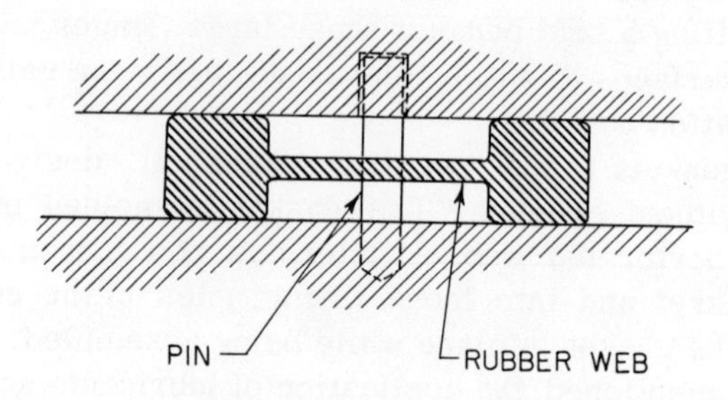

Fig. 4.13—Dumbbell design of rubber gasket.

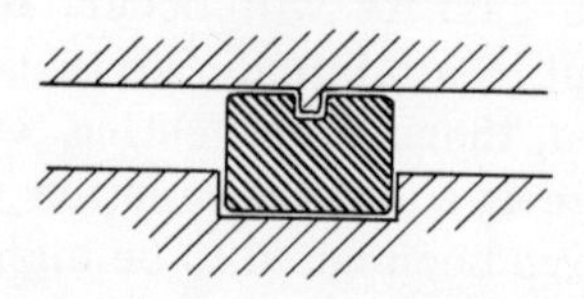

Fig. 4.14—Tongue on flange to minimize gasket loading.

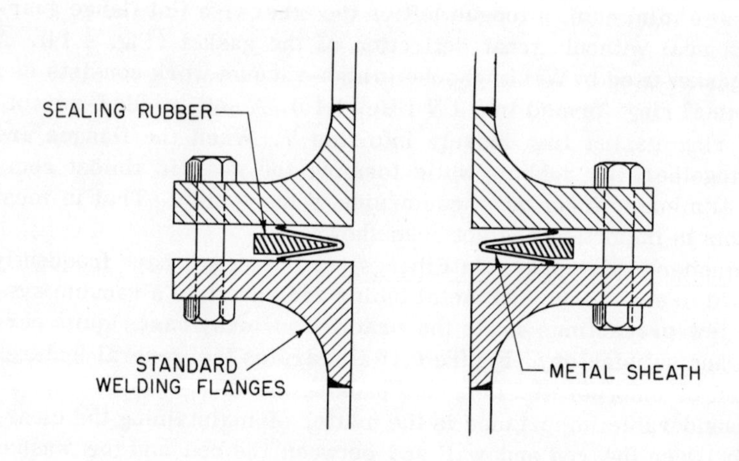

Fig. 4.15—Westinghouse design of flange gasket.

bered that the rubber is incompressible, for it is quite easy to collapse thin copper tubing by overtightening such a device. A soft to medium hardness of rubber will be useful as long as temperatures do not rise above 100°C. Because of differential expansion, these seals are prone to develop leaks after use at alternate extreme tempera-

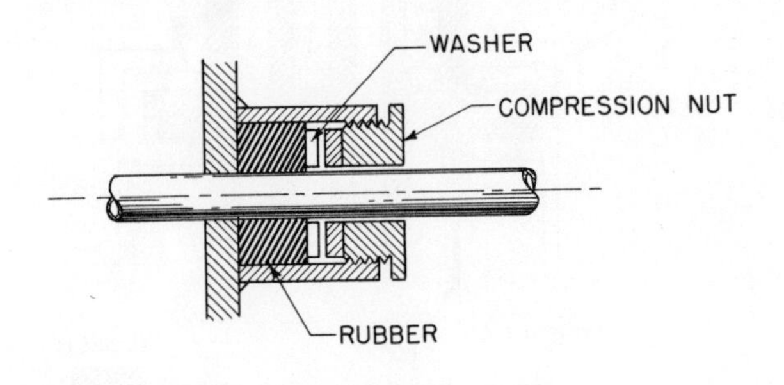

Fig. 4.16 — Packing gland.

tures. This type of seal has been very successfully used to seal glass tubing, as in ionization gauges, into a vacuum system.

A very satisfactory seal, developed for the entrance of tubing and electrical leads into an insulator entering a vacuum system, is diagrammatically shown in Fig. 4.17. This assembly, several inches in diameter, carries electrically insulated leads. Very little trouble has been experienced with this type of assembly. A medium-hardness rubber is used.

4.5 Metal Gaskets. Seals that must be maintained at temperatures higher than about 125°C, or in which rubber cannot be used owing to outgassing, utilize metal gaskets of some kind. Small gaskets of lead, copper, aluminum, silver, or tin have long been used for such service. Complete sealing demands high stresses and consequently very heavy and rigid flanges. When the size of the seal becomes more than an inch or so, extremely heavy fittings must be used. The difficulty of differential expansion can be overcome by using such a design that the elastic flexure of the flange and bolts due to tightening of the flange bolts will amply exceed the differential expansion between the gasket and the flange.

No large metal seals have been installed in the vacuum systems described, although at least one design was built and tested. This is shown in Fig. 4.18. Here the gasket is made of copper, cut from a piece of copper tubing. The assembly was made and held under high vacuum while it was alternately heated and cooled. No failure oc-

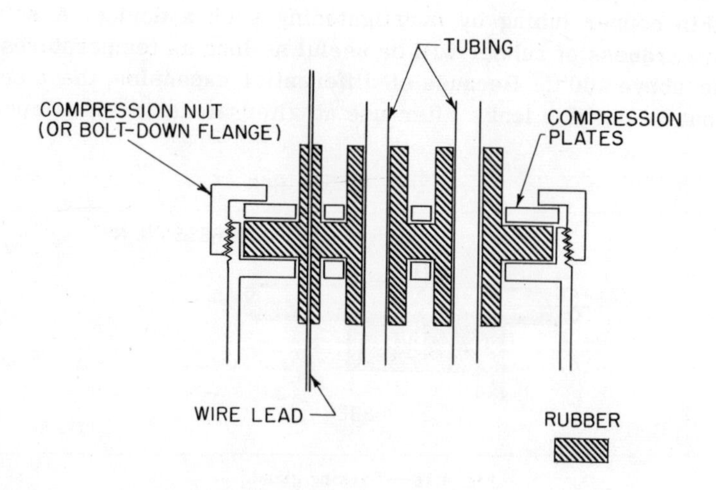

Fig. 4.17—Seal used to introduce tubing and electrical leads into vacuum chamber.

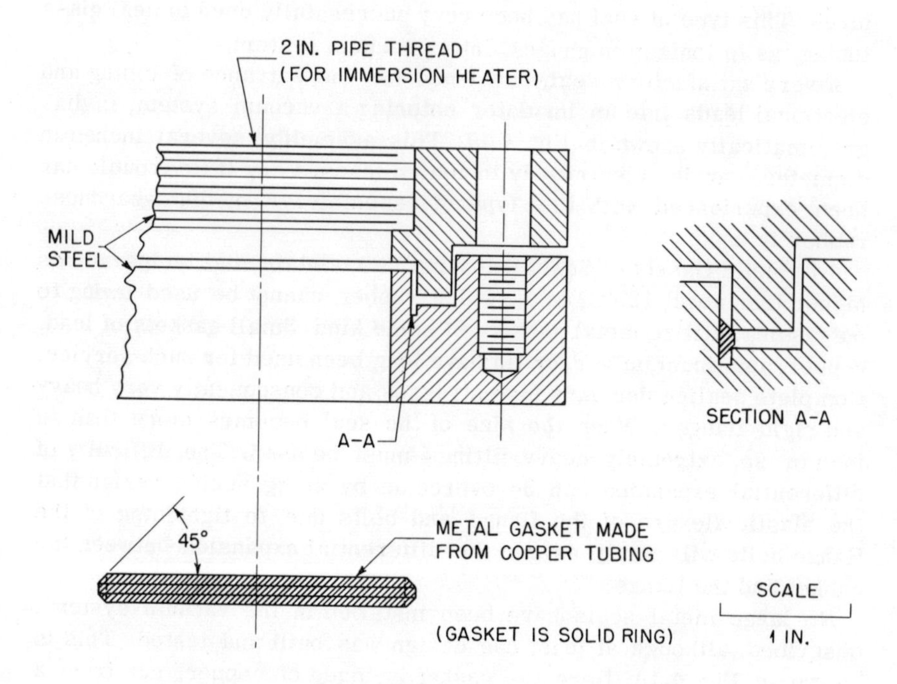

Fig. 4.18—Design of metal seal built at Radiation Laboratory.

curred during tests.[4] However, this gasket was never put into actual use.

Copper gaskets were used between tubing and the terminal flare fittings on the oil equalizing lines between the 8- and 20-in. diffusion pumps. These, when properly installed, gave no trouble at the temperature of the boiling oil (200 to 250°C).

4.6 Insulated Seals. In many instances in vacuum practice it is necessary to introduce electrical conductors from the atmosphere into the vacuum chamber. The insulating materials must be chosen on the basis of electrical, mechanical, and vacuum properties. In so far as vacuum properties are concerned the materials must not release gases to the vacuum system in such quantity as to impair the operation being carried out or result in appreciable loss of time. Various glasses and materials such as porcelain, Lavite, mica, quartz, micarta, etc., have commonly been used in this connection.

In glass vacuum systems it has been common practice to use metal-to-glass seals. Small wires of certain metals can be sealed directly to glass. Platinum can be sealed to soft glasses very satisfactorily, the coefficients of expansion being very nearly the same. Lead glass appears to be preferable to lime glass in this connection. Tungsten wire up to about 40 mils in diameter can be sealed to such glasses as Nonex Glass No. 772 or yellow "uranium" glass, provided suitable cleaning methods for the metal are adopted and careful annealing is carried out. Similar procedures will work with molybdenum, the seal being made to a glass such as Corning No. 750 AJ. Suitable transition glasses will allow these seals to be fused directly to the vacuum envelope. Another type of seal used to a large extent in the vacuum-tube industry is the pinch seal using Dumet.* Dumet is a copper-sheathed iron-nickel alloy. Outgassed fine wire of this material (up to 10 mils in diameter) can be sealed to glass without beading by inserting the wire in a hot glass tubing and pinching the opening shut.

The above seals are of use primarily in introducing fine wires into a vacuum system. There are a number of other types of seals that can be used for a rather wide range of sizes and shapes of metals. Kovar† and Fernico‡ are alloys of iron, nickel, and cobalt that have been developed for use in making glass-to-metal seals. Vacuum-tight seals can be made with relative ease with these materials if appropri-

*Dumet is the trade name for an alloy made by the Cleveland Weld Works, Cleveland, Ohio.

†Developed by Westinghouse Electric & Manufacturing Co. Exclusive fabricator and distributor, Stupakoff Ceramic and Manufacturing Co., Latrobe, Pa.

‡Developed by General Electric Company, Schenectady, N.Y.

ate glasses are chosen. These alloys are easily machined, brazed, and soldered, but are rendered porous by silver solder. However, they are not attacked by mercury. Seals of these alloys can be obtained in a variety of sizes and shapes from the manufacturers and are suitable for use on metal vacuum systems. Another type of glass-to-metal seal is that developed by Housekeeper[5,6] and named after him. Theoretically this type of seal should be possible with any metal, provided it has a low yield point and is wetted by the glass. The seal is most practical for copper and platinum, although iron, chromium, and nickel can be used. A final type of glass-to-metal seal is produced by soldering. The glass is platinized by means of a platinizing solution and then heated to around 650°C for a few min. Solder is applied to the platinum layer by means of a soldering iron, using a 60-40 solder with a flux of ammonium chloride in glycerol.

To introduce electrical leads into metal vacuum systems, particularly in the case of high-potential leads, vacuum seals with rubber gaskets are often used.

Glass-to-metal seals are in common use for high-vacuum systems. A number of such seals for high-voltage operation have been described in the literature. However, the fragility and lack of resistance to shearing force make glass unsuitable for many applications. For this reason, seals of ceramics (usually porcelain) to metal have been developed.[7] For many purposes, rubber-gasket seals are used, making seals between the vacuum envelope and the insulating ceramic. This is quite common practice in the case of large metal systems. Suitable brackets, of course, must be provided to press the insulator uniformly against the vacuum wall. This also applies to the supporting structure for the electrical leads. The usual precautions for obtaining tight seals with gaskets apply here with the added provision that a good deal of care must be taken to avoid straining the insulator. The method is of course applicable to glass and quartz insulators. It has been common practice in the Radiation Laboratory to seal cylindrically shaped insulators up to a diameter of about 1 ft by this method with quite satisfactory results.

Spark-plug-type fittings of laminated-mica construction have been used extensively in the Radiation Laboratory for carrying electrical leads and water lines into the vacuum system. These fittings are usually threaded into the system, a seal being effected by the use of solder or soft-copper gaskets. The best results have been obtained with the B-G-type mica spark plugs.

4.7 Sliding and Rotating Seals. Of great importance in vacuum processing equipment is the reliability of seals associated with moving parts entering the vacuum system. Of course, in many processes it is possible to produce a desired motion inside the vacuum chamber by means of magnetic forces. The usual procedure is to place a permanent magnet or an electromagnet outside a portion of the vacuum chamber, but as close as possible to the part to be moved inside the chamber—this part being constructed partially of magnetic material. Motion inside the vacuum chamber can then be produced by moving the permanent magnet or by passing current through the electromagnet. It is clear that the vacuum envelope in the region where this motion is to be produced must be constructed of nonmagnetic material. This method is most suited to carrying out a given well-defined motion inside the vacuum system. It does not lend itself to any precision of control, and it is not flexible in operation. The most general use of this method has been in connection with glass vacuum apparatus for such purposes as opening containers and operating vacuum cutoffs. However, it can be used just as effectively on nonmagnetic metal systems.

In many cases it has been found desirable to transfer motions through the vacuum-chamber walls by means of appropriate seals. Probably the earliest type of seal used for this purpose is the stopcock, in which a ground fitting is made and a lubricant is used. The most common type of material used for stopcocks is glass. However, "soft" metals such as brass and copper can be used if a good deal of care is exercised in construction and operation. More recent types of seals are those using metallic bellows or sylphons[8] as sealing agents, and those utilizing a rubber-to-metal seal, e.g., the Wilson seal.[9] The latter type of seal, for most purposes, has been found to be highly reliable and easily serviced. The reliability of the metallic-bellows type, although generally acceptable, is partially offset by the invariably difficult replacement problem.

Figure 4.19 illustrates the general assembly of a typical Wilson seal. The seal gland is either machined in the vacuum wall or, more generally, built as a separate unit. Two separators, as shown, hold two fairly hard rubber gaskets when compressed slightly by the compression nut. The base of the gland and the upper surface of the first separator are made to ensure that the gaskets will be held outward from the vacuum side of the seal. The gaskets fit snugly into the smooth inner surface of the cell, and the holes are approximately two-thirds (see Fig. 4.19) the diameter of the shaft. When assembled and suitably lubricated, the inner gasket forms the seal.

As the inner gasket receives the load of atmospheric pressure through the pump-out, it is thrust solidly against the shaft; thus the seal is maintained independently of the permanent set that the rubber might acquire. Suitably lubricated, this seal may be used for either a sliding shaft or a rotating shaft, or for both in combination.

Satisfactory use of the Wilson seal depends on several points of construction and assembly, as follows:

1. The shaft must be smooth (a semipolished surface).
2. The gaskets must fit the gland.
3. The gaskets must have smooth edges. A sharp circular cutter lubricated with soap solution produces such a smooth cut.

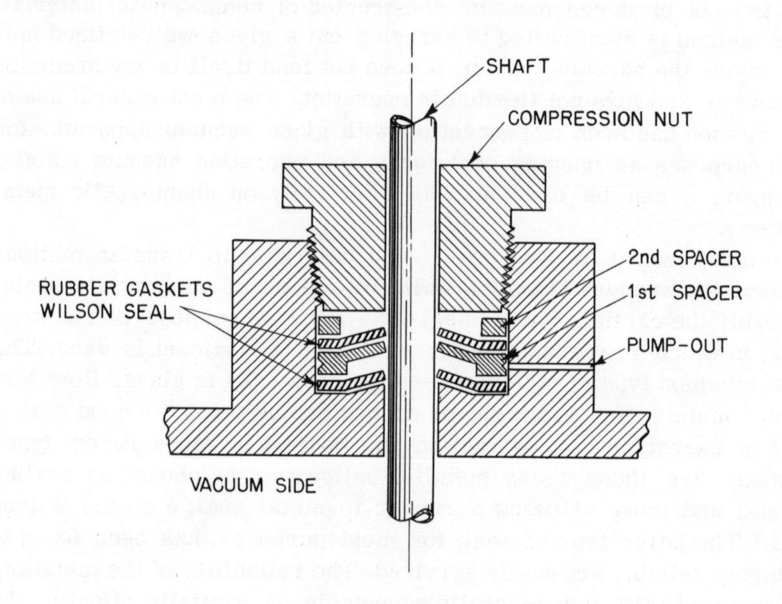

Fig. 4.19—Wilson seal.

4. Lubrication must be adequate. A good quality of vacuum grease sparingly used is recommended.
5. The compression nut must be just sufficient to seal. If the compression nut is forced down too tightly it will squeeze the rubber out of shape and generally permit leakage.

This seal may be tested by using soap solution on the pump-out, since a leak past the first seal will cause air to enter the pump-out. If leakage occurs, the pump-out may be attached to a vacuum line, and, if the outer seal is holding, the leak will be checked. The operation of this checking method assumes that the pump-out and the vents in the first spacer are not clogged with grease or soap. Proper assembly and maintenance will ensure this. It has been the practice of a few operators to assemble the Wilson seal filled with vacuum grease. This results in a good seal but makes checking impossible. In an emergency a Wilson-seal leak has sometimes been stopped by allowing vacuum grease to be drawn into the pump-out. It soon reaches the leaking section of the gasket, and the leak is stopped. Usually this procedure results in brief stoppage, and the seal must be replaced before really satisfactory operation can be obtained. Most seals run for many months without attention. A sliding seal of this type requires that the sliding rod be lubricated at frequent intervals.

A number of installations have been operated with a small vial on each Wilson-seal pump-out. This vial was filled with diffusion-pump oil on the assumption that as long as the oil remained in the vial the seal was certainly not leaking. However, it was found necessary to remove the vials since most of the Wilson seals installed were packed with grease, and the pump-outs, being plugged, failed to act as indicators owing to the fact that other leakage paths (generally through the second seal) developed and were not indicated.

A later variation of this seal is known as a "chevron seal." It consists of a gland similar to that of the Wilson seal, but containing several gaskets in a pile without spacers. These are heavily greased and afford a highly satisfactory seal. If a checking device is desired, a spaced gasket is placed outside the chevron group in an arrangement similar to that in the Wilson seal. In actual use this has proved to be a remarkably trouble-free seal for large, slowly rotating and sliding shafts.

Failure in these rubber seals occurs when the shafts become dry or when the temperature of the seal rises to excessive values. The effect of temperature is twofold. The greases used become fluid, and their ability to seal poor fits between the gasket and the shaft is seriously diminished. Also the permanent set of the rubber makes it possible for the hole in the gasket to become too large for the shaft. The use of silicone greases will largely prevent the former difficulty, and the rubber characteristics control the latter. Neoprene is less adaptable to elevated temperatures than butyl rubber. A durometer hardness of 50 to 60 is desirable in these gaskets.

Delsasso and Creutz[10] have described a simple, quick-acting vacuum lock for the insertion of samples into a beta-ray spectrograph. The sample is contained in a depression in a rod that slides through two neoprene gaskets. Provision is made for pumping out the space between the gaskets. This type of seal appears to be satisfactory for the purpose intended, but it is not suitable for general application. Cowie[11] has described a seal that permits translational and rotational motions of a tube. It was developed for use when space requirements make it impossible to use a Wilson seal. The seal consists essentially of a neoprene gasket through which the tube passes, the gasket being sealed by contact with beveled (45 deg) surfaces on two plates clamped together. Other types of seals involving the use of rubber gaskets have been described in the literature. However, the Wilson seal appears to be generally as satisfactory in most cases as any of these.

The use of metal bellows for driving a mechanism within a vacuum is an old method. Figure 4.20 shows a bellows adapted for use in sealing a sliding shaft to a vacuum wall. The usual bellows can be extended or compressed about 35 per cent of its initial length, but the manufacturer's specifications should be consulted in any particular case. It is important in all cases to prevent torque from being applied to these bellows. A rotating motion may be imparted to a shaft as indicated in Fig. 4.21. Many variations of these designs have been used experimentally. Rubens and Henderson[12] have described the use of spherical ground joints to introduce motions through a vacuum envelope. This method is widely used for making temporary connections.

Fluid-line Seals. Frequently electrically isolated sections of cooling lines must be included within the vacuum system. This calls for the use of gastight tubing couplings that will act as suitable electrical insulators and at the same time withstand the temperature fluctuations and extremes which are required.

The problem is greatly simplified if the temperature of operation is constant, but this is rarely the case. Several possibilities have been explored, e.g., (1) bakelite or micarta couplings used with standard flare fittings, (2) fiber couplings used with compression gaskets, and (3) metal-to-glass seals such as Kovar or copper. All these methods are only partially satisfactory. Leaks due to a permanent set of gaskets appear to be unavoidable. Properly installed Kovar-seal couplings seem to be the best solution.

Wherever actual electrical insulation is not required, soldered joints are far superior to removable joints. Great care must be exercised in forming such joints, however, to see that flux-filled holes are not allowed to exist. Thorough external cleaning of finished soldered joints and flushing of the lines with hot water for a considerable time before final testing effectively avoid subsequent opening of leaks due to dissolving flux plugs.

4.8 Valves for Vacuum Service.[13-15] Industrial applications have made necessary the development of large-aperture valves suitable for vacuum service. Early designs were based upon the remodeling of the usual type of fluid-control valves to meet the more rigorous demands of vacuum systems.

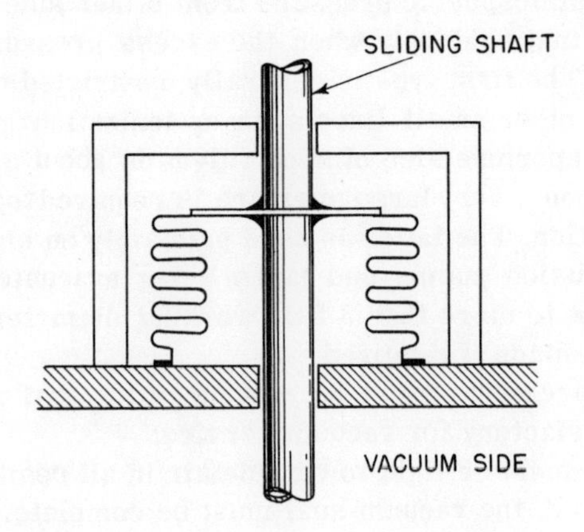

Fig. 4.20—Sliding shaft with metal bellows.

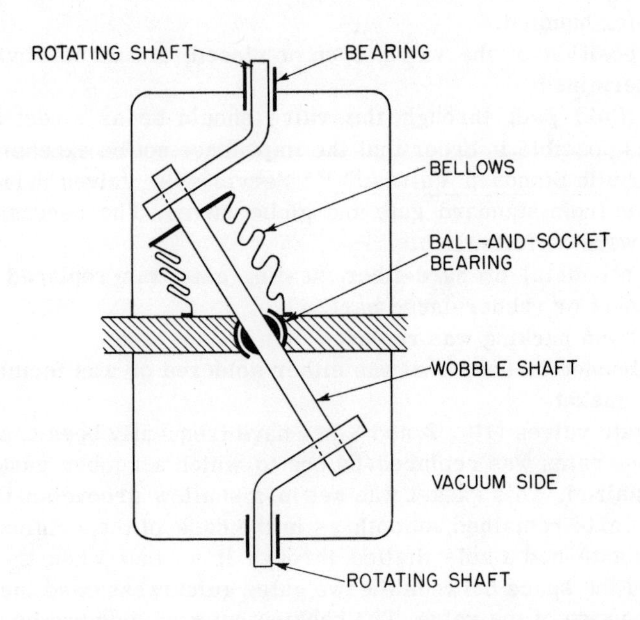

Fig. 4.21—Method of producing rotary motion inside vacuum chamber.

Two general classes of valves are now in use, namely, (1) valves that withstand atmospheric pressure from either side without leakage and (2) valves that hold only when the excess pressure is exerted in one direction. The first type is generally restricted to use in roughing lines or in other small lines such as ionization-gauge lines, etc. The maximum aperture size of such valves is about 6 in. The second type is used when a very large aperture is required together with high speed of operation. The latter is used primarily on high-vacuum lines connecting diffusion pumps and tanks being evacuated. Sizes range from about 4 in. to more than 3 ft in working diameter. Larger sizes could easily be made if required.

Several requirements must be met in order that a valve may be classed as satisfactory for vacuum service:

1. The valve must be tight to outside air in all positions.
2. When closed, the vacuum seal must be complete.
3. Action must be reasonably rapid.
4. Sealing parts must be replaceable.
5. Back-seating seals are desirable.
6. Sealing and moving parts should be noncorrosive in the atmospheres being handled.
7. The position of the valve (open or closed) should be obvious or easily determined.
8. The fluid path through the valve should be as direct and as straight as possible in order that the impedance not be excessive.

4.9 Rebuilt Standard Valves.[16,17] Serviceable valves have been constructed from standard gate and globe valves. The necessary alterations were as follows:

1. The all-metal or hard-fiber sealing gate was replaced with a rubber gasket or rubber-faced part.
2. The stem packing was replaced by a Wilson seal.
3. The bonnet-to-body seal was either soldered or was formed with a suitable gasket.

Crane gate valves ($1\frac{1}{2}$, 2, and 3 in.) have frequently been used. One of the brass gates was replaced by one to which a rubber gasket had been vulcanized. This gasket was set in a shallow groove so that the face of the gate remained smooth as in the case of the original. The remaining gate had a hole drilled through it so that when the valve was closed the space between the two gates quickly assumed the pressure of one side of the valve. The packing nut was replaced by a suitably designed Wilson seal. After assembly, the bonnet-to-body seal was formed by soft soldering. It was found that if the gates were held in an open position no damage was done to the rubber on the gate. These valves served in either roughing lines or high-vacuum service.

A precaution must be taken in the case of all cast-body valves. Tests should be made to determine the porosity of the casting. Some have been found unusable unless completely covered with soft solder or with suitable external coatings such as glyptal.

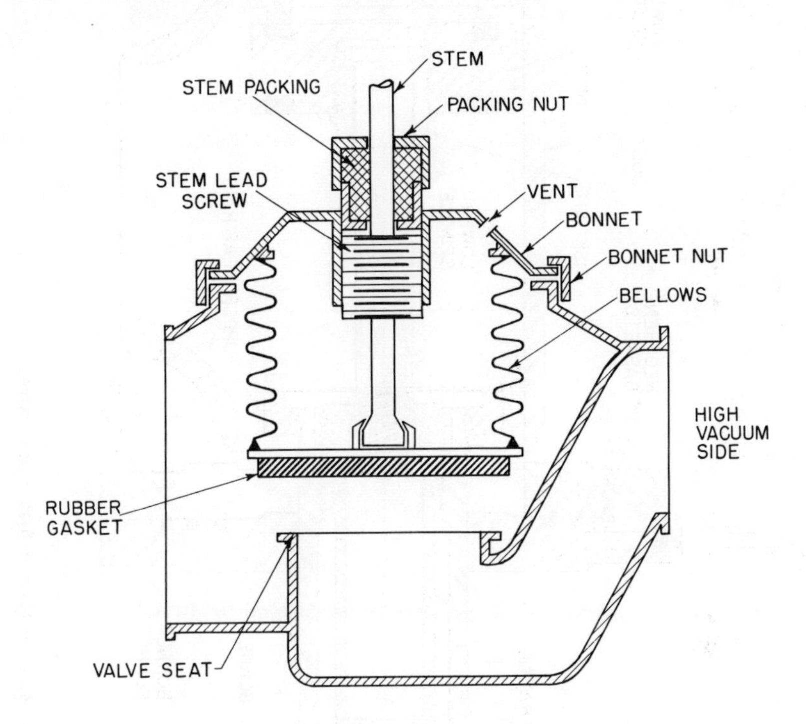

Fig. 4.22—Generalized globe valve with bellows.

A number of small valves, usually of globe or angle design, have been designed for gasoline or similar service. These valves are generally equipped with a metallic-bellows seal between the bonnet and stem and with a lead or aluminum gasket between the body and the bonnet. With suitable substitution of rubber for the usual metal or fiber sealing-gasket disk, these valves may sometimes be used without further alteration.

Three difficulties arise with these valves:

1. It is difficult to obtain a gastight seal between bonnet and body unless the gasket is replaced by a soft gasket. This replacement must be done with caution since any rotary motion of the bonnet when the valve is closed results in destruction of the bellows. A suitable gasket has been found to be a fiber one (such as is used for steam-line

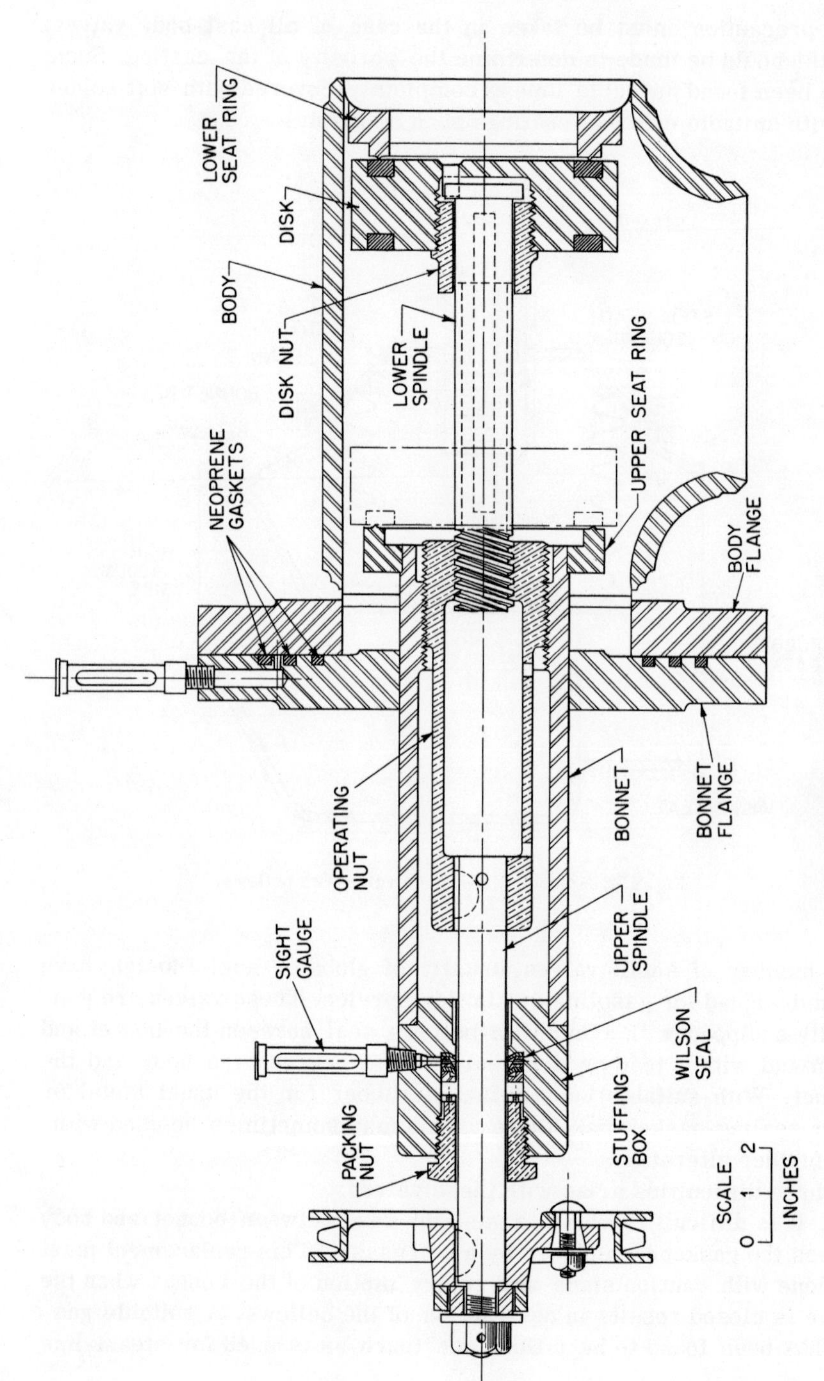

Fig. 4.23—Chapman 6-in. angle valve.

gaskets) which has been soaked in glyptal. This forms a good and permanent seal and is rigid enough.

2. The valve seats of some designs are not integral parts of the valve body but consist of elements threaded to the body. Gas leaks through these threaded joints are intolerable. Removal of the seat and coating the threads with glyptal together with subsequent tightening have seemed to cure all cases.

3. The bellows themselves are fragile and eventually crack. Replacement is then difficult.

In connection with bellows-seal valves (see Fig. 4.22), it is well to note that pressure applied on the inside of the valve in excess of a few (e.g., 10) pounds is likely to collapse the bellows and make further use impossible. Since some types of equipment are commonly tested up to pressures of 50 or 60 lb/sq in. during a hunt for leaks, caution should be used if bellows valves are in the lines being put under pressure. Large leaks in the bellows can be detected by observation of soap films on the bellows vent. In order to make this test effective, the stem packing must be tight. Small leaks are seldom detectable by this method since slightly changing temperatures in the bellows often far exceed the effect to be observed from the leak.

Attempts have been made to utilize standard valves by simply using a greased packing and a smooth stem. No completely successful installations of this kind have been seen by the writer. Ionization-gauge isolation valves of this type were used in some cases. These were provided with a sealing back seat, but, during travel, leakage usually was disturbingly great.

A very reliable general-purpose valve built by the Chapman Valve Manufacturing Company is a 6-in. (4-in. aperture) angle valve, as the general assembly drawing, Fig. 4.23, shows. This valve utilizes a Wilson seal on the stem and a back seat identical with the working seat. This is a highly successful valve seldom giving any trouble. The Wilson seal can be replaced when the valve is back-seated without any danger of leakage into the system. In the use of this valve one precaution should be noted. If the valve is back-seated when at atmospheric pressure, air is trapped behind the back seat. When the valve is closed, this will be released into the system. In order to avoid this the valve should not be back-seated until the system is fairly well evacuated.

A standard gas valve using a metal-diaphragm seal between the stem assembly and the valve disk is made in small sizes by Kerotest. This is a brass angle valve using either silver, tin, or fiber gaskets for sealing. The 3/8-in. size with fiber gasket has been used in most situations where small couplings or test gauges enter the vacuum system. The valve is reasonably reliable and rugged.

In general, it should be noted that valves should be so installed that in their closed position no moving seals or bellows are included on the process-tank side of the valve seat. This makes it possible for one to take accurate rates of rise when the valves are closed, independent of minor leaks in the stem seals or bellows. Other means are used in detecting these leaks.

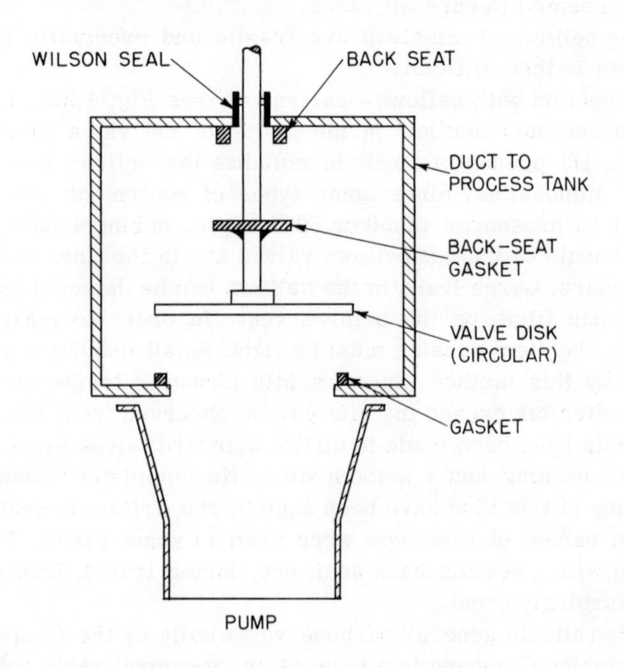

Fig. 4.24—General arrangement of disk valve.

4.10 Unidirectional Gate or Disk Valves. Since considerable time is required to heat up or cool a large diffusion pump, it is customary to leave such pumps in continuous operation. When a tank is let down to atmospheric pressure, a suitable valve between the tank and the pump is closed so that air will not reach the pumping system. Furthermore, since the duct between the diffusion pumps and the tank is necessarily very large, the valve cannot be allowed to be a serious constriction in the duct. Therefore very large valves are used. The use of these valves is restricted to that purpose noted above, and hence pressure from one side, and always from the same side, is all that such valves need be designed to stand. A typical arrangement is shown in Fig. 4.24. The valve disk is lifted by counterweight, or by geared mechanism, or by a pneumatic cylinder. The valve disk itself is faced off smooth, and the gasket is borne in a groove on the seat.

For disks up to 20 in. aperture, ¼-in. square rubber is used in a standard gasket groove. In some cases two concentric gaskets have been used to ensure sealing in case of failure of one of them.

An adaptation of this design, using an internal driving mechanism and having the gasket placed in a groove on the disk instead of the seat, has been widely used with 20-in. pumps (see Fig. 4.25).

Valves[18] 30 in. in diameter (see Fig. 4.26) are rapid-acting valves that also have the feature of a solid metallic seat with a raised tongue (Fig. 4.14) and a gasket molded in a groove on the disk. This is a very successful arrangement.

These valves hold well once atmospheric pressure is established on the upper side of the disk. Trouble is sometimes encountered in getting them to seal before such pressure is established. In order to accomplish this, some means of putting a force on the disk amounting to a large fraction of the working load of the gasket (see Table 4.1) before air is let into the system is required. It has been the normal practice to provide the initial pressure by means of the closing mechanisms (see Figs. 4.25 and 4.26). Some experimental valves were forced closed by a threaded nut on the stem, which engaged the threaded cell of the Wilson seal during the last inch or so of closing travel. This provided ample initial load. Care must be used in designing pneumatic closing systems so that the piston area is not only sufficient to afford adequate lifting but also to seal the valve initially. Unless specifically designed to take such a load, these valves should never be used to withstand atmospheric pressure from the wrong side. Not only will they leak, but there is also danger of complete and sudden collapse.

The heavily constructed Chapman 20-in. valve (Fig. 4.25) has a gate disk lifted by a screw similar to the usual jackscrew arrangement. This allows high initial sealing forces but is slow in operation if operated by hand. Motors are easily adapted to this drive, however, and good operation has been achieved with less than 30 sec being required for a 20-in. travel. Hammer gears are required for such drives unless excessively large motors are used.

Because of headroom limitations, the driving mechanism of the 20-in. valves was included inside the manifold. This has the twofold disadvantage of being necessarily improperly lubricated and also of preventing the use of a back-seating mechanism at the external connection of the drive. The vertically extended, externally driven arrangement (Fig. 4.24), such as is used on the 30-in. valves (Fig. 4.26), proved to be more satisfactory in many respects.

4.11 Leak Valves, Pressure Regulators, and Cutoff Devices. In many processes it is necessary to maintain the pressure in the vacuum chamber within fairly close pressure limits. There are two prin-

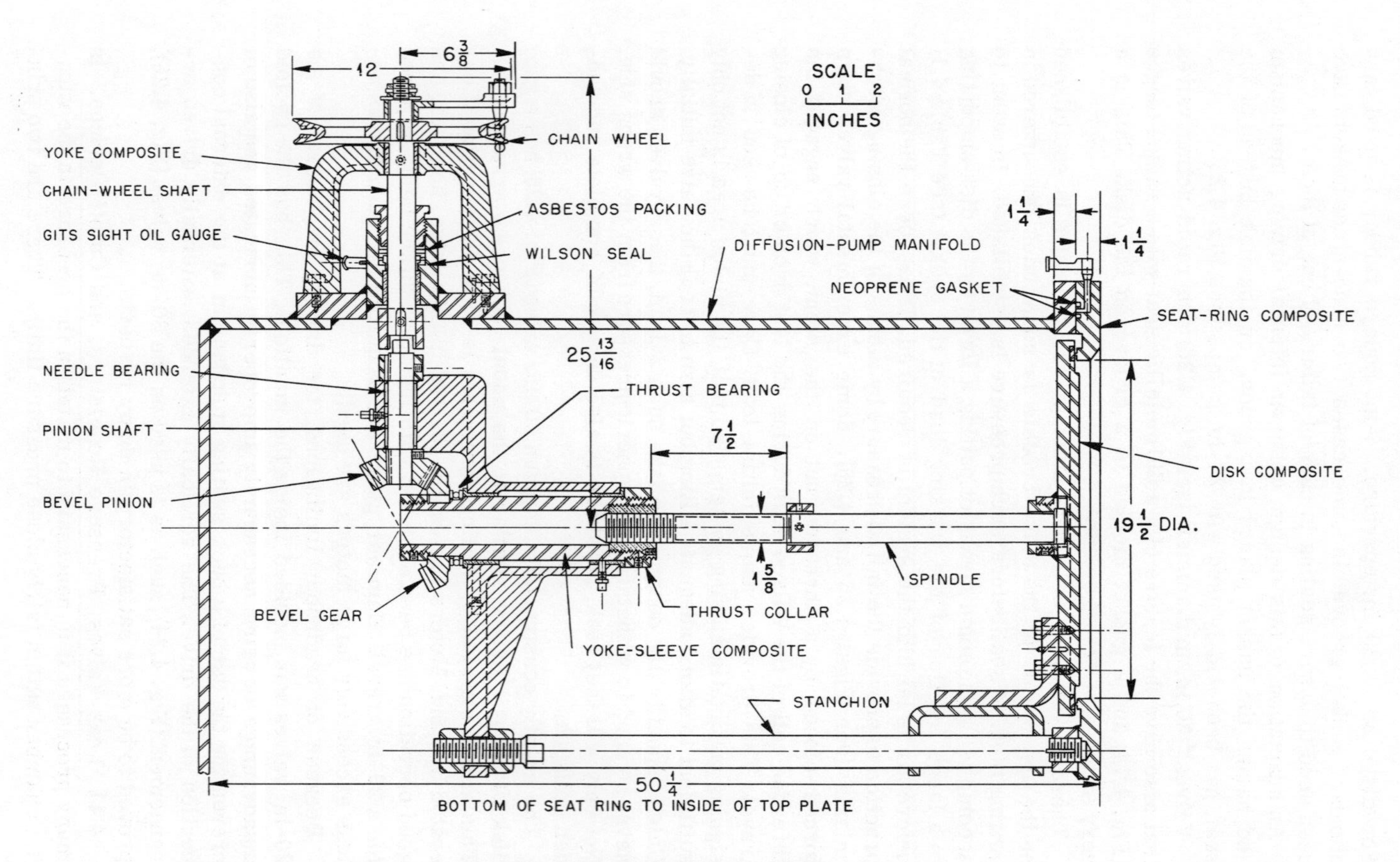

Fig. 4.25—Chapman 20-in. disk valve.

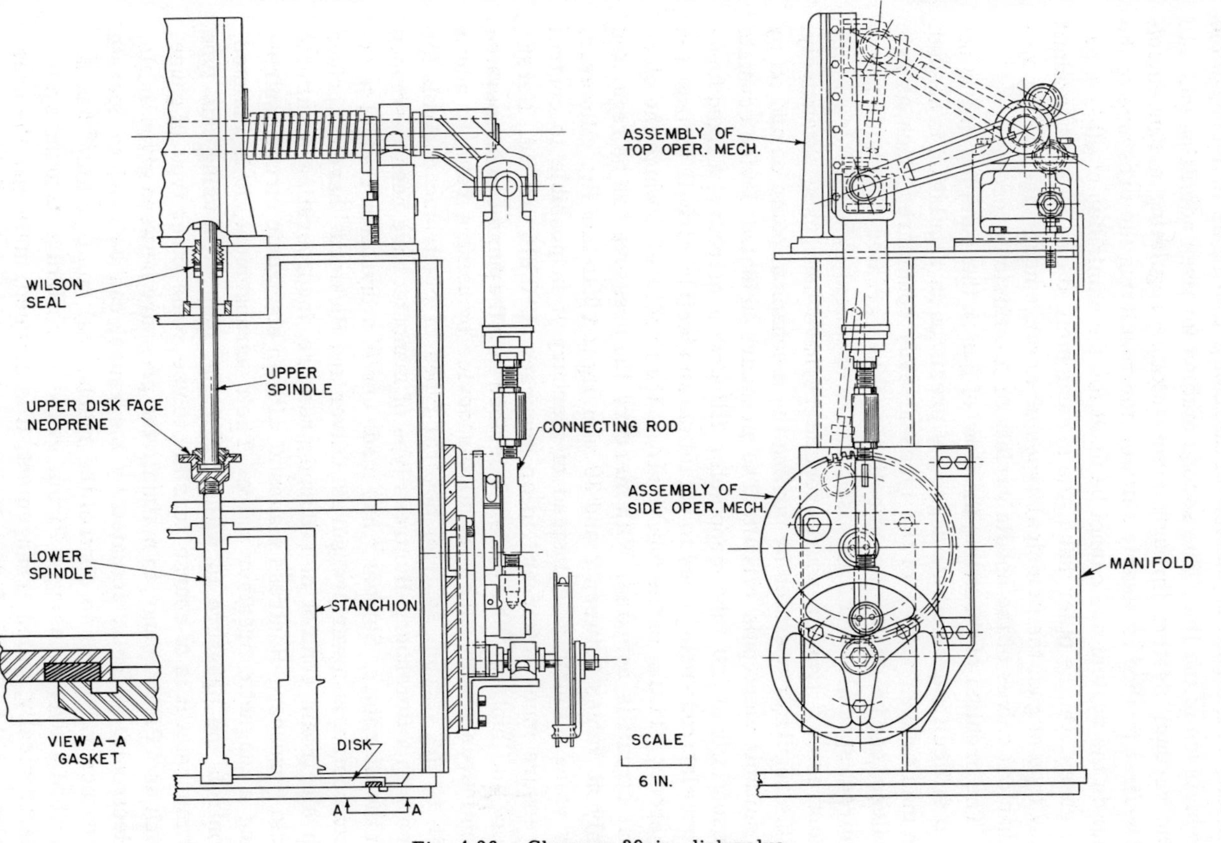

Fig. 4.26—Chapman 30-in. disk valve.

cipal methods by which this can be done: The first method involves the use of a throttling device in the pump line so as to increase the resistance of the line. The second method involves admitting gas into the vacuum system through some suitable regulating arrangement. The first method is clearly suitable for regulating the pressure of the gas in the system and cannot be used for the admission of other types of gases. On the other hand, the second method can be used to admit any type of gas, the principal types of arrangements used being mechanical valves of the needle variety or a diffusion process.

The problem of throttling the flow of gas in the pumping line is not too difficult unless a high degree of precision in regulation is needed. In many cases valves of the types already considered, such as gate valves, can be used quite effectively. When greater precision is required, special devices are used. In the chemical industry Hershberg-Huntress[19,20] type pressure regulators have been used extensively. This regulator operates by turning the mechanical pump on and off by a suitable electronic circuit. The pressure-actuated device consists essentially of a U-tube manometer filled with mercury, a fixed tungsten electrode being used to establish an electric circuit through the mercury. Tilting of the tube controls the pressure at which the electric circuit is actuated. With mercury the pressure can be regulated only at values between 2 and 30 mm Hg to ± 0.15 mm Hg. However, by using sulfuric acid instead of mercury it is possible to control pressure much lower and to an accuracy of ± 0.015 mm Hg. Hershberg and Huntress[20] have also described how the pump can be operated continuously with such a regulator device by using a relay to admit air to the vacuum system. Several types of electronic controls for use with a Hershberg-Huntress type of manostat have been described in the literature. Serfass[21] has made use of a thyratron control to effect control at lower pressures. Oliver and Bickford[22] have described an electronic control of reduced pressure incorporating a sulfuric acid Hershberg-Huntress manostat with an electronic circuit controlling a magnetic breather valve. Their arrangement, it is claimed, controls the pressure to within ± 20 μ Hg. Instead of using this type of manostat it is of course feasible to use some other type of gauge, such as a Pirani gauge, to maintain the pressure between given limits. Electronic controls, actuated by the gauge, can be used to operate breather valves or to control the mechanical pump. Smith[23] has described a system using a Pirani gauge to control a vacuum system electronically, which arrangement, it is claimed, maintains the pressure to within 0.01 to 0.02 μ Hg within the range of the gauge.

A type of arrangement that can be used to regulate the flow of gas in a pump line so as to control the pressure in a vacuum system is a cutoff device. Such a device is designed primarily to cut off the flow of gas in a pumping line completely. The usual method is to use a reservoir of mercury that is forced by atmospheric pressure to rise and fill a second reservoir where the flow of gas is interrupted. By only partially covering the opening through which the gas flows it is possible to regulate the pressure in the vacuum system. The principal disadvantages of such a system are that complicated stopcocks and large amounts of mercury are required, and the volume of the system is materially changed by the operation of the cutoff. Schmidt[24] has described an arrangement that eliminates these difficulties. He uses an iron or magnetic stainless-steel cap, operated by a magnet, to dip into a mercury reservoir and effect a seal (the cap or hat fits over the vacuum outlet). Serfass and Murasa[25] have used a ground steel ball seating in an opening in glass (ground) to effect a seal. Control is obtained by floating the ball in mercury. The main disadvantage to these types of cutoffs is that mercury is used, which limits their use primarily to glass systems. Also, because of the quantity of mercury involved, they are most useful for small vacuum systems.

The requirements of a valve used to admit gas into a vacuum system from the atmosphere or from a gas reservoir are determined by the pressure differential involved. The most common type of valve that has been used, regardless of the pressure differential, is the needle valve. Such a valve utilizes a metal-to-metal seal. In some cases a small amount of leakage, either from the air or from a gas reservoir attached to the needle valve by some such arrangement as a sylphon bellows, can be tolerated.[26,27] The smaller the pressure differential, the easier it is to construct suitable valves of this type. When it is desired to eliminate leakage to the system with the valve closed, it is possible to incorporate a suitable stopcock in the gas inlet to the valve. Stallman and Kruger[28] have described such a valve for the introduction of gas into a cyclotron.

A type of needle valve that has been used with satisfactory results at the Radiation Laboratory is shown in Fig. 4.27. This valve has been found to serve well in admitting atmospheric air into the system from complete shutoff to about 6 to 10 cc/sec. The characteristic features are (1) the long-taper pin creating a long path over which pressure drop is established and (2) a press-fitting soft-solder seat to ensure complete closure. If gases other than atmospheric are to be admitted, care must be exercised to see that the stem packing nut is actually sealing. For this purpose it is desirable to replace the packing assembly with a Wilson seal or a bellows mechanism of some sort. If fine adjustments are desired it is possible to obtain them by the use of two valves in series. The high-pressure valve is adjusted to take most of the pressure drop. The second valve can then be easily used as a fine adjustment, only slight changes in flow being caused by relatively large changes in the valve aperture.

The second principal method of introducing gas into a vacuum system involves the diffusion of gas through a semipermeable material. Probably the most commonly used material is unglazed porcelain.

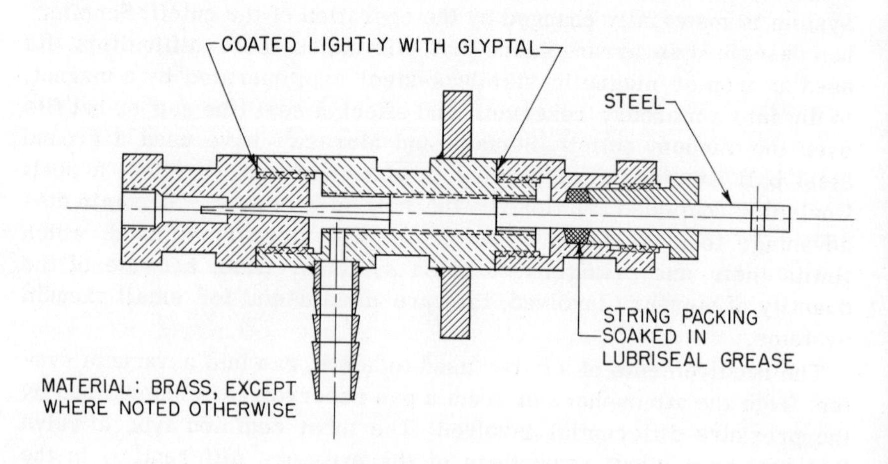

Fig. 4.27—Leak valve.

The arrangement usually is such as to allow the gas to diffuse through a porcelain tube at right angles to the axis of the tube, the control of the leak rate being determined by the proportion of the tube that is immersed in mercury.[29] Smythe[30] has described a porcelain leak valve in which the gas diffuses along the length of the tube, the rate of leak being controlled by mercury. Apart from porcelain, certain metals have been used effectively to introduce certain types of gases into vacuum systems. Silver has been commonly used to introduce oxygen into a vacuum system.[31] The rate of diffusion is determined by the temperature to which the metal is raised. Palladium has been used in the case of hydrogen and deuterium. Jossem[32] has treated the problem of admitting pure gases into a vacuum system in a fairly general way. He has considered hydrogen, deuterium, oxygen, nitrogen, carbon monoxide, helium, and neon and the metals to be used with these gases. A unique method of controlling the ratio of deuterium into a vacuum system has been reported by Bayley.[33] This method makes use of the fact that the viscosity of deuterium increases with an increase in temperature. By heating a capillary through which the gas flows it is possible to obtain a controlled rate of flow.

Apart from the principal methods outlined above, a number of simple and fairly effective methods have been reported in the literature. Two of these will be mentioned, owing to their wide usefulness and their simplicity. The first involves bending a flattened German silver tube into a U tube.[34] By fairly small changes in the shape of the U it is possible to obtain a controlled rate of flow. The second method is simply to clamp a heavy-walled rubber tubing to produce the leak, control being obtained by the amount of clamping.[35] Better control is effected by inserting a small wire into the rubber tubing.

It should be noted that, if a small tube is used between the leak valve and the vacuum chamber, a time delay will occur between the pressure change and the corresponding leak change. This time varies more or less as the length of the tubing and inversely as the cross section.

4.12 Protective Devices. In the operation of high-vacuum equipment various unexpected mishaps can result in considerable damage to the equipment. Not only may a loss in physical equipment occur, but the time lost in repair and cleanup, as well as in the operation of the process, may be of even greater consideration. Probably the most common sources of trouble in operating vacuum equipment are (1) a sudden rise in pressure due to such factors as leaks in the vacuum envelope, broken cooling or gas lines in the vacuum tank, and lack of refrigerant; and (2) insufficient cooling water for the diffusion pumps. Most of the automatic protective devices reported in the literature have been concerned with these difficulties. In the first case the diffusion-pump oil may decompose if the heaters are left on too long with a high pressure in the system. Of course, the use of silicone oils will overcome this difficulty to a large extent. However, loss of process time will still occur when using such oils. In the second case, pump oil will diffuse into the vacuum system causing loss of process time as well as time spent in cleanup. Apart from these important sources of troubles, difficulties may arise in some cases with the mechanical pumps. However, such difficulties are generally due to lack of adequate or proper servicing.

It is clear that some of the types of devices already discussed in Sec. 4.12 for pressure regulation can be adapted to give an alarm or to operate a circuit to isolate the diffusion pumps from the main vacuum system (or turn off the diffusion-pump heaters). Any pressure-regulating device that acts by throttling the gas flow from the vacuum chamber to the diffusion pump can be modified to act as a protective device against the pressure rising to too high a value, as long as this pressure lies within the pressure range of the instrument. The principal requirements of a device to protect the system against the pressure rising to too high a value are (1) pressure-indicating means and (2) means for using the signal from this pressure indicator to actuate an appropriate alarm system, to close a valve, or to turn off the diffusion pumps. A number of the pressure-indicating gauges already discussed in Chap. 3 have been used for this purpose, including Philips ionization gauges,[36] Pirani gauges,[37] manometers,[22] and thermocouple gauges.[36] In general it has been found simplest to insert the protective device on the fore-vacuum side of the diffusion pumps. Bainbridge and Sherr[38] have described the use of a Geissler tube for the protection of vacuum systems. A modified Metrovick type of Geissler tube was used. Various types of electronics control systems involving the use of relays, thyratrons, etc., have been used to apply the signal obtained from the pressure-indicating device.

Probably only one alarm system for indicating that the pressure in the vacuum system exceeds a predetermined value was developed to any extent in the Radiation Laboratory, and that used a hot-wire vacuum switch.[39,40] This system makes use of the expansion of a wire to operate an electric switch, which then opens an interlock circuit within a fraction of a second.

A 3-mil tungsten wire is used as the expansion element. Initial experiments indicated that this size of wire, when subjected to a controlled source of heat, could expand about 0.0002 cm per centimeter of length for a pressure change of from 20 to 200 μ Hg. By using a microswitch, at first type BFR and later type BFR-8, it was possible to use a 3-in. length of 3-mil tungsten wire. There appeared to be some tendency for the tungsten to change its expansion and resistance with use. The best results were obtained by leaving the wire in its annealed condition. Other metals, including platinum and Chromel C were tried, but they did not have sufficient tensile strength. Three-mil tungsten wire was found to be the smallest size practicable, having sufficient tensile strength to stand up under the 7- to 10-oz pull required for the type BFR microswitch (3 to 5 oz for type BFR-8) and being small enough to have a low heating-current requirement. The heating of the wire by a constant-voltage system and by a constant-current system was tried, the latter system being found better. A constant-voltage regulating transformer in series with the wire and with fixed and adjustable resistances was used. Change in length of the wire with change in pressure resulted from thermal transfer by the gas molecules as in the case of the Pirani gauge.

Owing to the small magnitude of expansion being utilized, it was necessary to choose a material having a very low coefficient of linear expansion for the mechanical support for the wire. Lavite and porcelain were tried, but the final material chosen was fused quartz. The manner in which the tungsten is mounted, together with other mechanical details and the electrical system, is shown in Fig. 4.28. It was found desirable to mount the switch assembly by means of springs since some trouble was experienced with vibration affecting the cutoff point.

The switch has given reliable operation for a cutoff point anywhere between 30 and 400 μ Hg (using the BFR-8 microswitch). It has been used as low as 10 μ Hg but there may be some variation in the cutoff point. The switch can be used on either the high-vacuum or the fore-vacuum side of the system, the former position being preferable from a contamination viewpoint. The initial setting of the cutoff point is made by using a vacuum system equipped with a calibrated leak and an appropriate gauge. In the Radiation Laboratory the switch has under normal conditions been set for cutoff at 150 μ Hg (see Fig. 4.29). A relay is incorporated in the unit to cut out part of the series resistance when the interlock operates, thus increasing the current so as to bring the reset pressure point to within a few microns (about 10) of mercury of the cutoff pressure point. This is shown in Fig. 4.29. A time-delay relay maintains the current for about 45 sec after the switch has closed the interlock circuit, preventing recycling near the reset point. The use of low voltage on the vacuum-switch contacts has made it possible to minimize difficulties with Geissler discharge and arc-over to ground under favorable pressure conditions. A relay shunted across the hot wire provides an alarm in case of a wire breakage. This is necessary because if the wire broke there would be no way of knowing that the vacuum protection was inoperative.

In large vacuum systems where dry-ice traps are employed between the diffusion pumps and the mechanical pumps, the oil in the latter pumps must be protected against lack of dry ice in the traps. If the temperature of one of these traps rises owing to lack of acetone–carbon dioxide mixture, the collected ice on the outside surface will melt and spoil the mechanical pump oil. Usually this difficulty is avoided by frequent inspection of the carbon dioxide traps. However, some device to give an alarm due to lack of carbon dioxide in a trap is clearly of considerable value in this connection.

The only alarm device that was developed at the Radiation Laboratory[41] for this purpose was of the following construction: A Penn Electric Switch Company pressure switch, type 260 AP01, model 1525,

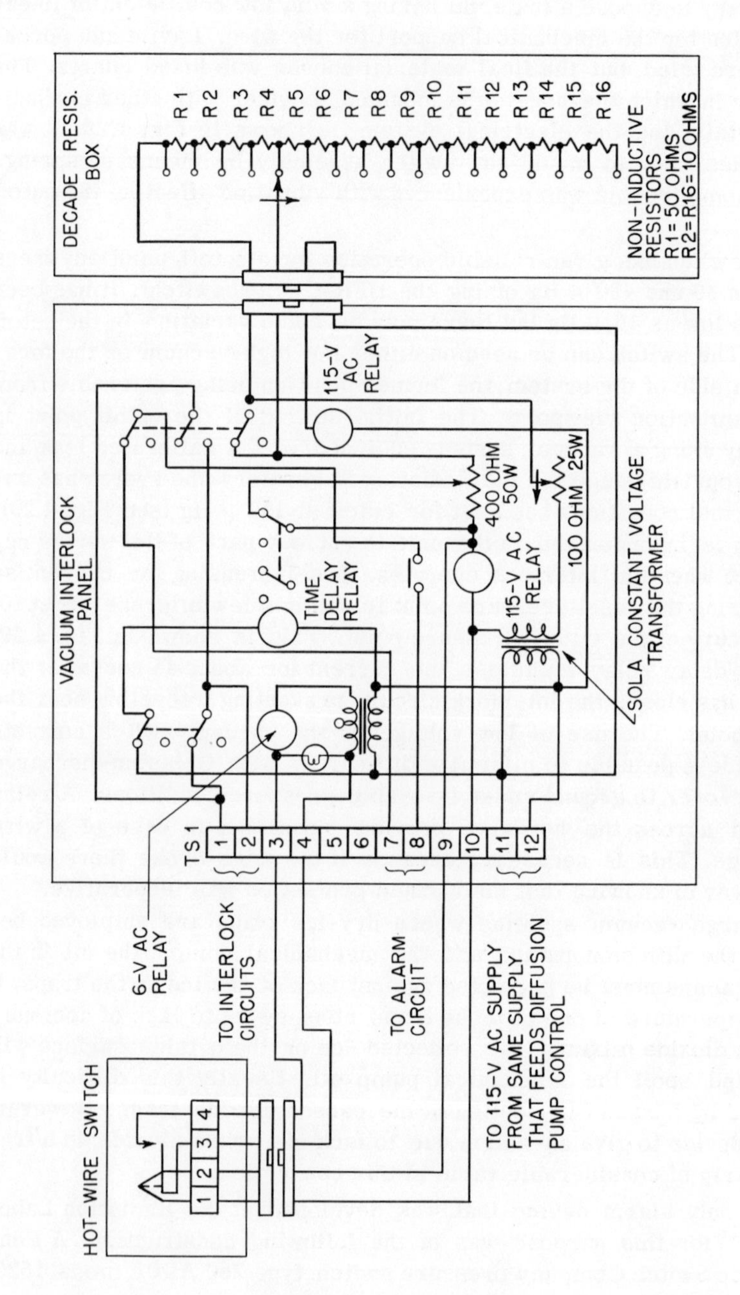

Fig. 4.28 — Electrical panel for hot-wire switch.

was used. A length of ¼-in. copper tubing, long enough to go over the edge and to the bottom of the trap, was sealed off at one end, and a ¼-in. flare nut was put on the other end. A small quantity of carbon dioxide in the form of dry ice was put in the bottom of the tube and left long enough to drive out all the air. Just enough carbon dioxide

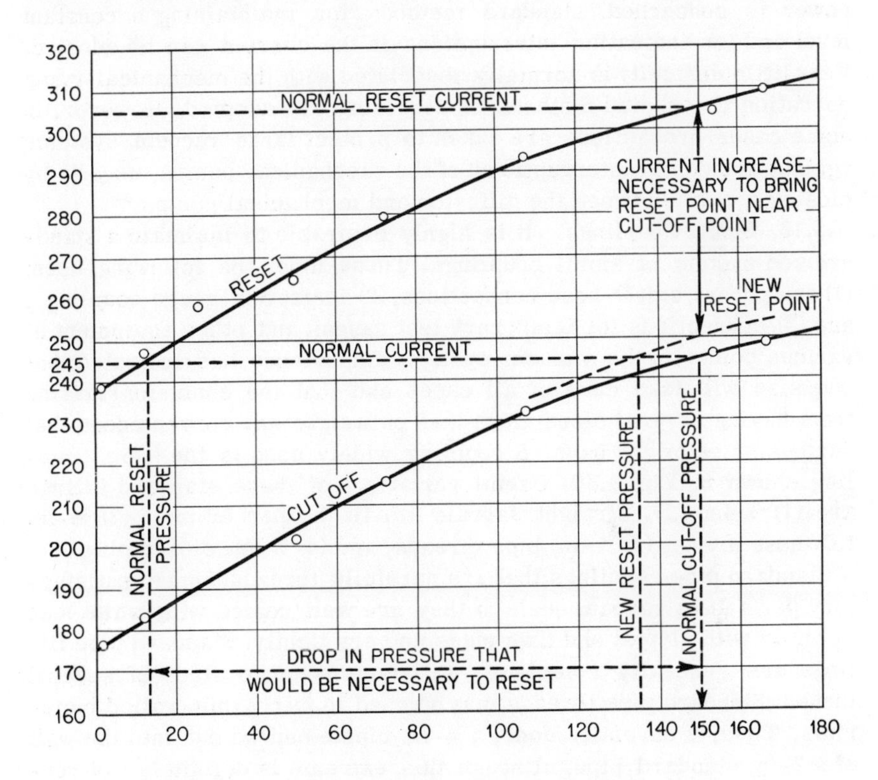

Fig. 4.29—Typical operation curves for hot-wire switch.

was left in the tube to build up a pressure of 45 lb at normal room temperature. This was found by first setting the pressure switch to trip at 45 lb by testing with a compressed-air supply and pressure gauge. Just enough carbon dioxide was then left in to trip the switch.

The copper tube was then placed in the carbon dioxide trap, and the switch was adjusted so that it would just stay open. The carbon dioxide in the tube is then under just enough pressure at the trap temperature to cause it to condense to the solid state. If the trap temperature rises a few degrees, the condensed solid carbon dioxide in the tube switch sublimates to the gaseous state, closing the pressure switch and ringing the alarm.

Problems associated with the operation of the diffusion and mechanical pumps are relatively easy to overcome. A suitable flow gauge can be inserted in the cooling system for the diffusion pumps so that when the water flow drops below the minimum required an alarm is actuated or the heaters are turned off. In so far as heater power is concerned, standard methods for maintaining a constant level and for indicating interruptions in the current can be adopted. Very little difficulty is normally associated with the mechanical-pump operation if accepted methods of servicing are adopted. However, in some cases precautions are taken to protect large vacuum systems against accidental interruptions of the mechanical pumps, usually by closing a valve between the diffusion and mechanical pumps.[42]

4.13 Small Couplings. It is highly desirable to maintain a standardized system of small couplings. These meet the following uses: (1) temporary small-hose connections, (2) ionization-gauge couplings, and (3) connections for temporary test gauges and other equipment at various points in the vacuum system. Experience has indicated that one size will take care of all cases and that the confusion arising from having several sizes more than outweighs any conveniences that various sizes might have. A coupling widely used is the ⅜-in. coupling shown in Fig. 4.30. Useful variations of these standard fittings are (1) ⅜-in. I.D. straight ferrule (to fit copper tubing), (2) ⅜-in. I.D. hose nipple, (3) ⅜-in. pipe threads, and (4) ⅝-in. closed plug.

Standard pipe couplings that are carefully threaded make satisfactory permanent vacuum seals if they are well coated with white lead in oil or with glyptal and then made up very tightly. Standard pipe fittings are generally completely satisfactory up to sizes of several inches. Standard pipe threads may be used in fairly thin-walled materials. Thus, if carefully done, a ⅜-in. nipple can be put into the wall of a 2-in. standard pipe, although this extreme is definitely not recommended. Such thin-wall connections are far better welded or soldered.

For larger sizes of pipe, standard welding flanges using the grooveless gaskets (Fig. 4.12) certainly represent the most practical type of installation.

4.14 Vacuum Greases, Waxes, Sealing Agents, and Miscellaneous Materials. Vacuum greases are commonly used to ensure vacuum tightness in various gasketed arrangements such as compression seals or Wilson seals as well as in stopcocks. Such greases must have low vapor pressures at the operating temperatures. Lubriseal has been used more extensively in the Radiation Laboratory than any other type of vacuum grease. The properties of this and other commercial greases are tabulated in Appendix H. For use at moderately high temperatures, Dow Corning Corp. silicone stopcock grease has been found most suitable.

Vacuum waxes are used to make temporary connections to vacuum systems as in ionization gauges and in many cases to make temporary repairs of leaks. In general, too much reliance should not be put on wax seals. Wherever possible it is preferable to use gasketed joints, solder connections, or the various types of glass-to-metal joints, such as Kovar, etc. The properties of a number of commercial waxes and cements are listed in Appendix H. Some of these materials are also discussed in Chap. 5.

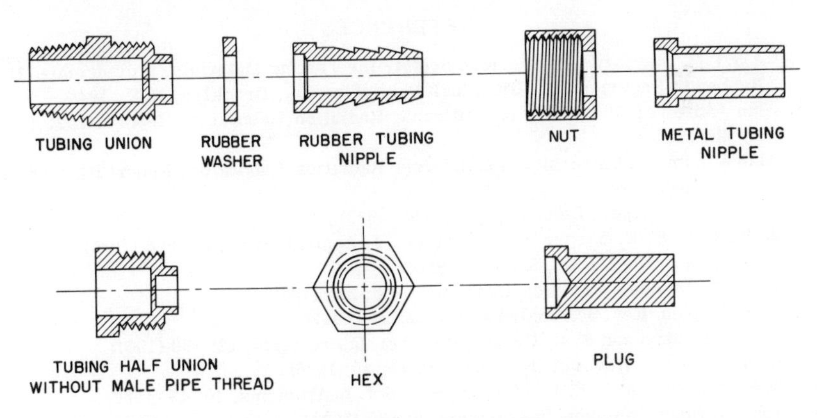

Fig. 4.30—Illustrations of ⅜-in. coupling.

Certain types of surface-coating materials as well as solders can be considered as sealing materials for use in vacuum practice. Surface coatings such as the glyptal materials and silicone varnishes are used to reduce outgassing of various surfaces as well as to prevent or repair small leaks. Little information has been gained in the California Radiation Laboratory regarding the outgassing characteristics of these materials. With regard to the use of surface-coating materials to reduce the outgassing of surfaces, the procedure has been to bake the material after application. During a vacuum shutdown this tends to reduce the adsorption of gases by the surfaces so treated. Various types of solders, as well as fluxes and brazing alloy, are listed in Appendix H.

The most commonly used materials for construction of small vacuum systems are glass and brass. Glass is fragile but has the advantage that alterations in the system are relatively easy to make. Also small leaks are often readily found (e.g., by the spark-coil method) and are easy to repair. Brass has been found to be a quite satisfactory construction material, particularly for its ease of working (machining, soldering, etc.). Its vapor pressure (when clean) is greater than that of glass. For large vacuum systems, of the type commonly used at the Radiation Laboratory, steel is used because of the cost factor. Some of the problems encountered in the use of this material have already been discussed in this chapter. Some properties of these materials are included in Appendix I.

REFERENCES

1. "A.S.T.M. Standards," American Society for Testing Materials, Philadelphia, 1944.
2. "Rubber in Engineering," Chemical Publishing Co., Brooklyn, N. Y., 1946.
3. Alan J. Samuel, University of California Radiation Laboratory Report RL 20.6.27, July 26, 1944.
4. Alan J. Samuel, University of California Radiation Laboratory Report RL 20.6.12, Sept. 6, 1943.
5. W. G. Housekeeper, Elec. Eng., 42: 934 (1923).
6. A. W. Hull, E. E. Burger, and L. Navias, J. Applied Phys., 12: 698 (1941).
7. W. E. Bahls, Elec. Eng., 57: 373 (1938).
8. J. W. M. DuMond, Rev. Sci. Instruments, 6: 285 (1935).
9. R. R. Wilson, Rev. Sci. Instruments, 12: 91 (1941).
10. L. A. Delsasso and E. C. Creutz, Rev. Sci. Instruments, 12: 450 (1941).
11. Dean B. Cowie, Rev. Sci. Instruments, 15: 46 (1944).
12. S. M. Rubens and J. E. Henderson, Rev. Sci. Instruments, 10: 49 (1939).
13. John E. Rose, Rev. Sci. Instruments, 8: 130 (1937).
14. R. J. Lang, Rev. Sci. Instruments, 10: 196 (1939).
15. H. Geissmann, Physik. Z., 44: 268 (1943).
16. L. N. Ridenour and G. P. Harnwell, Rev. Sci. Instruments, 12: 157 (1941).
17. E. Topanelian, Jr. and N. D. Coggeshall, Rev. Sci. Instruments, 17: 38 (1946).
18. K. M. Simpson, University of California Radiation Laboratory Report RL 20.6.21, Apr. 14, 1944.
19. E. H. Huntress and E. B. Hershberg, Anal. Chem., 5: 144 (1933).
20. E. B. Hershberg and E. H. Huntress, Anal. Chem., 5: 344 (1933).
21. E. J. Serfass, Anal. Chem., 13: 262 (1941).
22. G. D. Oliver and W. G. Bickford, Rev. Sci. Instruments, 16: 130 (1945).
23. R. A. Smith, Rev. Sci. Instruments, 11: 120 (1940).
24. Otto H. Schmidt, Rev. Sci. Instruments, 8: 68 (1937).
25. E. J. Serfass and R. F. Murasa, Rev. Sci. Instruments, 16: 225 (1945).
26. H. Kersten, Rev. Sci. Instruments, 6: 175 (1935).
27. W. L. Edwards and L. R. Maxwell, Rev. Sci. Instruments, 9: 201 (1938).
28. F. W. Stallman and P. Gerald Kruger, Rev. Sci. Instruments, 10: 242 (1939).
29. J. E. Dorn and George Glockler, Rev. Sci. Instruments, 7: 319 (1936).
30. W. R. Smythe, Rev. Sci. Instruments, 7: 435 (1936).
31. J. B. Taylor, Rev. Sci. Instruments, 6: 243 (1935).
32. E. L. Jossem, Rev. Sci. Instruments, 11: 164 (1940).
33. D. S. Bayley, Rev. Sci. Instruments, 13: 299 (1942).
34. D. Dudley Fowler, Rev. Sci. Instruments, 6: 26 (1935).
35. R. W. G. Wyckoff and J. B. Lagsdin, Rev. Sci. Instruments, 7: 35 (1936).

36. R. G. Picard, P. C. Smith, and S. M. Zollus, Rev. Sci. Instruments, 17: 125 (1946).
37. M. C. Henderson, Rev. Sci. Instruments, 10: 43 (1939).
38. K. T. Bainbridge and R. Sherr, Rev. Sci. Instruments, 10: 316 (1939).
39. Clarence Wieske, University of California Radiation Laboratory Report RL 20.6.15, Nov. 18, 1943.
40. Clarence Wieske, University of California Radiation Laboratory Report RL 20.6.41, Sept. 6, 1945.
41. Clarence Wieske, University of California Radiation Laboratory Report RL 20.6.7, Aug. 22, 1943.
42. J. P. Youtz, Rev. Sci. Instruments, 9: 420 (1938).

Chapter 5

LEAK-DETECTION INSTRUMENTS AND TECHNIQUES

By R. Loevinger and A. Guthrie

The locating and repairing of leaks in vacuum systems is probably the most troublesome aspect of high-vacuum technique. In this chapter a rough method of estimating the flow of various gases through small capillary holes will be described first, followed by a description of all the successful methods of leak detection normally available, and finally by an indication of the method of formulating quantitatively the performance of leak-detection techniques.

5.1 The Flow Characteristics of Small Capillaries. The most troublesome leaks to detect are, of course, the smallest ones. The term "size of a leak" means the amount of gas flowing through it into the vacuum system. This amount is assumed to be measured in micron-liters per second following the formulation of Chap. 1. Whether a given size of leak is large or small is of course a highly relative matter. With a mercury diffusion pump that has a speed of 5 liters/sec, a leak of 5×10^{-5} μ-liter/sec can be tolerated if a base pressure of 10^{-8} mm Hg is required—a pressure actually needed in the most refined mass-spectrometer work, for example. At the other extreme, with the very large industrial diffusion pumps of about 30,000 liters/sec and working pressures of 10^{-5} mm Hg a leak of 300 μ-liters/sec could just be tolerated. Thus the range in leak size with which designers and vacuum technicians must be prepared to concern themselves is very large indeed.

In order to arrive at any sort of quantitative formulation of the flow through small holes, it will be necessary to consider a rather special case, namely, that of a straight, circular cylinder of diameter D and length L. Then Knudsen's formula, Eq. 48 of Chap. 1, may be applied. This may be written in the form

$$C = \frac{1}{\Delta L} \left(aP + b\,\frac{1 + cP}{1 + fP} \right)$$

where ΔL is the length of a short segment in which the average pressure is P and the pressure drop is ΔP. Then the flow through that segment is

$$Q = \left(aP + b \frac{1 + cP}{1 + fP} \right) \frac{\Delta P}{\Delta L}$$

Integrating over the length of the capillary, the equation, since the flow Q is constant in a steady state, becomes

$$Q = \frac{1}{L} \int_{P_2}^{P_1} \left(aP + b \frac{1 + cP}{1 + fP} \right) dP$$

$$= \frac{1}{L} \left[\frac{a}{2} P^2 + \frac{bc}{f} P + \frac{b(d - c)}{f^2} \ln \left|1 + fP\right| \right]_{P_2}^{P_1} \quad (1)$$

where P_1 is the high pressure outside the leak, and P_2 is the lowest pressure reached inside the capillary itself. If $P_1 = 7.6 \times 10^5\ \mu$ Hg (i.e., 1 atm pressure) it is reasonable to suppose that $P_2 \ll P_1$. Then, taking $P_2 = 0$ and using the numerical values of the coefficients in Eq. 45, Chap. 1, the equation becomes

$$Q = \frac{10^{-6}}{L} \left[5.3D^4 \left(\frac{\eta_{air}}{\eta} \right) + 7.5D^3 \sqrt{\frac{M_{air}}{M}} + 0.91\ D^2 \left(\frac{\eta}{\eta_{air}} \frac{M_{air}}{M} \right) \right] \mu\text{-liters/sec} \quad (2)$$

This gives the flow through a straight circular cylinder of length L in centimeters and diameter D in microns for a gas whose coefficient of viscosity is η and whose molecular weight is M, at 20°C. The terms η_{air} and M_{air} are the viscosity and molecular weight of air, respectively.

From this equation, the flow has been calculated for air, helium, and carbon dioxide, for values of D of from 0.01 to 30 μ. The results are tabulated in Table 5.1. For air the flow is given directly in micron-liters, but for the other gases the flow is given as a ratio Q_{gas}/Q_{air}. It is clear that for large values of D this ratio approaches the value η_{air}/η_{gas}, which is a reasonable result, since the flow through large leaks will be essentially viscous flow and will thus be greatest for a low-viscosity gas. At the other extreme the flow ratio would approach $\eta_{gas}/\eta_{air} \cdot M_{air}/M_{gas}$, if sufficiently small leaks could be realized. Consequently, for very small leaks a high-viscosity low-molecular-weight gas flows through the leak most easily.

In Table 5.1 this flow ratio is given for helium, carbon dioxide, hydrogen, methane, and neon for the entire calculated range. The values for helium are plotted in Fig. 5.1. A sufficiently accurate figure for any other gas is easily produced by simply indicating in the

Table 5.1 — Flow Characteristics of a Circular Capillary Leak

Air			Other gases, Q/Q_{air}					
D, μ	Q, μ-liters/sec*	P_2	He	CO_2	H_2	CH_4	Ne	
Lower limit			7.7	0.53	6.9	1.07	2.45	$= (\eta/\eta_a)\ (M_a/M)$
0.01	9.9×10^{-11}	3.7 μ Hg	7.3	0.55				
0.03	1.0×10^{-9}	4.1 μ Hg	6.8	0.59				
0.1	1.7×10^{-8}	6.3 μ Hg	5.3	0.68				
0.3	3.2×10^{-7}	13 μ Hg	3.8	0.78				
1	1.4×10^{-5}	52 μ Hg	2.3	0.94				
3	6.4×10^{-4}	260 μ Hg	1.6	1.1				
10	0.060	2.2 mm Hg	1.2	1.20				
30	4.5	18 mm Hg	1.0	1.22				
100	470	170 mm Hg	0.93	1.24				
Upper limit			0.93	1.24	2.07	1.67	0.58	η_a/η

*Divide Q by length in centimeters to get flow for $L \neq 1$ cm.

graph the upper and lower limit and sketching in a transition between these limits, which roughly parallels the helium transition.

The calculations thus far assumed that the pressure inside the hypothetical cylindrical leak dropped to a low value P_2, negligible compared to atmospheric pressure. In fact the validity of this assumption can be checked. Inside the leak the velocity of the gas will rise from some small value at the inlet to a maximum value not greater than the velocity of sound under the temperature and pressure conditions prevailing. The velocity of the gas cannot exceed the velocity of sound. Now it is shown in kinetic theory that the velocity of sound in any gas is proportional to $\sqrt{P/\rho}$, where P is pressure and ρ is density. Then, if isothermal expansion is assumed, it follows from the isothermal equation of state, i.e., $P = R\rho T$, which is Eq. 4 of Chap. 1, that the velocity of sound is constant and equal to its well-known value in air, 3.4×10^4 cm/sec at 20°C. The assumption of isothermal expansion is probably accurate at the reduced pressures, since the mean free path (m.f.p.) becomes large compared with the very small diameters under consideration.

With these assumptions, a simple geometrical calculation gives for the lowest pressure inside the leak,

$$P_2 = 3.7 \times 10^6 \frac{Q}{D^2} \ \mu \text{ Hg} \tag{3}$$

where Q is the flow in micron-liters and D is the diameter of the leak in microns.

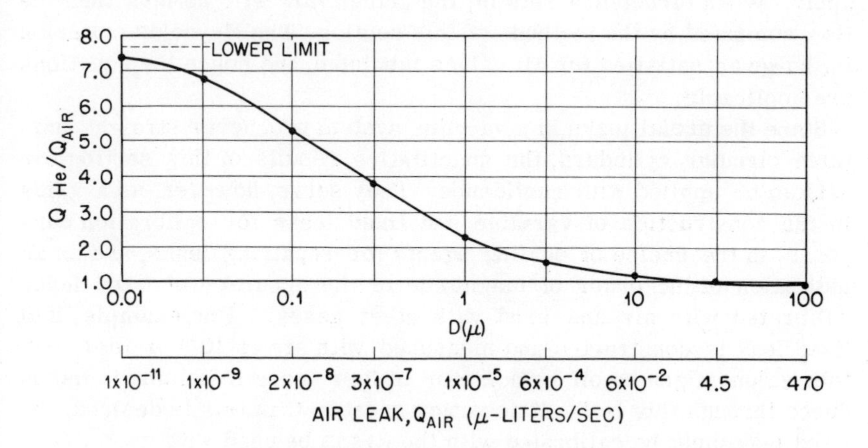

Fig. 5.1—Ratio of helium flow to air flow for a circular capillary.

Values of P_2 have been calculated for the values of Q and D given in Table 5.1 and are listed there. These values of P_2 have been checked against Eq. 1 to verify the validity of neglecting P_2 in Eq. 2. It is found that this is valid for $D \lesssim 30\ \mu$. For larger values of D, neglecting P_2 is not valid. However, for $D \gtrsim 30\ \mu$, the D^3 and D^2 terms of Eqs. 1 and 2 can be neglected compared to the D^4 term, and the flow may be computed from the equation

$$Q = \frac{10^{-6}}{L}\left[5.3D^4 \frac{\eta_{air}}{\eta}\left(1 - \frac{P_2^2}{P_1^2}\right)\right] \tag{4}$$

Substituting Eq. 3 in Eq. 4 permits solution for Q; in this fashion the Q for $D = 100\ \mu$ has been computed and given in Table 5.1. The corresponding value of P_2 is computed from Eq. 3.

This elementary calculation can hardly be significant if carried to values of D much larger than 100 μ (equal to 0.1 mm Hg). For exam–

ple, if D = 200 μ, Q = 5,000 μ-liters/sec by the method just described. But in Eq. 41 of Chap. 1 it was seen that it follows from the Reynolds number criterion that

$$Q < 10D$$

where D is in microns, if the flow is definitely to be viscous and not turbulent. Thus at D = 200 μ the equations of kinetic theory no longer apply. When turbulence sets in, the actual flow will be less than the flow computed by the methods of this section. The Reynolds criterion is, however, satisfied for all values tabulated, and hence the equations are applicable.

Since the actual leaks in a vacuum system are never straight, uniform circular cylinders, the quantitative results of this section can seldom be applied with confidence. They serve, however, as a guide in the construction of variable and fixed leaks for calibration purposes, in the choice of sealing agents for repairing leaks, and as an indication of the order of magnitude of the accuracy of fixed leaks calibrated with air and used with other gases. For example, if a fixed leak is constructed and measured with air as 10^{-5} μ-liter/sec, this value might be off by a factor of 2 or more if helium is introduced through this leak. If accuracy greater than this is desired, the fixed leak must be calibrated with the gas to be used with it.

5.2 Methods of Leak Detection. The term "leak detection" applies not only to the location of the leaks in a vacuum system with sufficient accuracy so that repairs can be made but also to the determination of the size of the leaks. The latter requirement in a leak-detecting method is not too stringent since it is usually of little advantage to determine the absolute size of leak in a vacuum system. In those cases where this is desirable, the methods of calculation outlined in the preceding section can be applied. However, it is normally desirable to obtain some idea of the magnitudes of the leaks in a vacuum system over and above those leaks present when the system is "tight" (i.e., when the system is at a pressure satisfactory for operation for the purpose at hand). Familiarity with the particular vacuum system being used as well as with the leak-detection methods being applied will usually give sufficient information about these magnitudes, as will be seen in later sections of this chapter. More accurate values of leak size can, of course, be obtained by making use of a calibrated leak.

A large number of leak-detection methods have been applied, some of which have been reported in the literature and others of which have come into use in various laboratories without having been made generally available. The purpose here is to discuss briefly some of the most useful methods, particularly as applied to large industrial vacuum systems. The systems to be discussed are as follows:

1. Spark coil passed outside vacuum system.
2. Discharge tube attached to vacuum system.
3. Rate-of-rise measurements.
4. Overvacuum or evacuated hood.
5. High pressure inside vacuum system, appropriate indicator on the outside.
6. Partial vacuum inside system, soap film applied inside.
7. Sealing substance on outside of system, change of pressure inside.
8. Probe gas on outside, change of apparent pressure or of nature of gas on inside of system.

It will become apparent that some of these methods are suitable primarily for a rather limited range of pressures but that others can be used at practically all pressures encountered in vacuum practice. Before discussing each of these methods some mention will be made of the requirements of an ideal leak-detecting method. The ideal leak-detecting method should be capable of both measurements of total leak and isolation of individual leaks, should be rapid in response, should not seal the leak more than momentarily, should be highly sensitive, should be capable of application to any vacuum system without loss of vacuum if necessary, and should make use of equipment that is simple and inexpensive to procure, maintain, and operate. Furthermore, it is highly desirable that the instrument used be selective, i.e., that it give nearly a zero reading for air and residual gases and respond only to a probe material. It will be seen later that the method involving the use of the indicating device known as the "helium leak detector" comes nearer to satisfying most of these requirements than any other one method. It is clear that a number of the leak-hunting methods listed above require the use of an appropriate indicating device. Most of these devices have been designed to indicate a change in pressure or apparent pressure when a gas or a condensable vapor is admitted into the vacuum chamber. Such instruments include the Pirani gauge, the mercury (or oil) manometer, the thermocouple gauge, the ionization gauge, the Knudsen gauge, and the Philips ionization gauge. These instruments make use of such properties of the gases or vapors as momentum transfer, thermal transfer, and ionization potential. No attempt will be made here to discuss them in detail since they have already been considered in Chap. 3. In a number of the methods visual observation is relied upon in the leak detection. The helium leak detector will be discussed in detail later in this chapter.

(a) Spark Coil Passed Over Glass. The method consists in passing the ungrounded high-potential electrode of a spark coil, such as a Tesla coil, over the outside surface of the vacuum system and observing the glow discharge produced inside. The glow occurs when the air pressure is roughly between a few millimeters and 5×10^{-2} mm Hg and is of a purplish-white appearance. It is clear that the method can be used only when the vacuum system is constructed, at least partially, of a nonconducting material and when a view of the discharge inside the system can be obtained. Consequently the method finds its greatest use in systems constructed wholly or partly of glass.

There are two techniques for locating leaks with a spark coil. The simpler of the two is to pass the tip of the coil over the glass parts of the system, watching the nature of the discharge. If the tip is within a centimeter or so of a small hole in the glass, a spark will run from the coil tip to the pinhole and into the vacuum. The hole itself glows white against the purplish discharge and is easily spotted. This technique is only possible several centimeters away from any metal, whether it is part of the vacuum system or not.

Another technique consists in obtaining a glow discharge with a spark coil and then applying illuminating gas, ether, or carbon dioxide gas to various portions of the vacuum system. When one of these materials enters the system through a leak, the appearance of the glow discharge is changed. With illuminating gas and ether, the discharge takes on a whitish appearance, and with carbon dioxide the appearance is bluish-green. If reasonable care is exercised in using these materials, leaks can be located quite accurately by this method. However, certain precautions must be observed in its application. The spark discharge must not be too strong, or there is danger of puncturing the glass. It is advisable to have a spark gap of ¼ to ½ in. in parallel with the high-potential electrode and ground. Puncturing of the vacuum envelope is also likely to occur if the spark coil is held in one spot for too long a time. The coil should be moved slowly over a portion of the system while the leak-hunting procedure is being carried out. There are certain fairly obvious limitations to the method. First, it cannot be applied to all-metal systems, and, second, it can be used only within certain pressure limits.

(b) Discharge Tube. Closely related to the spark-coil method of leak detection is the method involving the use of a discharge tube. Such tubes have already been described briefly in Chap. 3 in connection with the measurement of pressure. It will be recalled that the color of the glow discharge in such a tube depends on the pressure of the gas as well as on the nature of the gas (see Table 3.1). This forms the basis for the use of the device in leak hunting. By going over the outside of the vacuum system with a suitable vapor or gas, an indication of a leak will be obtained when the color of the discharge changes owing to the gas entering the system through the leak.

The discharge tube is normally attached to the vacuum system between the diffusion and mechanical pumps in order to have a sufficiently high pressure to obtain a glow discharge. Alcohol, ether, methane, and carbon dioxide are materials often used for covering suspected portions of the vacuum system. In so far as the sensitivity of the method is concerned, this is dependent primarily on two factors: the detectable color change and the ease with which the probe material passes through the leak. Normally the color change is observed visually, and therefore the amount of noticeable change is dependent on the observer. In so far as the ease with which the probe material passes through the leak is concerned, this depends on the physical characteristics of the materials, the important factors being viscosity and size of molecule. Because of these facts, vapors such as alcohol and ether are not so suitable for small leaks as are gases such as methane and carbon dioxide. The latter gas, owing to the pronounced color change produced and to its relatively low viscosity and molecular size, has proved to be quite sensitive when used in this method. Webster[1] has described the use of carbon dioxide in leak hunting with a discharge tube. He points out that in order to obtain the highest sensitivity with carbon dioxide there should be a pronounced positive column in the discharge. For a mixture of roughly equal parts air and carbon dioxide, the color of the positive column takes on that characteristic of carbon dioxide (bluish-green). This makes it possible to isolate two separate leaks of roughly equal magnitude. Several methods of applying the carbon dioxide, e.g., by use of cofferdams and gas masks, are also given by Webster. The properties of some liquids used in this method as well as in other leak-detection methods are included in Appendix I.

Attempts have been made to increase the sensitivity of this method by observing the positive column of the discharge with a spectroscope. Yarwood[2] lists the important spectral lines for various gases that can be used in this application. Such an optical spectrometer was considered for use in the Manhattan District on the K-25 project as reported by Jacobs and Zuhr.[3] They point out that the method is simple, gives instantaneous response, and has a high sensitivity for certain probe gases. However, it is unreliable owing to the uncertain "cleanup" of the discharge tube after exposure to different gases.

(c) Rate-of-rise Measurements. This method is not satisfactory for routine leak hunting, as it is too slow in application. However, it is very suitable for determining the portion of a vacuum system in which a leak is located or for finding out whether the trouble is in the pumps. For certain special purposes it is the most sensitive method available. The method is applied in essentially the following manner: The vacuum system or a portion of the system is isolated from the pumps by means of appropriate valves, gates, or stopcocks, and then the rate of rise in pressure in the isolated region is measured by an appropriate pressure-measuring device. It is clear that a continuously recording instrument, such as an ionization gauge, is preferable to an intermittent one, such as a McLeod gauge. The type of measuring instrument used will, of course, be determined by the pressure range in which the rate of rise is being taken. For example, if the pressure of the system does not come down below 100 μ Hg or so and the diffusion pumps cannot be turned on, then the rate-of-rise measurement could be made with a Pirani gauge, a thermocouple gauge, or some form of McLeod gauge. The method, if properly used, can produce some very useful information regarding leaks in a vacuum system. First the main vacuum system should be isolated from the pumps, and a rate-of-rise measurement made. If the value obtained is essentially that of a tight system (assuming that this value is known for the system) or is sufficiently low so that the required pressure should be attainable with the particular pumps and system being used, then this indicates that the pumps are not operating properly or that there is a leak in the pump system. Suppose, however, that the rate-of-rise measurement indicates a leak in the main vacuum system. A rough value for the size of leak can be found as follows: Suppose the vacuum system has a volume of 1,000 liters and that a rate of rise of roughly 0.5 μ Hg in 10 sec, starting at a pressure of 100 μ Hg, is obtained. Then the total leak is about 50 μ-liters/sec. This is, of course, far larger than the background leaks in a tight system. Knowing the over-all value of the leaks in the system serves as a guide in determining when the leaks of major size have been found.

Once it has been determined that leaks in the vacuum system definitely exist, the next steps are to isolate various portions of the system from the main part of the system if valves are available and to take rates-of-rise measurements. The results obtained may quickly indicate the portion of the system in which the major leaks are located. The actual location of the leaks is then carried out by one or more of the methods listed above. It is not necessary that a pressure-measuring device be connected with the part of the system being isolated. Suppose that for a vacuum system of volume V the leakage in some part of it of volume V′ is to be determined. Also suppose that the base pressure of the entire system is P_1. Volume V′ is closed off at pressure P_1. At a time t later the rest of the system is isolated from the pumps, and the valve between V′ and the remainder of V is opened. If at this time a pressure P_2 is observed, evidently the rate of rise inside V′ is just $(1/t)[P_2 (V/V') - P_1]$. In case it is not easily calculated, the ratio V/V′ is quickly measured from gas expansion.

This method is capable of great sensitivity, since t can be made as large as desired. For example, if a Geiger counter or a discharge tube is to be sealed off permanently, it can be tested for leaks by isolating it for several days. The principal contributions of the present method are, of course, the determination of the existence of leaks and a speedy way of isolating the portions of the vacuum system in which the leaks occur.

(d) Overvacuum or Evacuated Hood. In this method the pressure is reduced on portions of the outside surface of the vacuum system where it is suspected there may be leaks. While this is being done the vacuum system is kept on the pumps. When the pressure is reduced over a leak in the system this results in a drop in pressure inside the system (see Eq. 1 of Sec. 5.1). In order to reduce the pressure over a suspected portion of the vacuum system, use is made of appropriately shaped hoods that seal to the outside surface and are pumped down by a roughing pump. Except for small leaks it is necessary only to reduce the pressure to a few millimeters of mercury to get an indication of the leak. This is clear from an examination of Eqs. 1 and 2. The method is limited principally by the difficulty in devising hoods that can be sealed to irregular or curved parts of the vacuum system.

(e) High Pressure Inside Vacuum System, Appropriate Indicator on the Outside. One phase of this method is to raise the pressure inside the vacuum system above atmospheric so that gas leaks to the atmosphere. A soap solution is then painted over the surface of the system, and, when a leak is covered, a bubble will form. As well as giving the location of a leak the method will also give some indication of its size from the rate of growth of the bubble. The pressure inside the vacuum system may be anywhere from 16 or 17 lb/sq in. absolute to over 100 lb/sq in. absolute, depending on the mechanical construction of the system. In order to speed up the leak-hunting procedure it is advisable first to soap the most likely source of leaks, such as gasket seals, solder joints, etc. Another phase of this method is to immerse the system under study in water when at a pressure over atmospheric and to look for gas bubbles. This procedure is very effective for welded joints and solder seals. The method of immersion in water is of particular value in testing sections of a vacuum system prior to assembly. Its effectiveness is greatest, of course, in the cases of metal parts, e.g., with welded joints or solder seals where the pressure applied can be appreciable. The sensitivity of the method can be increased by choosing a light gas with a high rate of diffusion. For example, hydrogen will diffuse through leaks about four times as fast as air. As usual, the chief objection to the use of hydrogen is its inflammability. For this reason helium is usually used (diffuses about twice as fast as air).

To get a rough idea concerning the sensitivity of the method using pressure inside the vacuum system and soap solution applied outside, consider the following example: Suppose a soap bubble 1 mm in diameter is observed to form in 5 sec. Then a volume of air (or whatever gas is used inside the system) equal to $\frac{4}{3}\pi \times 0.05^3$ cc or 0.0005 cc at atmospheric pressure escapes in 5 sec, i.e., 0.0001 cc in 1 sec at atmospheric pressure. This corresponds to a leak of about 0.08 μ-liter/sec. This is actually a lower limit for the leak size. The leak will be larger than this estimate, owing to the surface tension of the bubble.

In the case of large leaks, where it is often impossible to produce bubbles with soap solution, it is common practice to pass a flame slowly over the surface of vacuum systems and to look for a wavering of the flame. Also large leaks can often be located by the hissing sound of the escaping gas. Instead of using a gas, in some cases a liquid is used. The presence of a leak is then indicated by a wetting of the surface in the vicinity of the leak. This procedure is suitable only for large leaks.

The principal modification of this method of filling the vacuum system with a gas or vapor under pressure involves the use of certain chemicals such as acidic materials, ammonia, or organic halides. The chemical (gas or vapor) is put into the vacuum system at a pressure above atmospheric so that it escapes through the leaks. The method of detection is then chosen on the basis of the chemical used. For example, if ammonia gas is used in the vacuum, hydrochloric acid is used as an indicator. The hydrochloric acid indicator is applied to various portions of the outside of the vacuum system. If the acid covers a leak, the escaping ammonia gas reacts with the acid to form ammonium chloride, which produces a white fog. The system could just as well be filled with carbon dioxide under pressure, using ammonia as the probe gas. The method is limited in application in such cases by the corrosiveness of the chemicals used.

A more suitable application of the method is the use of a halide gas in the vacuum system and a special type of torch as an indicator.[4] The type of equipment found to be quite effective is illustrated in Fig. 5.2. It consists of a burner operating on acetylene or some other halide-free gas. The air intake to the burner is through a tube about 3 ft long, which is the leak probe. Above the flame in the burner is a copper plate that becomes red hot. If a trace of a halide gas is sucked up in the air intake, it reacts with the hot copper plate, giving the bright-green flame characteristic of copper. Typical gases producing this effect are Freon, methyl chloride, methylene chloride, ethyl chloride, carbon tetrachloride, and chloroform.

Although any halide gas could be used in this test, Freon, CCl_2F_2, is the best with respect to sensitivity, vapor pressure, inertness, and

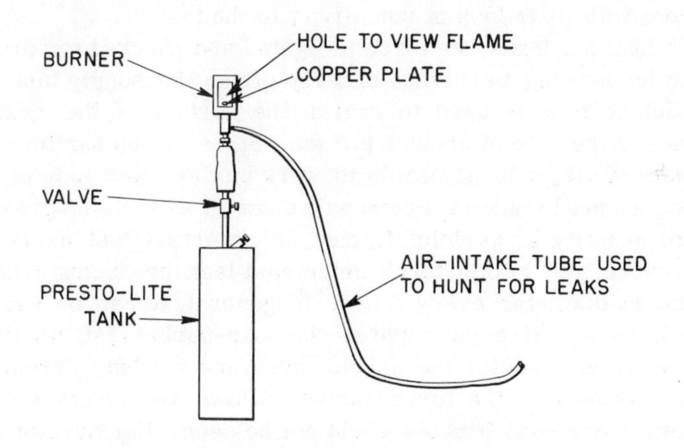

Fig. 5.2—Halide torch and auxiliary equipment.

safeness. The nearest substitute for it is methyl chloride, CH_3Cl, which has only one halide per molecule, has a vapor pressure only seven-eighths that of Freon at room temperature (73 lb/sq in. absolute against 84 lb/sq in. absolute), corrodes iron or steel in the presence of moisture, is explosive in a concentration between 8.1 and 17.2 per cent, and has a lingering toxic effect if breathed in a concentration greater than 4 per cent for over an hour. Freon, on the other hand, contains four halide ions per molecule, and is chemically inert so that it is noncorrosive, nonexplosive, and virtually nontoxic.

The test consists in filling the vacuum system, or some part of the system that can be isolated, with Freon and then probing the surface of the system to detect traces of gas that issue from the leaks. Depending on the size of the vessel and the sensitivity desired, the air may or may not be evacuated before the Freon is introduced. Evacuation takes longer and is not practicable for very small water pipes, but makes possible a pure Freon atmosphere that can be pumped back into the storage tank afterward. Many of the large steel vacuum tanks to which this method of leak detection has been applied can stand an absolute pressure of only around 21 lb/sq in. If Freon is added to air to bring the pressure up to that level, the resulting mixture is about one-third Freon, and 5 lb of liquid Freon can be used to test 30 cu ft of volume. The same 5 lb of Freon, if used without dilution can be used to test 10 cu ft of tank and can be recovered afterward. Most water pipe can be tested up to the full tank pressure of Freon at room temperature (84 lb/sq in. absolute). Accordingly, if the Freon is added to the air in the pipe, the resulting mixture could be five-sixths Freon, with little loss of sensitivity to the test.

To hunt for leaks, the torch is lighted and checked for proper operation by sucking in a trace of Freon from the supply tank. Then the air-intake tube is used to search the surface of the system being tested at the rate of about 1 in./sec. Since Freon has four times the density of air, it is advisable to work on the lower side of a possible leak. A small trace of Freon will show up as a Kelly-green flame, a large quantity as a violet flame. In an actual test using the above procedure, the halide torch detected a leak producing a soap bubble 1 mm in diameter every 5 sec. In general, it can be said that this test is as sensitive and rapid as the soap-bubble test, whether hydrogen or air is used for the excess pressure needed to create the bubbles. Moreover, the torch method allows the location of leaks in places where soap bubbles could not be seen. Furthermore, no residue of water and soap must be removed before the tested apparatus can be used. The technique is, of course, safer than any test involving hydrogen. Freon is noninflammable, and, once a leak is found, it may be soldered without fear of explosion.

Another phase of this method involves the use of helium and the helium leak detector, particularly for parts of a vacuum system that can be tested separately. This technique is described later in this chapter in connection with the instrument.

The various characteristics of these modifications of the pressure-testing procedure are listed in Table 5.2.

(f) Partial Vacuum Inside System, Soap Solution Applied Inside System. This method involves applying soap solution inside the vacuum system with the system partially evacuated. The method obviously has quite limited possibilities, being applicable only in the case of quite large vacuum systems. The procedure is for a man, equipped with oxygen mask, to get inside the vacuum system, which is then partially exhausted (to perhaps ¾ atm). The man can then apply soap solution to the inside surface of the system and look for the formation of soap bubbles. During this procedure the most careful precautions must be taken. The man inside the vacuum system should be under observation at all times so that any signs of exhaustion or other difficulties will immediately be apparent. A continuous and uninterrupted source of oxygen must always be available. Also every precaution must be taken so that there is no chance for the valve between the vacuum system and the pumps to be opened wide by mistake. The real value of the method lies in finding large leaks in parts of the surface of a large vacuum system that are not accessible from the outside.

Table 5.2—Pressure-testing Procedures*

Test medium	Probe	Response	Leak size at 45 psia, μ-liters/sec	Remarks
Air-nitrogen	Flame	Wavering	40	Draft-free room
	Sound	Hissing	40	Low noise level
	Soap film	Bubbles	0.04	Each area to be observed under good light for at least 5 min and soap film maintained
	Immersion	Bubbles	0.16	5 to 15 min observation; occluded air on surface must be avoided
Organic halide	Halide torch	Flame color change	0.04	
Acidic gas (CO_2 or SO_2)	Ammonia	Fumes	0.04	
Ammonia	CO_2, HCl	Fumes	0.04	
Liquid under high pressure		Wet exterior surface		

*Taken from Jacobs and Zuhr.[3]

(g) Sealing Substance on Outside of System, Change of Pressure on Inside. The procedure here is to paint, brush, or spray a sealing substance over various portions of the vacuum system until a change in pressure inside the system indicates that a leak has been covered. The indicating device may be any of the above-mentioned gauges, such as the Knudsen gauge or the ionization gauge, depending on the pressure in the system. The sealing substance may temporarily or permanently seal the leaks. Substances such as glyptal lacquers, shellac in alcohol, a mixture of beeswax and resin, and cellulose acetate solution will often produce permanent sealing, and the covering of a leak is indicated by a decrease in pressure (Appendix H). Materials such as water, acetone, and alcohol seal the leak temporarily, and air cannot enter the vacuum system (Appendix I). Instead the vapor of the particular material used gets into the system, and a change in pressure is indicated.

The indication obtained when a leak is covered with temporarily sealing substances depends on the nature of the substance, the type of pressure gauge used, and the manner in which the gauge is used. For most gauges and substances the indication is a decrease in pressure shown by the gauge due to the fact that the vapor pressures of the substances used are lower than atmospheric pressure. This applies to Pirani, Knudsen, and thermocouple gauges. Cuykendall[5] has described a simple laboratory-type Pirani gauge involving the use of two 50-watt carbon-filament lamps suitable for leak hunting. He discusses its use with alcohol, glyptal, and other materials. The indication of a leak is given by the deflection of a galvanometer needle. The indicated decrease in pressure is greater if a cold trap, such as a liquid-air trap, is placed in the vacuum system in the line leading to the gauge. Since the vapors of the temporarily sealing substances are condensable this trap prevents them from reaching the gauge. With such a trap an ionization gauge will indicate a reduced pressure for these substances. However, since such a gauge depends on the ionization potential of the gas surrounding its elements, with no trap the indicated change in pressure may be an increase, depending on the properties of the substance being used. For example, with alcohol and acetone such a gauge will indicate an increased pressure. Manley, Haworth, and Luebke[6] have described the effects of ether, acetone, amyl acetate, alcohol, glyptal thinner, and carbon tetrachloride on an ionization gauge (tungsten filament). They found that the order of efficacy of the liquids corresponded to the order of both vapor pressure and viscosity. Ether produced the greatest effect, this being about 10 times the effects of all the other liquids except acetone. Acetone gave a large initial effect, but the response quickly dropped to a small value and then slowly recovered to a value somewhat less than that for ether. This behavior was attributed to a poisoning of the filament by the acetone. Ether gave the most reproducible results. Amyl acetate tended to close the leak partially. Lawton[7] has also described some results obtained with carbon tetrachloride. He found that this material tends to increase the emission from the filament (tungsten). He points out that measuring the change in emission of the filament due to entrance of a foreign gas or vapor into the vacuum system provides a more sensitive and satisfactory method of detecting leaks than measuring the ion current. In general, it is advisable to protect this type of gauge with a liquid-air trap in its vacuum line to avoid poisoning effects.

Nothing has been said about the effect of temporary sealing substances on manometers, e.g., a McLeod gauge. Owing to the nature of this gauge it is seldom used in leak-hunting procedure where speed is an important factor. This type of gauge will not show the pressure of condensable vapors, and consequently it will indicate a reduction in pressure when a leak is temporarily sealed with some substance such as water or alcohol.

The temporary sealing substances are quite effective in leak-hunting procedure for all sizes of leaks except the very smallest. In this case the diffusion rate becomes an important factor, owing to the relatively large size of molecule used. On the other hand, the permanent sealing substances are most effective for the small leaks. For large leaks it is not possible to obtain a permanent seal since the material is sucked into the vacuum system. The permanent sealing substances give fairly satisfactory results with leaks in metal plates, in soldered and welded joints, and in glass systems. However, it is not so satisfactory as a final repair obtained by reworking the material of the vacuum system by soldering or welding of metal or fusing of glass. In general, the use of permanent sealing substances for repairing leaks in gasket seals is not satisfactory.

(h) Change in Pressure or Nature of Gas Inside Vacuum System, Probe Gas Outside System. This method resembles quite closely that described in Sec. 5.2g, with which temporary sealing substances are used. However, in the latter case it is normal practice to use a material that is liquid at room temperature. Consequently the vapors entering the vacuum system are condensable, and a cold trap before the indicating device inside the system will produce a pronounced effect in the pressure readings obtained. In this method a permanent gas, usually helium, is used. A light gas is chosen so as to increase the rate of diffusion through the leak. The effect of the gas on the pressure-indicating device inside the vacuum system will depend on the nature of this device. For example, the substitution of helium for air will decrease an ionization-gauge reading owing to the small mass of the helium molecules and their high ionization potential. On the other hand, helium will make a Pirani gauge read high owing to the high speed of the helium molecules, which remove heat from the Pirani element more effectively than is the case with air.

The sensitivity of this method of leak detection clearly depends directly on the type of device used to detect the test gas in the vacuum system. When a pressure-indicating instrument is used, its nature will be determined by the pressure range within which the leak hunting is carried out. For example, when the leaks are such as to make it impossible to operate the diffusion pumps, a gauge such as a Pirani or thermocouple gauge would be used. Kuper[8] has described a Pirani-gauge circuit so arranged that when a response is obtained it is indicated by a loudspeaker, thus facilitating the leak-hunting procedure. It is clear that such an arrangement can be used with temporary sealing substances such as ether as well as with the permanent gases. At pressures of the order of 10^{-4} mm Hg it would be possible to use an ionization or Knudsen gauge.

Lawton[7] has described the effects of oxygen and hydrogen on the emission of a tungsten filament in an ionization gauge. He found that both of these gases decreased the emission. The oxygen appeared to be adsorbed on the filament. The hydrogen was believed to be dissociated to atomic hydrogen by the filament. This atomic hydrogen then reacts with oxides on the surrounding walls of the vacuum chamber, producing water vapor. A diode type of ionization gauge used with oxygen as a probe gas has been reported by R. B. Nelson.[9] The emission of the tungsten filament (temperature limited) changes when oxygen reaches it; the same result was reported by Lawton.

H. Nelson[10] has described a special type of ionization gauge for use with hydrogen as a probe gas. A sealed-off ionization gauge (at about 2×10^{-7} mm Hg pressure) is used with a section of the gauge constructed of palladium sheet. This sheet is heated to about 800°C, which renders it highly permeable to hydrogen gas but to no other gases or vapors. The hydrogen entering the gauge increases the ionization current. After a leak has been located by this gauge it is pumped down (through the palladium) for further use. High sensitivity is claimed for this type of gauge. Brubaker and Wouk[11] have described a frequency-modulated oscillator for use with an ionization gauge in leak hunting. Their arrangement converts the variable d-c voltages produced in the ionization-gauge circuit to an audible signal so as to speed up the leak-hunting process. The indicating device known as the "vacuum analyzer" is also used with this method, although there are certain disadvantages attending its use. This instrument detects the atoms of the probe gas by mass-spectrographic principles. Details will not be given here since it will be described later in the chapter.

Probably the most effective instrument for use in this method is the helium leak detector, which is a further development of the vacuum analyzer. In view of the fact that this instrument has rather unique features and is a very important instrument in leak-detection procedure, it will be described in great detail later in this chapter. In this connection, various steps in the application of the present method are described. Consequently, further discussion of this method will be postponed to the treatment of the helium leak detector.

Most of the methods of leak detection discussed are not particularly suitable for obtaining an accurate determination of the size of a leak. On the other hand, in most cases this is not too important, the problem being to locate the leaks and repair them in the shortest time possible. Of course, if the geometrical form and arrangement of the vacuum system and the pumping speed are known, it is possible to obtain some idea of the leak size with a number of the leak-detecting methods by suitable calibration against a known leak. Also experience with a given vacuum system will often make it possible to estimate the size of a leak with a fair degree of accuracy. Probably the method best adapted to determining accurately the size of a leak is the rate-of-rise-measuring procedure.

5.3 Pump-outs. Owing to the difficulty of locating leaks in gaskets, a special device called a "pump-out" is incorporated very often in vacuum equipment, particularly when this equipment is of a large size and requires the use of a number of gaskets. The device has been described briefly in Chap. 4. It consists essentially of two gaskets separated by a space that is accessible from outside the vacuum.

Several of the methods of leak hunting already discussed can be used to find leaks in the vacuum-sealing gasket or inner gasket. A common procedure is to pump out the space between the two gaskets with a fore pump. If there is a leak in the vacuum-sealing gasket, this is manifested by a drop in pressure in the vacuum system. Also the methods involving the use of temporary sealing substances or probe gas together with appropriate pressure-indicating devices inside the vacuum system are often used. Soap solution is often applied to the opening to the space between the gaskets. A leak will be indicated by the soap bubbles drawing in. The use of permanent sealing substances is not to be recommended in view of the fact that they may result in blocking of the opening to the intergasket space, thus destroying the usefulness of the pump-outs. The methods using pressure inside the vacuum system may also be applied with the usual indicating devices such as soap solution, the helium leak detector, etc.

Pump-outs are often used in the case of welded joints (see Chap. 4). Dams are constructed between inner and outer welds so as to leave a pump-out space between the dams. This space is available from outside the vacuum system through a suitable opening, usually a drilled hole. Leaks in the inner weld (next to the vacuum) can then be detected by applying the same types of methods as described above for the gasket pump-outs.

5.4 The Vacuum Analyzer. In certain types of processes a knowledge of the residual gases in a vacuum system may be of great value to an understanding of the process in question. An apparatus that would give the requisite knowledge should be semiquantitative in action and should be suitable for continuous operation. Such an apparatus has been developed and called a "vacuum analyzer." This instrument has been found to provide much useful information regarding the nature of the gases and vapors inside a vacuum system, but it is

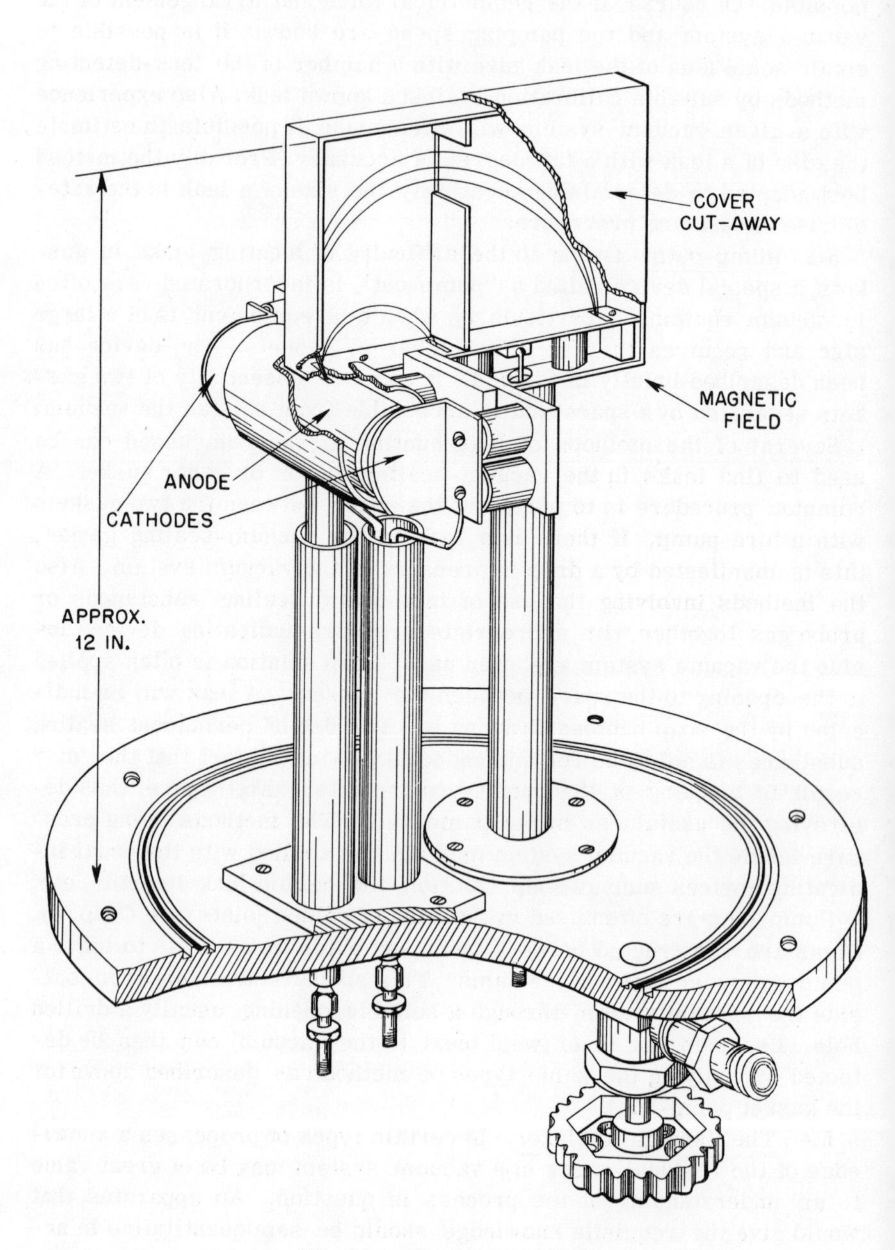

Fig. 5.3—The vacuum analyzer.

not particularly adapted to routine leak hunting. However, modifications of the instrument have resulted in the helium leak detector, which is designed specifically for routine leak hunting.

The vacuum analyzer is a small-radius mass spectrometer using a cold-cathode ion source for the production of positive ions, and cathode-ray scanning for a detector. The origin of the vacuum analyzer lies in experiments carried out by Backus[12] in which a Philips ionization gauge (abbreviated as P.I.G.) was used as a positive-ion source for a small mass spectrometer that separated the gases in the vacuum up to masses of about 50.[13-15]

In Fig. 5.3 is shown a schematic cutaway drawing of the vacuum analyzer as developed at the Radiation Laboratory. This analyzer was designed to be mounted on a port in a large vacuum tank, which was inside a uniform magnetic field. Thus numerous conditions entered into the design other than just the performance of the mass spectrometer. The electrical leads, the insulators, etc., are all covered with grounded shields necessitated by material in the tank, which spoiled the insulation. The salient features are the simple cylindrical anode (1 in. in diameter, 3 in. long) with cathodes covering the ends, these cathodes being just flat pieces of metal, and the simplest possible mass spectrometer. None of the spacings are critical, except that the gap between the two $\frac{1}{32}$- by $\frac{3}{4}$-in. slits (acceleration system) should be quite small, e.g., about $\frac{1}{32}$ in. The materials of construction are not critical, except that the cathodes wear rapidly owing to bombardment, unless they are made of tantalum or tungsten.

In Fig. 5.4 the simplest circuit that was used is shown. The sweep circuit shown will obviously sweep the voltage from ground up to a maximum equal to twice the peak voltage of the secondary of the sweep transformer. Thus it will sweep over all masses down to a certain minimum mass, set by the sweep-supply variac. In a rather obvious extension of this method, a voltage divider was put across the secondary of the sweep transformer, so that width of the sweep could be adjusted independently of the bias. Thus the width of the mass spectrum being examined could be set from a few mass units to the full spectrum. This simple system is useful up to mass 50, approximately. By refinement of the circuits and substitution of a hot-cathode ion source for the simple cold-cathode P.I.G. source shown here the method may be extended to much higher masses.[16]

The development of the P.I.G. source for use in a vacuum analyzer was guided by two main requirements: (1) the ion source must give a sufficient supply of ions at pressures at least down to 10^{-5} mm Hg, and lower if possible, and (2) the ion beam must be sufficiently homogeneous in energy so that the desired resolution is obtained. If ions of charge ne and mass M (on the scale O = 16) are moving perpendicularly to a magnetic field of strength B gauss with a velocity $\sqrt{2neV/M}$, then the following relation obtains:

$$\rho B = 144.5 \frac{MV}{n} \tag{5}$$

where ρ is the radius of curvature of the ion in centimeters, n is the number of times the ion is ionized or the effective number of charges

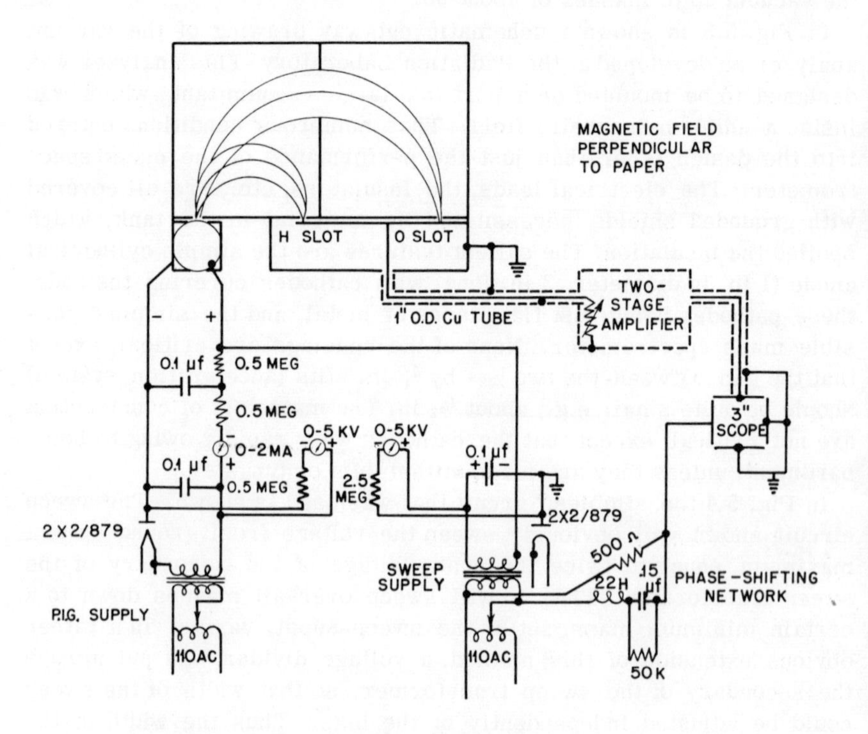

Fig. 5.4—Schematic circuit diagram for the vacuum analyzer.

carried by the ion, V is the potential in practical volts through which the ion has been accelerated, c is the velocity of light, and e is the charge of the electron. The constant 144.5 is equal to $(2c^2/e)$ ($\frac{1}{16}$ mass of O atom in grams/300). In order to get the condition for resolving adjacent atoms in the neighborhood of $O^+ = 16$, Eq. 5 is differentiated to obtain $-dV/V = dM/M = \frac{1}{2}/16 = \frac{1}{32}$, which gives the order of magnitude of the allowable voltage spread in the energy of the ions.

In order to satisfy the first condition above, it was found necessary to expand the anode in the standard P.I.G. to a cylinder about 1 in. in diameter and to draw the ions out through a slit parallel to an element of the cylinder. The second condition was satisfied only after the anode was lengthened to about 3 in.

The plasma inside the anode is essentially at anode potential so that ions enter the grounded spectrometer box with an energy given by the potential of the P.I.G. anode with respect to ground plus or minus their random energies. In the instrument being described there are two slots ahead of the single collector, one the "hydrogen" slot on a 2.85-cm radius, and the other the "oxygen" slot on a 6.35-cm

Table 5.3 — Voltages for the Various Masses to Fall on the Collector Slots at Magnetic-field Strength of 3,600 Gauss

Mass	Radius of 6.35 cm	Radius of 2.85 cm
1		5,000
2		2,500
4	6,240	1,250
7	3,550	714
8	3,120	625
10	2,500	
12	2,160	415
14	1,780	358
15	1,670	334
16	1,560	313
17	1,470	294
18	1,380	278
28	900	179
32	780	156
35	714	143
40	625	125

radius. The voltages at which the various atomic weights fall on these collector slots for a magnetic-field strength of 3,600 gauss are given in Table 5.3. Thus, for the radii chosen, H_2^+ falls in the hydrogen slot at the voltage for which $M = 10$ could fall on the oxygen slot. Both slots are ½ mass unit wide for $M = 16$.

There are ±10-deg defining vanes for the oxygen slot placed at the 90-deg position, but there are none in the case of the hydrogen slot (see Fig. 5.3). The angular spread corresponding to a voltage spread of ½ mass unit for $M = 16$ is 10 deg. The voltage spread of the ions from the P.I.G. source described was found to be of the order of ±20 volts at 2×10^{-4} mm Hg and ±100 volts at 0.1×10^{-4} mm Hg. If these values are compared to $dV = V/32 = 1{,}560/32 \approx 50$, it is seen that, with the geometrical form and field described, the resolution in the neighborhood of $M = 16$ should be good at pressures below 10^{-4} mm Hg and increasingly poor at pressures above this value.

The electrical circuits used with the instrument will not be described in detail here, Fig. 5.4 being sufficient for our purpose. The circuits used with the instrument as converted for helium detection (see helium leak detector) will be described in more detail in the following section. The types of peaks obtained with the instrument are shown in Fig. 5.5.

The vacuum analyzer has been used for leak-hunting purposes primarily with helium or methane gas. Helium gives much more sensitivity than methane in leak hunting, although the vacuum analyzer

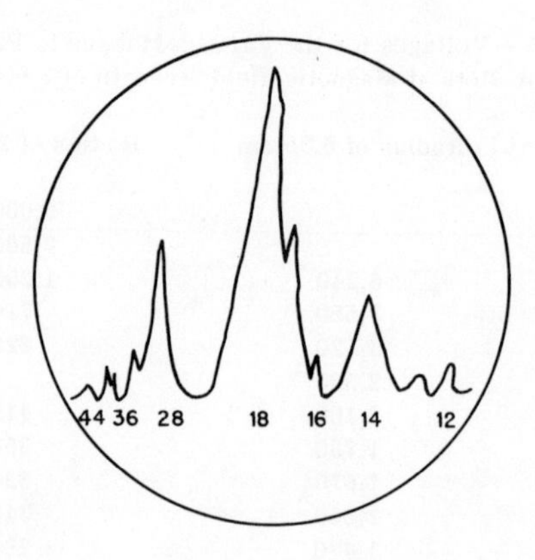

Fig. 5.5—Typical peaks obtained with vacuum analyzer.

when used with the latter is still more sensitive than the Western Electric ionization gauge. The usefulness of methane lies in the fact that it produces peaks not normally present and at much lower voltages than the helium peak. With a rather small leak the mass-15 peak (CH_3^+) appears, and the 16 (CH_4^+) and 16 (O^+) peak increases in height. If the leak is somewhat larger, the 13 (CH^+) and 12 (C^+) peaks appear in addition but are not over one-tenth the height of the 15 and 16 peaks. At pressures less than 10^{-4} mm Hg the resolution is so sharp in the neighborhood of M = 16 that the 15 peak rises from the zero line on the introduction of methane.

5.5 The Helium Leak Detector.[16,17] The principle of operation of this instrument is the same as for the vacuum analyzer. However, its design is directed toward obtaining a portable self-contained unit for the detection of helium atoms introduced into a vacuum system in the process of leak hunting. The general design of the leak-detector unit proper follows quite closely that of a vacuum analyzer. However, the magnet provided must be portable, and an independent vacuum system for the unit must be used. Also only one collector slot is used since the whole purpose of the instrument is the detection of helium ions alone. The helium ions are collected at about 180°C, as shown in Fig. 5.6. The output current is approximately 5×10^{-11} amp for 1 part

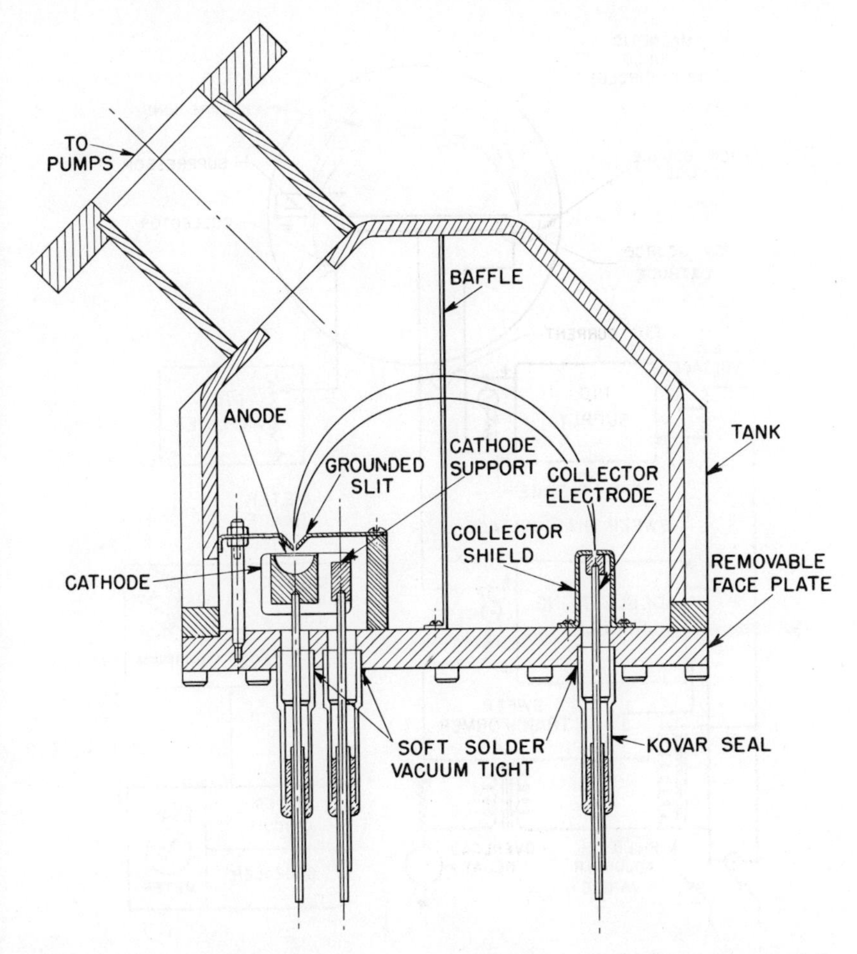

Fig. 5.6—Cross section of mass-spectrometer tank of cold-cathode helium leak detector.

of helium in 75,000 parts of air. The general arrangement of electrical components is indicated in Fig. 5.7, and the relation of the leak-detector unit with respect to the vacuum chamber being studied is shown in Fig. 5.8. A general description of a type of leak detector system found to be satisfactory will first be given, followed by a more detailed description of the various component parts of this type of system. At the time of writing four mass-spectrometer helium leak detectors were available commercially. The first was developed by A. O. Nier[19] et al. of the University of Minnesota and is produced

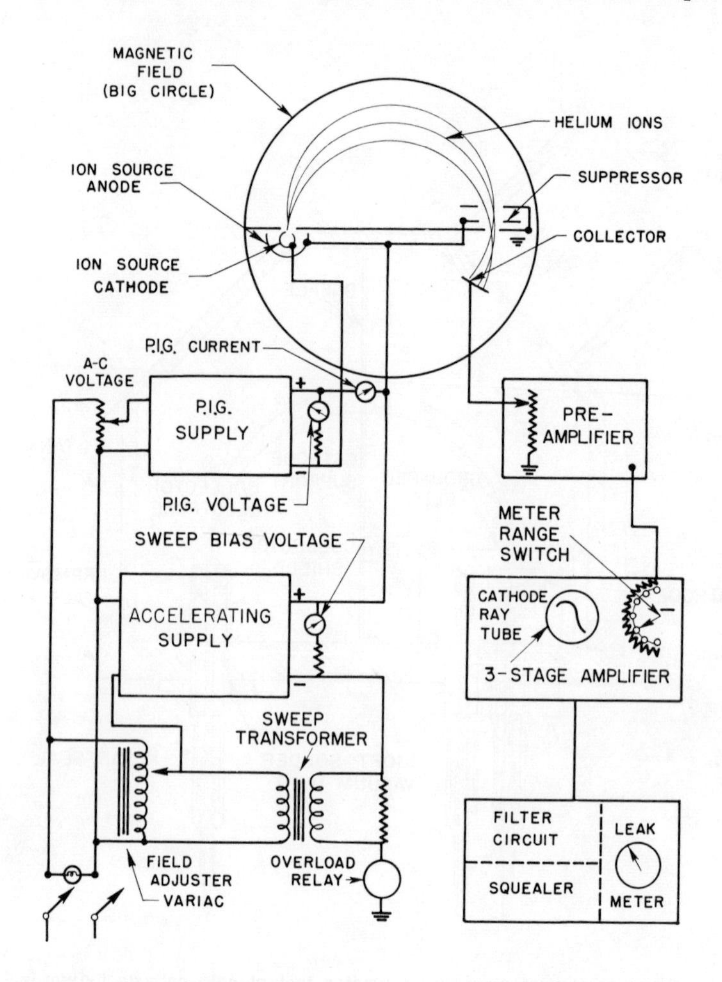

Fig. 5.7—Schematic circuit diagram for helium leak detector.

by the General Electric Company. The second was developed by the Westinghouse Electric & Manufacturing Company,[20] and since then such instruments have been produced by Consolidated Engineering Corporation and National Research Corporation. All these are portable self-contained vacuum systems, with a hot-filament ion source in the mass spectrometer. Since the cost of these units puts them beyond the reach of any but the largest institutions, it is considered worth while to describe in some detail the somewhat simple cold-cathode leak detector developed at the Radiation Laboratory during 1945 and 1946, since any competent physicist or engineer can construct his own.

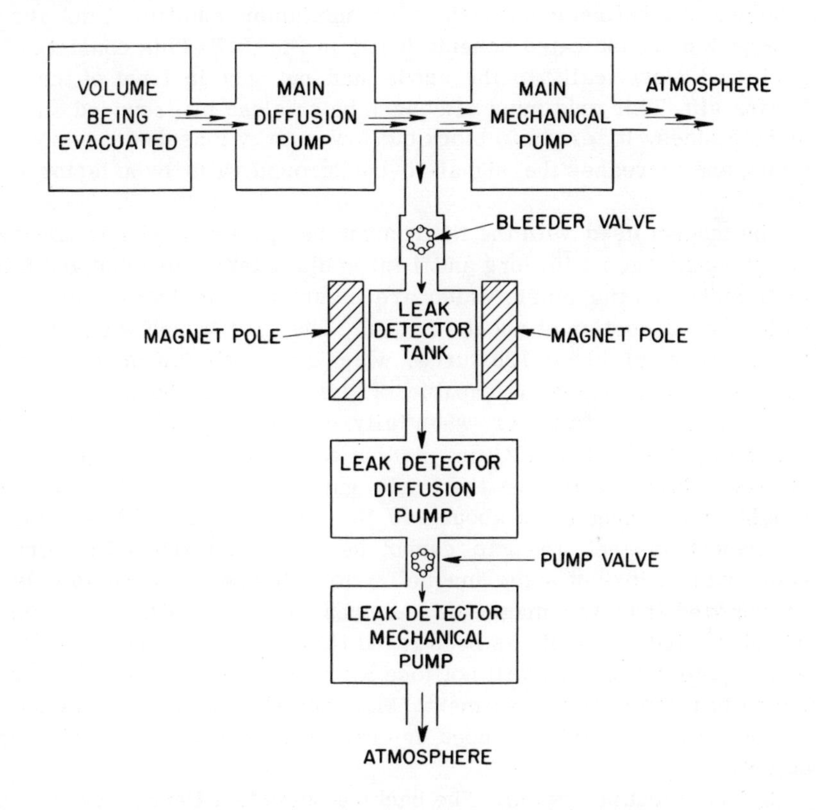

Fig. 5.8—Pumping system with helium leak detector.

(a) Leak-detector Tank and Magnet. The arrangement of the tank is such as to facilitate reservicing (see Fig. 5.5). The tank is supported by the vacuum line. The P.I.G. source and the collector, as well as a baffle at the 90-deg position, are attached to a faceplate constructed of nonmagnetic material (brass). This makes it possible to remove the whole assembly for servicing or for replacement without disturbing the magnetic field, which is produced by a permanent magnet. The inside of the chamber is covered with a silicone lacquer baked so as to minimize the cleaning problem and in particular to reduce the absorption of moisture. The side walls of the chamber are constructed of magnetic iron 9/16 in. thick, which constitute the magnetic-pole faces. The inside spacing of these walls is 1⅛ in. The length of the P.I.G. discharge (distance between cathodes) is about ⅝ in., the length of slit in front of the discharge is about ½ in., and the accelerating slit is about 9/16 in. long and 1/32 in. wide.

There is a refinement possible for maximum sensitivity, not shown on Fig. 5.6 but indicated schematically in Fig. 5.7. This consists of a grid, tied electrically to the anode, and put just in front of the collecting slit. This grid must of course be shielded by grounded shields on both sides. It serves to block out low-energy ions due to gas scattering and increases the signal-to-background ratio by a factor of 5 or so.

The magnet used with the instrument being described contains two alnico slugs, each 4 in. long and 4 in. in diameter on one end and 5 in. in diameter on the other, which are mounted in an iron-return path with a cross section of about 16 sq in. They are wound with 100 ft of No. 12 wire, or about 125 turns, which are used for magnetization purposes. The magnet is capable of giving up to 2,700 gauss over a 1-in. gap 5 in. in diameter, when fully magnetized. The gap between the ends of the alnico is 2¼ in., so that the walls of the tank are made of iron 9/16 in. thick to give the 1⅛-in. gap that is used. The over-all weight of the magnet is about 200 lb. With this, as with any other permanent magnet, the gap cannot be increased above its normal value without loss of some magnetization. Hence, when the tank is to be removed from the magnet for any reason, a magnetic keeper must be substituted for it. It has been found that the alnico used is magnetically quite rugged and will not lose its magnetization even when subjected to rather rough treatment. Mechanically, however, it is not so strong, and it is easily chipped or cracked if hit with any hard sharp object.

(b) The Vacuum System. The backing pump is a Cenco Hyvac, supported on a spring suspension to damp out its vibrations. Some Hyvac pumps will hold a vacuum for a long period while not pumping, but others, presumably those which are somewhat worn, will let down to atmospheric pressure in 4 or 5 min. When this happens, mechanical-pump oil is sometimes pulled back into the diffusion pump, which of course spoils the diffusion-pump oil. For this reason a Kerotest valve, called here the "pump valve," is mounted on the mechanical pump. It has been found desirable to include an oil trap on this pump because it threw oil over into the diffusion pump. This trap is mounted right above the mechanical pump, so that any oil in it will run back where it belongs.

The mechanical pump is coupled to the diffusion pump with a short section of rubber tubing ¼ in. I.D. with walls ¼ in. thick. Tubing with thinner walls collapses after a period of time. The speed of 6 in. of ¼-in. I.D. tubing is about 0.2 liter/sec, which is ample for the Hyvac, which has a speed of about 0.1 liter/sec. Air-cooled diffusion pumps with rated speeds between 10 and 25 liters/sec were found to be satisfactory for use on the unit. The greatest amount of experience was obtained with a Distillation Products pump, designated VMF 10, which has a rated speed of 10 liters/sec at 0.1 μ Hg and a base pressure of 0.001 μ Hg. It requires a fore pressure of 100 μ Hg or less.

There are two specially adapted valves on the leak detector being considered. The pump valve, located at the top of the Hyvac pump, is a Kerotest valve to which a microswitch has been added. This switch is placed so as to operate appropriate signal lights as the valve is turned. The bleeder valve is a Kerotest valve of the same type, which is fitted with a worm-gear drive, with a 15 to 1 ratio. This gives about 27 turns on the handle from open to closed. The valve is fitted with a mechanical system that actuates a microswitch, when the valve is turned, so as to operate signal lights. Helium should not be put into the vacuum inlet to test the bleeder valve seat. This gets helium into the valve parts, and it may take hours to clean it out. The base pressure should be noted when the valve is closed and the inlet is evacuated by a roughing pump, and then it should be observed if the base is appreciably higher when the inlet is suddenly let down to atmospheric pressure. If it is not, the valve is tight enough.

(c) The Electrical Circuits. In Fig. 5.7 is shown a block diagram of the electrical system of the leak detector, except for the a-c control circuits. An understanding of Fig. 5.7 is sufficient for purposes of operation. As there is nothing unique about the control circuits for the instrument, they will not be discussed here.

The high-voltage supplies for the P.I.G. source and for the acceleration of the ions are quite standard in design. It will suffice to say that the P.I.G. supply should give voltages up to about 2,000 volts, and the accelerating supply should give voltages up to whatever is required for the field and radius chosen. In the latter case the current requirements are quite low, but the voltage regulation should be good to a few per cent. A half-wave supply with a resistance-capacitance filter is adequate for the P.I.G. source.

The Amplifier. The amplifier power supply is a conventional, filtered, and regulated power supply furnishing the required voltages. The first stage of the amplifier shown in Fig. 5.9 is located in a spring-suspended box near the leak-detector tank. This serves to keep the input lead short, thus keeping input capacity low, and also serves to damp out the vibrations from the floor and the air, which otherwise would go through the amplifier like an ordinary signal. The first stage is a 9001 pentode, followed by a 9002 used as a cathode follower. The output voltage appearing across R_7 is fed back into the input through C_2 (Fig. 5.9). The effect of this feedback is to give an improved signal-to-noise ratio. The cathode follower serves to give a low output impedance, so that the cable running from the chassis connector J_1 to the amplifier is not sensitive to pickup.

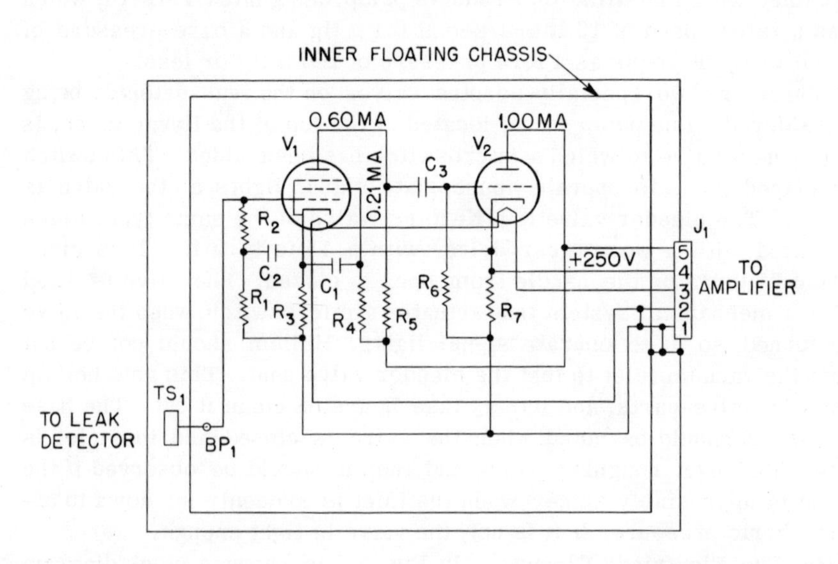

Fig. 5.9—Preamplifier schematic diagram for a helium leak detector. C_1, 0.5-μf 600-volt capacitor; C_2, 0.1-μf 600-volt capacitor; C_3, 0.005-μf 600-volt capacitor; R_1, 20-megohm ½-watt resistor; R_2, 500-megohm 1-watt resistor; R_3, 1,500-ohm 1-watt resistor; R_4, 1.0-megohm 1-watt resistor; R_5, 0.25-megohm 1-watt resistor; R_6, 2.0-megohm ½-watt resistor; R_7, 10,000-ohm 1-watt resistor; V_1, 9001 tube; V_2, 9002 tube.

The main part of the amplifier, which is shown in Fig. 5.10, carries the cathode-ray tube. The input resistance to the first 6SJ7 consists of a selector switch and four resistors constituting the meter range switch. There are three stages of conventional resistance-coupled amplification, and the signal then goes through C_{15} to the vertical plates of the cathode-ray tube. The rectifiers Se 1 and Se 2 furnish d-c filament heating for the first four tubes (three stages of amplification and the cathode follower). The a-c sweep signal from the sweep transformer in the high-voltage power supply comes in on pin 4 of plug J_3 and goes through the bleeder R_{38}, R_{39}, R_{40}. The center of the potentiometer R_{40} goes to the horizontal plates of the cathode-ray tube, providing the horizontal gain control. The rectifier tube V_4 is a special circuit to block one-half of the cycle, so that both the forward and the return sweep will not appear simultaneously on the cathode-ray tube. Binding posts BP_1 and BP_2 are directly across the vertical plates of the cathode-ray tube. If this tube is broken or inoperative, or if it is desired to omit the tube in general, the signal can be viewed equally well by connecting BP_1 and BP_2 to the input of any scope. The input to the squealer and meter circuit is connected to these binding posts.

It is seen from this circuit that the horizontal sweep of the cathode-ray tube is thus a sine wave in phase with the sweep inside the leak-detector tank, which is also a sine wave. Thus the pattern looks somewhat different than when a scope with an internal saw-tooth sweep is used. When an external scope is used, it is synchronized to 60 cycles, and the helium peak appears as a single peak but not necessarily in the middle of the trace.

The Squealer and Meter Circuit. The output signal from the a-c amplifier is applied to the squealer circuit through terminals 3 and 4 of TS_1 as shown in Fig. 5.11. It then goes through half of a 6SN7, which has a gain of about 2½ and which also serves as a signal limiter to protect the meter that follows.

The output of this tube goes into a special filter circuit designed to filter out all frequencies but the signal frequency. This is accomplished by taking the relatively high voltage (480 volts) from the power winding of the transformer T_2 and putting this through the 5-megohm resistors R_{27} and R_{28} on the grids of the 6SN7 (V_5), which is used as a synchronous filter. This has the effect of causing each half of the tube to conduct for half a cycle only, since during the negative half cycle the grid is completely blocked, and during the positive half cycle the drop across the resistor holds the grid current down to a reasonable value. The plate voltage on each half of the tube is the B+ voltage plus the signal from the previous stage. The plate current follows the plate voltage. Random frequencies average to zero on the two sides of the meter, but a 60-cycle signal in phase with the 60 cycles on the grids of the tube averages positive on one side of the meter and negative on the other and hence gives a net d-c deflection. All this is shown in Fig. 5.12, where the effect of signals of various frequencies is shown. Since the two plate currents are on opposite sides of the output meter M_1, an increase in current on one side causes the same deflection as an equal decrease in current on the other. The largest deflection is given by a signal equal in frequency and phase to the grid signal, but it is seen that a part of other frequencies does get through, so that it is not a perfect filter.

The zero set for the meter is shown as R_{32}, Fig. 5.11. The time constant of the meter is set by R_{31} and C_{12} and C_{13} and is about 1 sec.

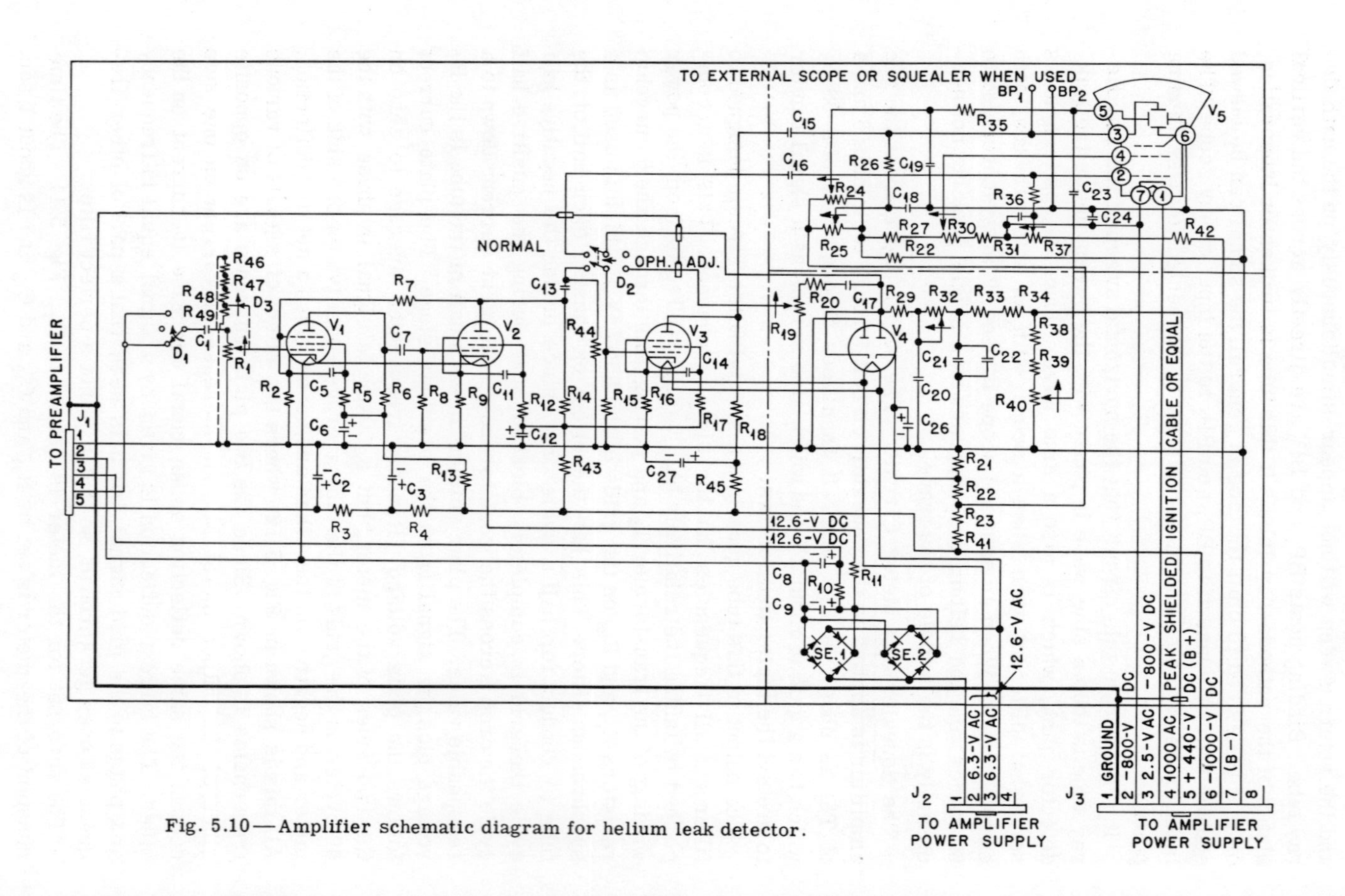

Fig. 5.10—Amplifier schematic diagram for helium leak detector.

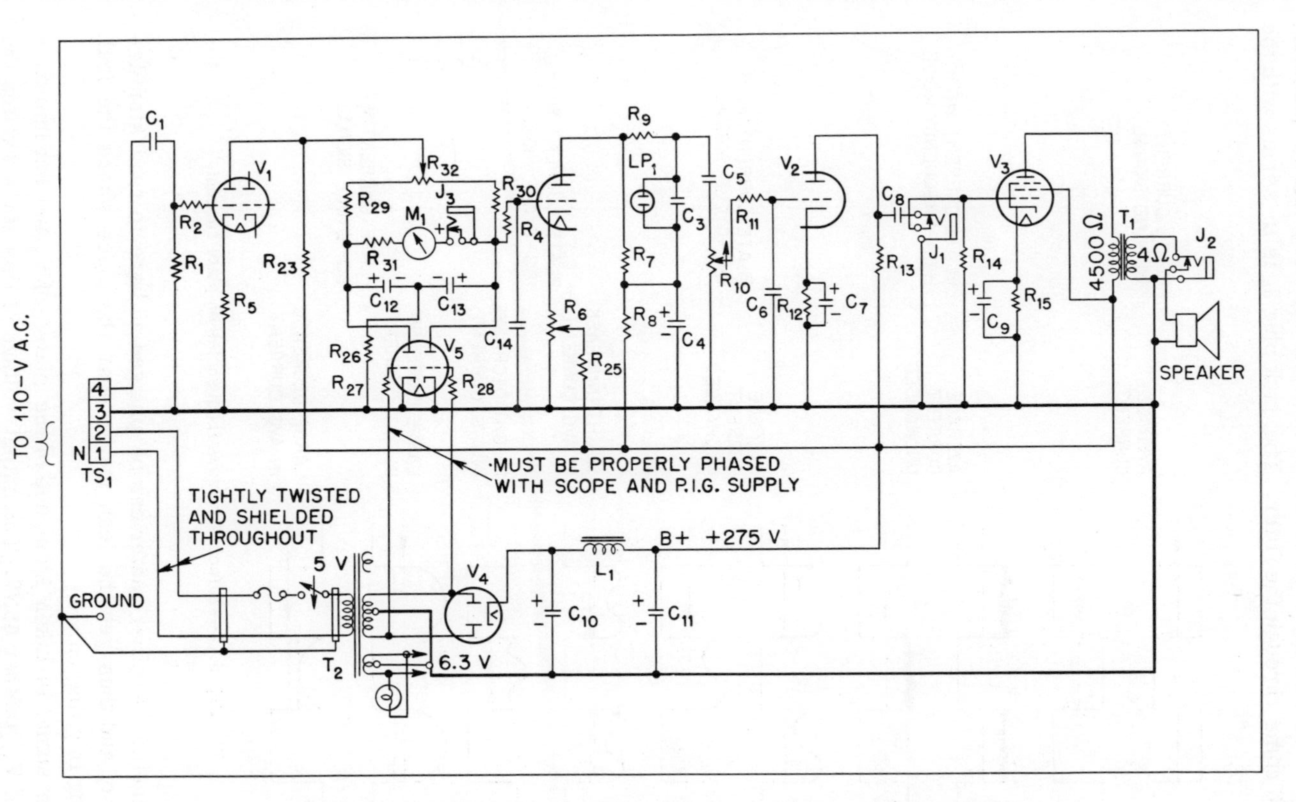

Fig. 5.11 — Squealer and meter schematic diagram for helium leak detector.

It has to be this slow in order to take out the very low frequencies, which come through the filter. The jack plug J_3 is in series with the

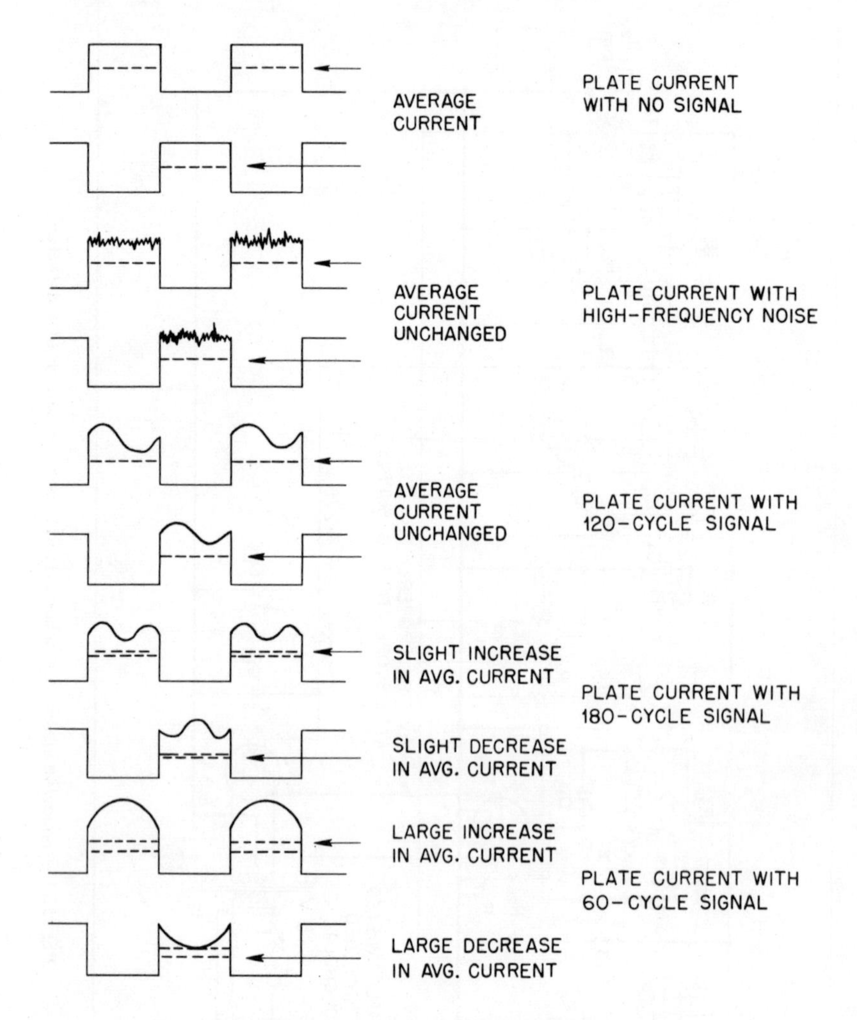

Fig. 5.12 — Effect of various frequencies on plate current.

leak meter. Another meter can be plugged in here to read simultaneously and thus get the leak meter near the place where the leak hunting is going on.

The signal is taken from one of the plates of V_5 and put into one-half of V_2, another 6SN7. The output voltage of this stage excites the relaxation oscillator composed of C_3 and the neon bulb LP_1, the potentiometer R_6 being used to set the quiescent frequency of the oscillator.

The oscillator tone goes through one stage of amplification, thence to a phone jack plug, and then through another stage to a speaker and a speaker jack plug. R_{10} is the volume control. The two jack plugs are so wired that, if either a headphone or an external speaker is plugged in, the speaker on the panel is cut out. It is intended that the top tone of the oscillator be around 1,000 cycles with a very large signal.

The meter does pick up some 60-cycle signal from the sweep voltage. The grid phases on V_5 are so chosen that this pickup is negative (between 5 and 10 μa on the most sensitive scale). Then the residual helium and the ion-current background in the tank, when at operating pressure, give a small positive signal, and hence the average background should be close to zero in the absence of a helium leak.

(d) Sensitivity of the Instrument. The helium leak detector is a very sensitive instrument and should be capable of detecting 1 part of helium in 200,000 parts of air. However, if not properly used, it might fail to detect a very large leak, or it might give a very big indication on an insignificant leak. The considerations that govern its sensitivity will be discussed here. If these are understood, procedures can be adopted to make it a reliable instrument.

The notion of limiting sensitivity of any measuring instrument is an arbitrary one. Suppose that the leak detector shows a background of 5 μa in the absence of any helium and that the needle wanders by 2 or 3 μa owing to various instabilities. Then a reading of 15 μa is certain to be helium, 10 μa is on the border, and 7 μa might be helium or might be a fluctuation. Thus the sensitivity of the instrument is made sufficiently high so that we can safety disregard readings in the uncertain range near the base noise level.

The base noise level is due to random noise inherent in any a-c amplifier, pickup of stray frequencies near the signal frequency, ion background from elements other than helium inside the leak-detector tank, and a helium background that will be at least 1 in 670,000 (the normal atmospheric concentration) and very often much greater due to contamination, leaks, etc. In the leak detector considered here this background should be not over 10 per cent of full scale on the most sensitive scale. If it is greater, the instrument is not in proper adjustment, but it still might operate satisfactorily.

The arbitrary criterion used for limiting sensitivity with this instrument has been the mixture ratio of helium in air that gives a deflection twice the noise level. In order to determine the sensitivity it is necessary to secure a known mixture of helium in air. A very simple way to do this is to prepare a known mixture in a fixed volume, which is the so-called "static" method. The best way to do this is to pump down some small system with a diffusion pump until the pressure is about 0.1 μ Hg or less. Then shut off the diffusion pump and let helium leak in, raising the pressure to around 15 μ Hg with helium alone. Following this, the helium is shut off, and the system is let down to atmospheric pressure by opening a valve. As soon as the air stops rushing in the valve is closed. For example, if the helium pressure was n microns, the mixture ratio is n/760,000.

In measuring the pressure when a large amount of helium is present it should be remembered that an ion gauge reads approximately five times low for pure helium and that a Pirani gauge reads approximately 30 per cent high for pure helium. The ion-gauge effect is due to the small size and high ionization potential of the helium atom. The Pirani effect is due to the low mass and consequent high velocity and greater cooling effect of the helium atoms. As a result, a McLeod gauge must be used in measuring pressure for this work.

If possible, making mixtures in long hose connections should be avoided. There is considerable danger that the air in rushing in will not give sufficient turbulence to give a uniform mixture but will tend to push the helium to one end, giving a richer mixture at that end. If a hose cannot be avoided as part of the mixing system, at least half an hour should be allowed for equilibrium to be established. In introducing the mixture into the leak detector, it is necessary, of course, to evacuate the connections between the mixture and the leak detector with an auxiliary mechanical pump. It is clear that all the connections, as well as the leak detector itself, must be free of leaks. They should be tested with helium in the usual way.

A second method of measuring sensitivity is the fixed-leak or so-called "dynamic" method. Suppose a very small leak is made, as can be done, for example, by collapsing a piece of small copper tubing. By connecting it to a manometer and measuring the rate at which the bubble moves, it may be calibrated. If it is measured as A cubic centimeters per second, the flow through the leak is 760A μ-liters/sec. It is best to perform this calibration with helium, but if air is used the correction factor can be estimated from Fig. 5.1. This leak can then be installed on the same vacuum system to which the leak detector is connected. Hence, if S is the pumping speed of this system in a region where the pressure is P, the total gas handled is PS micron-liters per second, and the mixture ratio of helium to air is 760 A/PS.

Consider a numerical example. Suppose a fixed leak is calibrated at 0.02 μ-liter/sec. This leak is put on a 43-cfm Kinney pump (divide speed in cubic feet per minute by 2.1 to get liters per second) operating at 50 μ Hg. At this pressure the Kinney pump is about 60 per cent efficient, and hence $S = 0.6 \times 43 = 26$ cfm. Also, $P = 50\ \mu$ Hg, so that the mixture ratio is $(0.02 \times 2.1)/(50 \times 26) \approx 1/30{,}000$. This represents the mixture ratio as pure helium at approximately atmospheric pressure is put into the leak. Then, by simply connecting the leak detector and sampling this known mixture in the usual way, the sensitivity of the instrument is determined.

It is possible to measure the sensitivity over a range of mixture ratios by using two leaks. For example, if a mixture of 1 in 10,000 is prepared, and if this is let into the test system through a variable leak, and simultaneously there is a metered air leak, the mixture ratio can be varied from 1 in 10,000 to 1 in 500,000 with no difficulty.

(e) Response and Cleanup Time. From the viewpoint of the operator, the response time is the time from the application of helium to the suspected point of leak until the appearance of an appreciable response at the indicating meter. There are three places where there may be some delay: the regions outside the vacuum wall, the volume inside the vacuum system, and the indicating circuits. In order to interpret the results it is necessary to understand clearly under what circumstances these delays can be very large.

If there is any large volume between the place where helium is applied and the place where it leaks in, the response may be delayed by several minutes. An extreme example is a long water line. If helium is applied without pressure at one place, it will take many hours to diffuse to the other end. However, if it is allowed to flow in one end and out the other until the line is full of helium, the response is immediate. Likewise, the line can be cleaned out rapidly by blowing air through it.

With a pump-out this is not possible. A good procedure here is to apply helium under pressure, then release the pressure, then apply it again, etc. A few repetitions of this cycle will get the helium all the way into the system. The only way to get it out rapidly is to apply vacuum, but this can be done with any pump that goes down to a few millimeters of mercury pressure.

By noting the speed of response and cleanup it is often possible to say immediately that the leak is or is not at a certain place. This will greatly speed up the leak hunting. Sometimes it is obvious that the helium will penetrate rapidly into a closed region only by shooting it in as a jet with appreciable velocity. The exact methods depend on the circumstances and the alertness and ingenuity of the operator.

It is shown in Sec. 5.10 that the 90 per cent response time of a vacuum system is $T = 2.3\ V/S$, where V is the volume and S is the pumping speed. When a diffusion pump is used, this is ordinarily a fraction of a second. But when a mechanical pump evacuates a large volume the response time (which is the same as the "cleanup time") becomes often many seconds or minutes.

For rapid movement of the helium from the leak to the mechanical pump (where the leak detector is connected) it is necessary to have small volumes, low pressure, fast pump lines, and fast pumps. It should be noted that the requirements of small volume and fast pump line are in a sense contradictory. If, in the attempt to speed up response and pump speed, the connecting lines are made too large, the added volume, requiring more helium to give a required concentration, will actually slow down the response. The two factors governing the line size are similar to resistance and distributed capacity in an electrical line. There is actually a most favorable line diameter. A consideration of the experience with systems in use must be the guide for new installations. Response times up to 45 sec have been noted with 6-in. lines about 30 ft long at a pressure of about 100 μ Hg. This is not satisfactory, and long lines should be avoided for this reason.

In general, the response time will not be in the leak detector itself. Since the pressure inside the leak detector, from the bleeder valve in, is about 2 μ Hg or less, and the volume is small, there is no appreciable delay in the leak-detector system. The slowest part of the instrument is the output meter, which is usually damped to a time constant of about 1 sec. This will usually be less than the delay in the main vacuum system.

The connecting line from the main vacuum to the leak detector may cause considerable delay if it is small or if the pressure is high. If it is between ½ and 1 in. in diameter and not over 2 or 3 ft long, it will cause no delay below 100 μ Hg pressure.

(f) Use of the Instrument in Leak Detection. Figure 5.8 shows a generalized block diagram of a typical high-vacuum system and a sampling-type helium leak detector. No matter how tight and dry the main vacuum tank is, gas is always being pumped out of it. This gas goes through the diffusion pump, where the pressure rises to some value between 10 and 100 μ Hg. It then goes through the mechanical pump, where the pressure once more rises, this time to atmospheric pressure. Now this leak-detector tank must operate at a pressure of about 1 μ Hg. Thus, by connecting the leak detector to the line between the main diffusion pump and mechanical pump, just enough gas can be bled off to raise the leak detector to its operating pressure, adjusting this pressure to its proper value by adjusting the bleeder valve. The gas going through the main mechanical pump is many thousand times greater in amount than that going through the leak detector. However, the gas going through the leak detector is the same in composition. Consequently the instrument that is able to detect the presence of a very minute amount of helium actually continuously samples the gas in the main vacuum system for helium.

Thus, if helium is used to go over the outside of the vacuum tank under test, the leak detector will give an indication when it is in the vicinity of a leak. It will not indicate helium at any other time, since the amount of helium in the atmosphere is very small, about 1½ ppm. The instrument could be set for gases other than helium. Helium is used because it is light and hence diffuses rapidly into a leak, because it is relatively cheap and easy to get, and because it cannot explode or catch fire.

Hood and Line Testing. Determination of the over-all leakage of any unit is most conveniently done by covering the unit with a hood and flooding the inside of the hood with helium. The unit can be evacuated by either a mechanical pump alone or a diffusion pump backed by a mechanical pump. The helium indication on the leak detector is a function not only of the size of leak but also of the amount of helium in the hood, the pressure inside the vacuum dock, the pumping speed of the mechanical pump, the pressure inside the instrument, and the length of time since application of the helium to the hood. As a result, specific rules as to procedure must be set up for each installation where hood testing takes place, and these should be followed exactly by the operator.

Water lines can be tested in essentially the same fashion as with hood testing. With the unit evacuated, apply a helium hose to one end of the line, leaving the other end open. If a number of lines are connected in series, this applies to the entire group as a unit. Let the helium flow through until it is judged that the air is displaced and then cap the open end and raise the pressure of the helium to the value specified for the unit in question. Since a high pressure can be used, this method will detect very small leaks. As with hood testing, the procedure laid down for a given installation should be followed exactly in order to get quantitative results.

Leak Hunting. For this purpose the helium leak detector is unexcelled, but some practice is needed before the full advantages of the instrument can be utilized. Unlike hood and line testing, the procedure will vary to suit the special circumstances. The unit will initially be evacuated as usual. Since response time is a major consideration in this procedure, it is necessary either to use a diffusion pump or else have the volume of the system small enough so that the mechanical pump can pull it down and clear it up in a reasonable time. The considerations involved are discussed in Sec. 5.5e.

A helium probe should be available for this work. This should be attached to a long flexible line from the reducing valve on the helium tank. There should be a small valve on the end of this line so that the helium can be conveniently turned off when not needed. If the helium is allowed to flow indiscriminately, not only will the gas be used up much faster than necessary, but also the helium will get into the leaks when and where it is not expected, and the issue will be badly confused. This probe should taper to a point a few inches long and a few millimeters in diameter. It will be advisable to put on a very fine point if it is necessary to differentiate between small, near-by parts.

The hunt should usually be started by using a moderate flow of gas, e.g., one that is easily felt on the hand. It can then be played over broad areas without too close attention to details. As soon as some indication is noted, the helium stream can be turned down to a very fine one so that it can just be detected by holding the tip up to the lips or cheek, and then the indication is followed to the leak itself. Since helium is lighter than air, it is necessary to start at the top and to work down. If the gas stream is too strong, it will shoot past the part being tested and probably hit a leak at some point that is not noticed. Paper, cardboard, scotch tape, cloth, a glove, or anything else that will be helpful in isolating one section from another should be used. Sometimes it will be necessary to build a small hood to go over one part in order to separate it from near-by parts.

The most natural procedure when in the neighborhood of a leak is to apply the helium to the suspected spot, then remove it, then apply it again, etc. Sometimes this is all right, but very often it leads to the conclusion that the leak has been found when actually it is many inches or feet away. The helium diffuses so rapidly that this mistake is easy to make. The best procedure is usually to move the probe around until a maximum is obtained. It will often be necessary to turn the leak detector to the least sensitive scale in order to remain on scale in the immediate neighborhood of the leak. By doing this, and watching or listening for a maximum indication, the leak can usually be spotted to within a fraction of an inch. For the best results, turn the helium stream down low, move the probe slowly, and always try to get a maximum indication. Sometimes it is useful to have an air line in one hand, using it to blow helium away from certain parts while testing others.

The speed of response and, even more, the cleanup time often give a considerable clue as to the nature of the leak. If there is an enclosed space at atmospheric pressure surrounding the leak, it will take from several minutes to many hours before the helium cleans up. Blowing air into the volume will, of course, tend to clean it up.

When very large areas are to be covered, use a strong stream of helium. Occasionally it has been found useful to turn an electric fan on an inaccessible region and put the helium into the fan. It may be necessary to put the helium probe on a long rod and poke it into inaccessible regions. If the operator shows both ingenuity and patience, any leak large enough to be of significance in ordinary high-vacuum work can be located.

The instrument is provided with a jack plug, so that a portable meter can be used in series with the fixed one. Any meter of the same sensitivity as the leak meter can be used on a cord with an ordinary phone jack. Thus the meter can be taken to wherever the operator is working.

The Squealer. In order to free the eyes and hands of the operator for leak hunting, a squealer circuit (see Sec. 5.5c) has been added to the leak detector. This gives an audio signal that is almost as sensitive as the reading of the leak meter. In the instrument being described there are two adjustments on the squealer: volume and threshold. There is a small speaker on the squealer panel, and two jack plugs are provided for a portable speaker and a headphone. Plugging in either one takes the fixed speaker out of the circuit. The headphone is by far the most useful method, particularly in a noisy environment.

The use of the volume adjustment is obvious. The threshold adjustment allows the operator to set the base tone to something not too objectionable to his ears. Usually it is best to set the base to a barely audible clicking sound. Then the indication of helium is a rise of frequency that saturates at about full scale on the meter. If there is a high helium background for any reason, the squealer can still be adjusted to a fairly low tone that is quite tolerable to listen to for extended periods. The squealer oscillator will not give a tone above about 1,000 cycles, and hence, if the starting tone is already a high one, a helium indication may not be noticed. The squealer changes range with the meter, so that the threshold may have to be adjusted after changing the range. The squealer, like the meter, is protected by saturation of earlier stages in the amplifier, so that it can never be injured by a large signal.

The Water-line Sniffer. A special method has been tested for leak hunting on water lines. This consists of putting helium into the lines under pressure and then sniffing over the outside with a special needle valve attached to the vacuum inlet of the leak detector. The needle valve is on the end of about 10 ft of vacuum tubing. The tests made have shown this method to be extremely sensitive, accurate, and rapid in response and cleanup.

With this type of sniffer it is very important that the line used be free of excessive outgassing. It should be treated to remove free sulfur from the rubber. The best treatment is boiling in a 15 per cent solution of potassium or sodium hydroxide, followed by application of castor oil to the outside. However, a prolonged pumping will probably be sufficient with most tubing. The sniffer line may be evacuated through the leak-detector system if the diffusion pump is cooled first. If the detector is devoted exclusively to this kind of detection, then this is the best way to evacuate the line, but, if it is used for this purpose only occasionally, it would be preferable to have a by-pass system to rough the line down first with an auxiliary pump.

5.6 General Leak-hunting Procedure. Up to this point a number of leak-hunting methods have been described. Little has been said regarding the various steps to be taken after first starting up a vacuum system to the point where the system can be used for the purpose at hand. The discussion to follow is applicable primarily to large metal vacuum systems, since these are of the greatest importance industrially and have not been treated as thoroughly as glass systems in the literature.

Suppose, for example, that a vacuum system is roughed down after having been let down to atmospheric pressure or after some major accident. If a McLeod gauge, Pirani gauge, or some other gauge suitable for the measurement of pressures of the order of millimeters of mercury indicates a pressure of much over 100 μ Hg, it is clear that the diffusion pump cannot be turned on. The first step is to try to find the general region of the system in which the leak is located. This is best done by isolating certain parts of the system, by means of valves, from the fore pumps and then taking rates-of-rise measurements. The main part of the vacuum system, including the diffusion pump, should first be isolated from the fore pump. If there is no indication of a leak in the main vacuum system, the oil in the mechanical pump should be inspected, since it may be low or contaminated. Once it is fairly clear that there is a leak in some portion of the main vacuum system it is first advisable to check such obvious sources of leaks as gasket seals, which should be tightened. If this gives negative results, one or more of the leak-hunting techniques discussed earlier in the chapter, suitable for the pressures involved, should be used. It is clear that instruments such as the ionization gauge or Knudsen gauge are unsuitable for this purpose. A Pirani gauge and gas such as methane, propane, or helium could be used. Also the system can be tested under pressure, using air or helium and soap, helium and a leak detector, or any of the other methods already discussed. Once the pressure indicated by the McLeod or Pirani gauge reads below about 100 μ Hg, the diffusion pumps can be turned on.

If, after the diffusion pumps have been on for an adequate length of time, the pressure is too high to be read on a pressure-measuring device such as an ionization gauge or for the operation of a helium leak detector directly connected to the system, it will be necessary to resort to the types of leak-hunting procedures used above. If the difficulty lies in the diffusion pumps this can usually be proved by isolating the vacuum system from the diffusion pumps and taking a rate-of-rise measurement. After the pressure has dropped to a point where such gauges as the ionization gauge can be used but still too high for operating the process in question, any of the leak-hunting procedures suitable to low pressures can be used. It is advisable at first to use procedures suitable for application with the system evacuated so as to speed up the process. Probably the most rapid method is the use of helium for probing the outside surface of the system in conjunction with a leak detector. If such an instrument is not available, one of the other methods such as the application of a gas outside with an ionization gauge or other suitable gauge reading the response inside can be used. The use of pressure (air or helium) may be necessary if the above procedures fail to locate the leaks.

5.7 Repairing of Leaks. The most frequent sources of leaks in a vacuum system are the gasket seals, flare fittings (for gas, water, etc.), solder seals, and welded joints. If a leak is located in a rubber gasket, the gasket should be tightened but not too much (see Chap. 4). When this procedure fails to stop the leak, the system should be shut down and the gasket examined. If the gasket is in bad shape, it should be replaced. However, it is often sufficient simply to clean it and the surfaces that it meets, as well. Vacuum greases can be used if the pumping speed of the system is adequate. It is inadvisable to try to stop leaks in gaskets with some sealing material such as glyptal, owing to the fact that such a repair is usually only temporary and also that the gasket is likely to be rendered of little further use.

Flare fittings are constructed of a soft metal, usually copper, which "gives" enough when two surfaces are compressed against each other to provide a vacuum seal. If a leak is found in a fitting, the nut by which the compression is obtained can be tightened moderately. Tightening too much is likely to twist the tubing passing into the fitting. If this fails to stop the leak, it will be necessary to break the joint open. Annealing the copper flare will almost always give a tight seal. If this is not practical, a thin coating of glyptal can be applied to the surfaces that make contact.

In solder seals and welds, if the leaks are small enough so that the vacuum system is very near operating pressure, clear glyptal can be used. On leaks too large for that, but small enough so that the pressure goes down to diffusion-pump operation, red glyptal can be used sparingly. It is advisable to make every effort to locate the leak accurately before applying glyptal indiscriminately. Leaks that are too large to be stopped by the above methods should be repaired by remaking the solder seal or weld that is at fault or by replacing a portion of the vacuum system that includes the leaks.

In the case of glass components of a vacuum system, leaks usually occur in glass-to-metal seals (waxes, etc.), glass-to-glass joints, cracks in the glass, and stopcocks. In the case of glass-to-metal seals, the repairing procedure depends on the nature of the seal. For wax seals it is sometimes necessary to rework the seal or replace it. In other cases the application of some sealing compound such as glyptal is adequate. Leaks in glass-to-glass joints or through cracks and pinholes in a glass section of the system, if small enough, can be repaired by the use of materials such as glyptal, which can be applied at room temperature. Often a wax can be used (such as picein) by heating the glass and pouring on the wax over the leak. If the leak is too large, it will be necessary to rework the glass or replace the part of the system where the leak is located. Often electrical power is brought into a vacuum system through glass members (usually tubular), which provide electrical insulation. These glass components are usually sealed by means of gaskets. The same procedure in repairing leaks as described above is applicable here. However, much greater care must be taken in exerting pressure on the glass member.

One component of a vacuum system that is likely to give rise to leaks unless suitable precautions are taken is a sliding seal, such as a Wilson seal. When a leak occurs in such a seal, more vacuum grease such as Lubriseal should be applied to the moving member, and this member should be operated several times through the seal. Tightening the retaining rings on the seal may also stop the leak. If these steps do not stop the leak it is necessary to dismantle the seal and examine the component parts. Such an examination may show the need for new gaskets, for resurfacing of some of the metal parts (particularly the movable member), or for complete replacement of the unit.

5.8 Outgassing. In both glass and metal systems the materials in the vacuum region may release adsorbed gases and vapors that give the indications of a leak. This phenomenon is, of course, most prevalent in new vacuum systems or in systems that have been let down to atmospheric pressure. Also it often occurs when new materials are installed in the vacuum system. When a system is put on the pumps, a good deal of effort can be expended in leak hunting when actually the difficulty lies in outgassing of various surfaces. Consequently a knowledge of the gas-adsorption properties of various materials intended for vacuum use will result in a saving in time and effort.

The treatment of certain materials prior to use in vacuum systems so as to reduce pump-down time and incidentally time lost in leak hunting will be considered briefly. The general procedure for outgassing of most materials is to heat the material in air, vacuum, or hydrogen. Heating glass in air, in either an oven or a flame, is satisfactory. Most of the gases are driven from soft glasses by prolonged heating at about 150°C, and the monomolecular film of water vapor and adsorbed gases is removed at 300°C. Lime glass and hard glass have to be heated to temperatures of 400 and 500°C, respectively. Higher temperatures than the above should be avoided owing to softening and deterioration of the glass.

Most metals in vacuum give off adsorbed gases as well as gases from the decomposition of oxide near the surface. To minimize this the metals are heated in vacuum or in hydrogen. Tungsten, molybdenum, and graphite should be heated in vacuum to about 1800°C. Gas adsorbed by subsequent exposure to atmospheric pressure can easily be removed by heating to moderate temperatures. Many metals may be heated in hydrogen to remove surface contamination. In this case the dissolved gases near the surface are replaced in part by the hydrogen, which comes off readily when the metal is subsequently heated in vacuum either in a bake-out oven or by induction heating.

Apart from the above methods of avoiding outgassing, when a low ultimate pressure (10^{-6} mm Hg or better) is required without too long a waiting period great care must be taken in choosing the vacuum materials. This applies to vacuum greases, rubbers, and various sealing compounds. The vapor pressures of a number of materials are listed in Chap. 4 and the appendixes at the end of this volume, and data on other materials can be found in the "Handbook of Chemistry and Physics" and in the "International Critical Tables." Reference to such information is of great value in designing vacuum systems. Where a system is intended to be sealed off after being pumped down, so as to remain at a low pressure for appreciable periods of time (e.g., radio tubes, cathode-ray tubes, etc.), use is made of the "gettering" process. This process involves making use of chemically active metals such as barium, aluminum, calcium, tantalum, and magnesium to remove residual gases in the vacuum system. The getter is electrically volatilized in the vessel when the pressure has been brought to the required point and before the sealing-off operation is carried out. The getter, during volatilization, combines with the residual gases in the vessel, which deposit as chemical compounds on the walls of the vessel. Also some getters, particularly barium, will adsorb small quantities of gas after the vessel has been sealed off from the pumps. A good deal of useful information regarding the application of getters in the vacuum-tube industry is contained in Yarwood's "High Vacuum Technique," and reference should be made to it for a more detailed discussion.

In the case of large metal vacuum systems provided with adequate pumping speed and required to produce an operating pressure of about 10^{-5} mm Hg, there is no need for outgassing of metals and glasses. However, care must still be taken in choosing appropriate materials for use inside the vacuum system. For example, common paints and lacquers and rusty iron surfaces should be avoided as much as possible. Also care must be taken to prevent water from getting into the system. Liquid water, being incompressible, will ruin a mechanical pump. Also its vapor pressure is about 18 mm Hg at room temperature. The initial rapid evaporation of water under reduced pressure will reduce the temperature of the remaining water sufficiently to freeze it. The subsequent evaporation is of course greatly reduced. This results in a long period of time being required to remove the water even with the use of cold traps. The loss of time due to the presence of water in the vacuum system has resulted in the use of various drying agents and freezing mixtures. The effectiveness of the more common drying agents and freezing mixtures is indicated in Appendix G. All the drying materials have vapor pressures less than 10^{-4} mm Hg, as long as they are thoroughly baked and melted before use.

5.9 Virtual Leaks. Vapors condense on freezing traps when their partial pressures are above the vapor pressure corresponding to the trap temperature. When this condition is not satisfied, vapor can escape from the trap and give all the indications of a leak (called a "virtual" leak). Unless the mechanism involved is understood, a good deal of time can be lost in leak hunting. In view of the fact that water vapor is the most common vapor met with in vacuum practice, consider the case of a trap containing dry ice and acetone. At the temperature of this mixture (–78°C), the vapor pressure of water is 10^{-3} mm Hg. When the system has been pumped down to a pressure below this value, water vapor escapes from the surface of the trap, giving rise to a virtual leak. It is clear that in order to reach pressures below 10^{-3} mm Hg it is necessary to use materials other than dry ice and acetone, if a lower temperature is to be reached. Liquid air is commonly used for this purpose, with the trap inserted between vacuum chamber and diffusion pump. However, even in this case virtual leaks can arise owing to the fact that, as the level of the liquid air drops, the ice (water) above this level on the outside of the trap can rise in temperature. One method of avoiding this difficulty is to fill the liquid-air trap only part full at first and then to complete the filling after the pressure has come down to the operating value. Also, if sufficient care is taken in keeping the liquid-air trap filled, the difficulty with virtual leaks can be minimized.

Even when all possible precautions are taken to keep the liquid-air level constant, the symptoms characteristic of a virtual leak develop, particularly in the cases of large vacuum systems. This is due to the fact that ice is a poor conductor and that, as a layer builds up on the liquid-air trap, the surface exposed to the vacuum region can reach an appreciably higher temperature than that next to the trap. The only way to avoid this difficulty is to remove the traps periodically and clean them. How often the traps must be cleaned is dictated primarily by the nature of the process being used.

5.10 Theory of Leak Detection. In the preceding sections of this chapter the general considerations applying to the various types of leak-detection apparatus have been given. With the very large vacuum systems now becoming important in industrial practice it is essential that efficient methods of leak detection be considered when designing the vacuum plant. Proper planning can result in immense savings in assembly, maintenance, and operation. In this section the sort of generalized theoretical approach that can be used in planning for high-efficiency leak detection will be indicated. Just two cases will be examined. The same method can be applied to other situations and techniques, as desired. This section is based on the kinetic-theory developments of Chap. 1.

(a) Leak Detector on High-vacuum Space. Consider a vacuum system evacuated by a diffusion pump, with a leak-detecting device of some sort connected to the high-vacuum vessel (see Fig. 5.13). The notation is as follows:

Q = total undetected leakage plus outgassing, μ-liters/sec

q = detected leak under consideration, μ-liters/sec of air

kq = detected leak under consideration, μ-liters/sec of probe gas

V = volume of vacuum vessel, liters

P = air pressure, μ Hg

p = probe-gas pressure, μ Hg

S = speed of diffusion pump, liters/sec of air

KS = speed of diffusion pump, liters/sec of probe gas

t = time in seconds, starting at application of probe gas

T = time required to reach 90 per cent of equilibrium

f = ratio of detector response, probe gas/air

In the following considerations the time elapsing after covering the unknown small leak with probe gas until this gas starts entering the vacuum system is justifiably assumed to be very small compared with the time required for the system to reach a new equilibrium pressure. In other words the time t = 0 represents the time that probe gas starts entering the vacuum system. If the inflow plus the

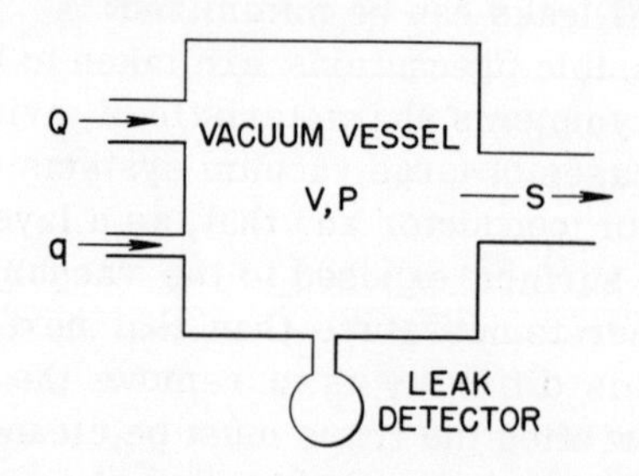

Fig. 5.13—Schematic diagram of leak detector working out of the high vacuum.

outflow of probe gas is equated to the change in amount of gas in the tank, this differential equation results.

$$kq\,dt - pKS\,dt = V\,dp \tag{6}$$

If the initial condition p = 0 when t = 0, then Eq. 6 integrates to

$$p = \frac{kq}{KS}\left(1 - e^{-KSt/V}\right) \tag{7}$$

If now a detector that responds to partial pressure only (e.g., a Pirani gauge detecting hydrogen through hot palladium) is used, it is clear that any desired sensitivity may be attained by simply throttling down the diffusion pump, since p is inversely proportional to S. However, since $e^{2.3} = 10$, the time constant for 90 per cent equilibrium is

$$T = \frac{2.3}{K}\frac{V}{S} \tag{8}$$

Thus, if the diffusion pump is made too slow, the time to reach equilibrium becomes so long that the effective sensitivity is decreased.

The more usual case is that of a detector responding to both air and probe gas. In this case the rate of change of the air pressure is also needed. The differential equation for the air, corresponding to Eq. 6 is

$$Q\,dt - PS\,dt = V\,dP \tag{9}$$

Here again it is assumed that the time required to pump out the air in the unknown leak after covering it with probe gas is very small compared with the time required to reach a new equilibrium pressure. Integrating Eq. 9 with the initial condition

$$P = P_0 = \frac{Q + q}{S}$$

where t = 0, the equation becomes

$$P = \frac{Q}{S} + \frac{q}{s} e^{-St/V} \tag{10}$$

Therefore the fractional change in the reading of the detector due to the probe gas, making use of Eqs. 7 and 10, is

$$\frac{1}{P_0}(fp + P - P_0) = \frac{q}{Q + q}\left[f\frac{k}{K}\left(1 - e^{-KSt/V}\right) + e^{-St/V} - 1\right] \tag{11}$$

Now, since normally K > 1, the dominant exponential as the system approaches equilibrium is the second, and hence the time for 90 per cent equilibrium is now approximately

$$T = 2.3\frac{V}{S} \tag{12}$$

Moreover, differentiation of the right-hand member of Eq. 11 shows that the reading reaches a maximum value at time

$$t_{max} = \frac{K}{K - 1} T \log fk \tag{13}$$

The equilibrium fractional change in the reading is

$$\frac{q}{Q + q}\left(f\frac{k}{K} - 1\right) \tag{14}$$

It is to be noted that the equilibrium reading is independent of the pump speed. Thus the equilibrium sensitivity depends upon the pump speed only in that it is advantageous to have the detecting gauge operating in its most sensitive region.

In addition, it should be noted that, in general, f, k, and K are functions of the pressure, so that it could happen that $fk \approx K$ in one pressure region, and the equilibrium change would be negligible.

As an example consider an ionization gauge as a detector and helium as a probe gas. If the pressure is somewhat below 1 μ Hg, the

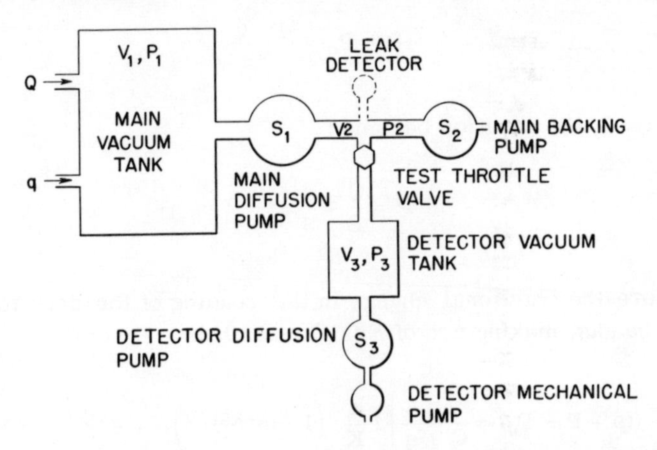

Fig. 5.14—Schematic diagram of leak detector working out of the backing space.

gases will pump independently, the flow into the diffusion pump will be just the free-molecule flow, and the ratio of the pumping speeds for helium and air will be

$$K = \sqrt{\frac{29}{4}} = 2.7$$

since 29 and 4 are the molecular weights of air and helium, respectively. From Fig. 5.1, k = 1 for leaks of the order of 1 μ-liter/sec. It has been found experimentally (see Chap. 3) that $f \approx 1/5$ for an ion gauge. Then the equilibrium fractional change in the gauge reading is $-0.9[q/(Q + q)]$. Thus, if the gauge is steady to about 2 per cent, a leak that is about 2 per cent of the total gas being handled may be detected, but not much better may be expected.

Here the minus sign means a decrease in the reading of the indicating device. It is clear that in the case of helium and an ionization gauge there is no amplification of response. If it were possible simply to close the unknown leak, the equilibrium fractional change in gauge reading would be $-q/(Q + q)$. When leak detection is to be performed on a large scale, the constants involved should be determined, experimentally when necessary, for the whole pressure range to be used.

(b) Leak Detector on Backing Space. Consider a vacuum system evacuated by a diffusion pump of speed S_1, backed by a mechanical pump of speed S_2, as shown in Fig. 5.14. The leak detector to be considered is either connected to the backing space of volume V_2 directly or else bleeds off V_2 through a throttle valve into an auxiliary vacuum system. The notation of the preceding paragraph will be used here, with the appropriate subscripts added as indicated in Fig. 5.14.

From the results of the preceding paragraph the pressures of air and probe gas in the main vacuum vessel are given by

$$P_1 = \frac{Q}{S_1} + \frac{q}{S_1} e^{-S_1 t/V_1} \tag{15}$$

$$p_1 = \frac{kq}{K_1 S_1} \left(1 - e^{-K_1 S_1 t/V_1}\right) \tag{16}$$

Assume that the throttle valve into V_3 is closed. Then the differential equation giving the rate of change of probe-gas pressure in the backing space is

$$(K_1 S_1 p_1 - K_2 S_2 p_2)\, dt = V_2\, dp_2 \tag{17}$$

With the initial condition $p_2 = 0$ when $t = 0$, and using Eq. 16, Eq. 17 integrates to

$$P_2 = \frac{kq}{K_2 S_2} \left(1 - e^{-K_1 S_1 t/V_1}\right) \left(1 - e^{-K_2 S_2 t/V_2}\right) \tag{18}$$

which is the partial pressure of the probe gas in the backing space.

By the same method, the air pressure in the backing space is

$$P_2 = \frac{Q}{S_2} + \frac{q}{S_2} \left[e^{-S_1 t/V_1} + e^{-S_2 t/V_2} - e^{-(S_1/V_1 + S_2/V_2)t}\right] \tag{19}$$

Where $t = 0$, $P_2 = (Q + q)\, S_2 = (P_2)_0$. Suppose now that there is a detector (e.g., a Pirani gauge) located in the backing space, shown dotted in Fig. 5.14. Then the fraction change in the detector gauge reading due to the probe gas is just

$$\frac{1}{(P_2)_0}\left[fp_2 + P_2 - (P_2)_0\right] = \frac{q}{Q+q}\left\{\frac{fk}{K_2}\left[1 - e^{-K_1S_1t/V_1} - e^{-K_2S_2t/V_2} + e^{-(K_1S_1/V_1+K_2S_2/V_2)t}\right] + e^{-S_1t/V_1} + e^{-S_2t/V_2} - e^{-(S_1/V_1+S_2/V_2)t} - 1\right\} \quad (20)$$

Now the gases in the backing space, where P_2 is of the order of 10 to 100 μ Hg, can be considered to be in viscous flow. Therefore the various gases flow together, and $K_2 = 1$. Moreover, $K_1 > 1$, as shown above, and hence the time for 90 per cent equilibrium is either

$$T_1 = 2.3\frac{V_1}{S_1} \text{ or } T_2 = 2.3\frac{V_2}{S_2} \quad (21)$$

whichever is larger. Clearly the system must be designed so that neither T_1 nor T_2 is excessive if it is to have a rapid response. The right-hand member of Eq. 20 has a maximum value, which can be found by differentiation, and then it drops off to an equilibrium value of

$$\frac{q}{Q+q}\left(\frac{fk}{K_2} - 1\right) = \frac{q}{Q+q}(fk - 1) \quad (22)$$

since usually $K_2 = 1$. This is the equilibrium value of the fractional change in the detector reading, when the probe gas is substituted for air. It should be noted that the equilibrium sensitivity is independent of S_1, S_2, or K_1, except in so far as it is advantageous to have the gauge operating in its most sensitive region.

By comparison of Eq. 22 with Eq. 14 of the previous section, it may be seen that putting the detector in the backing space has removed K_1 from the expression for the equilibrium sensitivity. This would be a disadvantage with the example cited in the previous paragraph, helium and an ion gauge, for which $fk/K_1 \approx 1/10$. It would be an advantage for hydrogen and a Pirani-gauge detector. For such a combination f has been found experimentally to be about 2. From Table 5.1 it might be estimated that k is approximately 2.5 for a leak of the order of 10^{-2} μ-liter/sec. Therefore $fk - 1 = 4$, and it follows from Eq. 22 that, if the gauge is accurate to 2 per cent, a leak that is about ½ per cent of the gas being handled can be detected. Thus in this case the amplification factor of the response is about 4.

Now consider the case of the helium leak detector, which is a separate vacuum system bleeding off the backing space, as indicated in Fig. 5.14. It is assumed that, since it is specially designed for this work, it will have a time constant

$$T_3 = 2.3 \frac{V_3}{S_3} \tag{23}$$

which is negligible compared with the time constants T_1 and T_2. Then the speed of response is set by either T_1 or T_2, Eq. 21, whichever is larger. Consequently the same design considerations hold as before.

The flow through the throttle valve into V_3 will be viscous, and hence the gases flow together, and the concentration of the probe gas at the throttle valve is p_2/P_2. But the flow out of V_3 is molecular flow, so that the gases flow independently, and, neglecting the time response of the leak detector, the concentration of the probe gas in the detector vessel is p_2/K_3P_2. This concentration is then, at equilibrium,

$$\frac{p_2}{K_3P_2} = \frac{k}{K_3}\frac{q}{Q} \tag{24}$$

Now, for helium of molecular weight 4 in air of molecular weight 29,

$$K_3 = \sqrt{\frac{29}{4}} = 2.7$$

Also $k \approx 1$ for large leaks, and about 2.2 for very small leaks of about 10^{-5} μ-liter/sec. Thus for the smallest leaks the concentration of the probe gas in the mass-spectrometer tank will be about ¾ (q/Q). Thus, if the mass spectrometer has an inherent sensitivity of 1 part of helium in 10^5 parts of air (a feasible value), the detector will just be able to detect an air leak $q = 1.3 \times 10^{-5}Q$. This is about the limit of sensitivity of any leak-detecting device at the present time.

As an example, suppose that

$$S_1 = 100 \text{ liters/sec} \qquad P_1 = 10^{-5} \text{ mm Hg} = 10^{-2}\ \mu\text{Hg}$$

Then $Q = 1$ μ-liter/sec, and the smallest detectable leak is 1.3×10^{-5} μ-liter/sec. A leak of this size would require about three years to raise a volume of 1 liter up to 1 mm Hg pressure.

REFERENCES

1. D. L. Webster, Rev. Sci. Instruments, 5: 42 (1934).
2. J. Yarwood, "High Vacuum Techniques," John Wiley & Sons, Inc., New York, 1945.
3. Robert B. Jacobs and Herbert F. Zuhr, J. Applied Phys., 18: 34 (1947).
4. A. C. Schmidt, University of California Radiation Laboratory Report RL 20.6.5, Sept. 6, 1943.
5. T. E. Cuykendall, Rev. Sci. Instruments, 6: 371 (1935).
6. J. H. Manley, L. J. Haworth, and E. A. Luebke, Rev. Sci. Instruments, 10: 389 (1939).
7. E. J. Lawton, Rev. Sci. Instruments, 11: 134 (1940).
8. J. B. H. Kuper, Rev. Sci. Instruments, 8: 131 (1937).
9. R. B. Nelson, Rev. Sci. Instruments, 16: 55 (1945).
10. Herbert Nelson, Rev. Sci. Instruments, 16: 273 (1945).
11. W. M. Brubaker and Victor Wouk, Rev. Sci. Instruments, 17: 97 (1946).
12. John Backus, Chap. 11 in "Characteristics of Electrical Discharges in Magnetic Fields," National Nuclear Energy Series, Div. I, Vol. 5, McGraw-Hill Book Company, Inc., New York, 1949.
13. R. Loevinger, University of California Radiation Laboratory Report RL 20.6.23, May 6, 1944.
14. R. Loevinger, University of California Radiation Laboratory Report RL 20.6.34, Sept. 26, 1944.
15. J. Backus, University of California Radiation Laboratory Report RL 20.6.36, Mar. 19, 1945.
16. A. T. Founester and W. B. Whalley, Rev. Sci. Instruments, 17: 549 (1946).
17. R. Loevinger, University of California Radiation Laboratory Report RL 20.6.38, June 12, 1945.
18. R. Loevinger, University of California Radiation Laboratory Report XL 20.6.806, July 2, 1945.
19. A. O. Nier, C. M. Stevens, J. A. Hustrulid, and T. A. Abbott, J. Applied Phys., 18: 30 (1947).
20. H. A. Thomas, T. W. Williams, and J. A. Hipple, Rev. Sci. Instruments, 17: 368 (1946).

Appendix A

LIST OF SYMBOLS

a = length of side of a rectangular or triangular duct
A = cross-sectional area of an aperture, pipe, or thimble
A_0 = cross-sectional area facing an aperture or pipe inlet
α = correction factor in molecular-conductance formula for short circular pipe
b = length of side of a rectangular duct
B = total perimeter of the cross section of a pipe
$\beta = \sqrt{m/2kT}$
C = conductance of an aperture or pipe
D = diameter of a circular pipe or aperture
D_0 = diameter of a circular region from which a pipe or aperture is conducting
η = coefficient of viscosity
f = frequency of rotation of cylinder in mechanical pump
γ = mass of gas in volume V, and also ratio of specific heats of a gas
Ho = ratio of rate of gas removal by a given jet to that which would occur if the jet were replaced by a perfect vacuum
i = subscript to designate one of several kinds of molecules
J = correction factor in Knudsen's general circular-pipe-conductance formula
k = 1.38×10^{-16} dyne-cm/deg (Boltzmann's constant)
K = correction factor in Knudsen's molecular-conductance formula
κ = thermal conductivity
ln = natural logarithm
log = common logarithm
L = length of a pipe
λ = mean free path of a molecule
m = mass of one molecule
m.f.p. = mean free path of a molecule
M = molecular weight of a gas
μ Hg = microns of mercury pressure
n = number of molecules per unit of volume
N = total number of molecules in volume V
N′ = number of molecules crossing a plane per unit of time
P = pressure
P′ = time rate of change of pressure = dP/dt
P_0 = base pressure
P_1 = pressure in region from which gas flows, also partial pressure
P_2 = pressure in region into which gas flows, also partial pressure
$\bar{P}$ = average pressure in a pipe
P_{atm} = atmospheric pressure
ΔP = pressure rise due to a leak
Q = PV′ = amount of gas flowing by a certain plane
Q_0 = a fixed leak into a pump or vacuum system

r = a ratio, either P_2/P_1 or b/a
r_c = critical pressure ratio
R = k/m, the gas constant
Re = Reynolds number
ρ = density of a gas
S = pumping speed in general
S_p = pumping speed of a pump
σ = diameter of a molecule
t = time
t_1 = initial time
$t_{1/2}$ = time for pressure to fall to one-half initial value
T = absolute temperature
v = velocity of a single molecule and also velocity of a streaming gas
$\bar{v}$ = average molecular velocity
v_s = root-mean-square velocity = $\sqrt{\overline{v^2}}$
V = fixed volume of a vessel
V' = volume of gas flowing past a plane per unit of time
V'_{atm} = volume of gas flowing into a leak per unit of time measured at atmospheric pressure
x = distance along a pipe
Y = correction factor in rectangular pipe, viscous-conduction formula
Z = vacuum impedance

Appendix B

SUMMARY OF FORMULAS USEFUL IN VACUUM DESIGN

The formulas most frequently used in vacuum design work are presented here. They are given in two types of units, which were chosen because they are convenient and frequently used.

Table 1

	Metric laboratory units	Mixed metric and English laboratory units
a,b = length of side of rectangle	Centimeters	Inches
A = cross-sectional area	Square centimeters	Square inches
C = conductance	Liters per second	Liters per second
D = diameter of a circular pipe or aperture	Centimeters	Inches
γ = mass of gas in volume V	Grams	Grams
L = length of a pipe	Centimeters	Feet
λ = mean free path	Centimeters	Inches
M = molecular weight of gas	Atomic-weight units	Atomic-weight units
P = pressure	Microns of mercury (μ Hg)	Microns of mercury (μ Hg)
Q = PV′ at constant T, flow	Micron-liters per second	Micron-liters per second
S = pumping speed	Liters per second	Liters per second
t = time	Seconds	Seconds
V = volume of vessel	Liters	Liters
V′ = volumetric flow	Liters per second	Liters per second
Z = impedance	Seconds per liter	Seconds per liter

Table 2

	Metric laboratory units	Mixed metric and English laboratory units
Mass of gas at 20°C	$\gamma = 5.44 \times 10^{-8}$ MPV grams $\gamma = 1/56 \times 10^{-6}$ grams/μ-liter for air	
Mean free path in air at 20°C	$\lambda = \dfrac{4.86}{P}$ cm	$\dfrac{1.91}{P}$ in.
Impedance and conductance definition	$\dfrac{1}{Z} = C = \dfrac{Q}{P_1 - P_2}$ liters/sec P_1 is upstream, P_2 is downstream pressure	
Pumping speed, definition	$S = \dfrac{Q}{P}$ liters/sec	
Series impedances	$Z = \sum Z_i \qquad \dfrac{1}{C} = \sum \dfrac{1}{C_i}$	
Parallel impedances	$\dfrac{1}{Z} = \sum \dfrac{1}{Z_i} \qquad C = \sum C_i$	
Pumping speed through an impedance Z of a pump with speed S_p	$\dfrac{1}{S} = Z + \dfrac{1}{S_p} = \dfrac{1}{C} + \dfrac{1}{S_p}$	
Viscous conductance, thin small aperture, air at 20°C $P_2/P_1 \leq 0.1$	C = 20A liters/sec or $C = 16D^2$ liters/sec	129A liters/sec $100D^2$ liters/sec
Molecular conductance, thin small aperture, $\lambda \gg$ aperture size	C = 11.6A liters/sec or $C = 91.D^2$ liters/sec	75A liters/sec $59D^2$ liters/sec
Aperture pumping speed; P_1 and P_2 are upstream and downstream pressures, respectively	$S = C\left(1 - \dfrac{P_2}{P_1}\right)$ $S = C$ for $\dfrac{P_2}{P_1} < 0.1$	
Molecular flow through large aperture	Multiply preceding formulas for small apertures by $A_0/(A_0 - A)$ or by $D_0^2/(D_0^2 - D^2)$ if aperture is circular	D_0 A_0 A D
Reynolds number: In general	$Re = Dv\rho/\eta$	
Air at 20°C and circular pipe	Re = Q/89D	Q/226D
Turbulent to viscous transition, air at 20°C	Flow is turbulent if $Q > 2 \times 10^5 D$ Flow is viscous if $Q < 10^5 D$	$Q > 5 \times 10^5 D$ $Q < 2.5 \times 10^5 D$
Viscous to molecular transition, air at 20°C (Gives conductances accurate to 10%); $\bar{P}$ is average pressure	The flow is viscous if $\bar{P}D > 500$ μ-cm, $\lambda < D/100$ The flow is molecular if $\bar{P}D < 15$ μ-cm, $\lambda > D/3$	$\bar{P}D > 200$ μ-in., $\lambda < D/100$ $\bar{P}D < 6$ μ-in., $\lambda > D/3$
Viscous conductance, long circular pipe, air at 20°C; $\bar{P}$ is average pressure	$C = 0.182 \dfrac{D^4}{L} \bar{P}$ liters/sec	$0.25 \dfrac{D^4}{L} \bar{P}$ liters/sec
Viscous volume flow, long circular pipe, air at 20°C	$V' = 0.182D^4 \left(\dfrac{P_1 - P_2}{L}\right)$ liters/sec $= 0.182D^4$ liters/sec/unit pressure gradient	$0.25D^4 \left(\dfrac{P_1 - P_2}{L}\right)$ liters/sec $0.25D^4$ liters/sec/unit pressure gradient

Table 2 — (Continued)

	Metric laboratory units	Mixed metric and English laboratory units
Viscous conductance, long rectangular duct, air at room temperature (see Sec. 1.14, Chap. 1)	$C = 0.26 \frac{a^2b^2}{L} \bar{P}Y$ liters/sec $Y = 1$ for $a = b$	$0.36 \frac{a^2b^2}{L} \bar{P}Y$ liters/sec
Viscous volume flow, long rectangular duct, air at room temperature (see Sec. 1.14, Chap. 1)	$V' = 0.26a^2b^2Y \left(\frac{P_1 - P_2}{L}\right)$ liters/sec $= 0.26a^2b^2Y$ liters/sec/unit pressure gradient	$0.36a^2b^2Y \left(\frac{P_1 - P_2}{L}\right)$ liters/sec $= 0.36a^2b^2Y$ liters/sec/unit pressure gradient
Impedance of any short pipe	Add impedance of aperture to impedance of pipe computed from long-pipe formula	
Molecular conductance, long circular pipe, air at 20°C	$C = 12.1 \frac{D^3}{L}$ liters/sec	$6.5 \frac{D^3}{L}$ liters/sec
Molecular conductance, short circular pipe, air at 20°C	See Sec. 1.15, Chap. 1, if accurate formula is needed	
Molecular conductance, long circular annulus, air at 20°C (see Sec. 1.15)	$C = 12.1 \frac{(D_1 - D_2)^2 \quad (D_1 + D_2)}{L} K$ $D_1 > D_2$, $K = 1$ for $D_1 \gg D_2$	$6.5 \frac{(D_1 - D_2)^2 \quad (D_1 + D_2)}{L} K$
Molecular conductance, long rectangular duct, air at 20°C (see Sec. 1.15)	$C = 30.9 \frac{a^2b^2}{(a + b)\,L} K$ liters/sec $K = 1.11$ for $a = b$	$16.6 \frac{a^2b^2}{(a + b)\,L} K$ liters/sec
Molecular conductance, long equilaterally triangular duct, air at 20°C	$C = 4.79 \frac{a^3}{L}$ liters/sec	$2.58 \frac{a^3}{L}$ liters/sec
Molecular conductance, thin slitlike tube, air at 20°C	See Chap. 1, Sec. 1.15	
Molecular flow at bends and elbows. For each bend allow for an effective length in the range indicated by the inequality	$L_{axial} < L_{eff} < L_{axial} + 1.33D$	$L_{axial} < L_{eff} < L_{axial} + 0.11D$
Pumping speed of pump of speed S_p through impedance Z	$1/S = Z = + 1/S_p$ sec/liter	
Pumping speed of pump of speed S_p near base pressure P_0	$S = S_p (1 - P_0/P)$ liters/sec	
Pump-speed formula, metered-leak method	$S_p = 760 \ V'/\Delta P$ liters/sec	V' = leak in cc/sec of free air ΔP = pressure rise in μ Hg
Pump-speed formula rate-of-rise method	$S_p = \frac{P_2' - P_1'}{P_2 - P_1} V$ liters/sec	V = volume of vessel P_1', P_2' = rates of rise corresponding to operating pressures P_1, P_2, respectively
Evacuation rate, time to fall to one-half pressure	$t_{1/2} = 0.7 \ V/S_p$	V = volume of system S_p = pump speed

Appendix C

SOME CONVENIENT CONSTANTS AND CONVERSION FACTORS

Number of molecules in a mole = 6.02×10^{23}
$k = 1.381 \times 10^{-16}$ dyne-cm/deg (Boltzmann's constant)
1 atomic-weight unit = 1.660×10^{-24} g
1 atm = 760 mm Hg at sea level = 760,000 μ Hg
1 μ Hg = 10^{-3}mm Hg
1 microbar = 1 dyne/sq cm = 0.745 μ Hg
1 poise = 1 g/cm/sec (c.g.s. unit of viscosity)
1 liter/sec = 2.12 cu ft/min = 2.12 cfm
1 cc/sec at atmospheric pressure = 760 μ-liters/sec
1 liter = 61.0 cu in. = 0.0353 cu ft

Appendix D

Table 1 — Physical Properties of Certain Gases and Vapors

Gas	M, molecular weight	m, mass of a molecule, 10^{-24} g	$\bar{v}$, average velocity of a molecule at 15°C, km/sec	λ, m.f.p. at 15°C and 1 μ Hg pressure, cm	σ, diameter of a molecule, 10^{-8} cm	κ, thermal conductivity at 0°C, 10^{-3} cal/cm/sec/°C	η, viscosity at 15°C, micropoises	Relative diffusion into air, arbitrary scale
H_2	2.02	3.35	1.74	8.97	2.74	0.416	87	1.0
He	4.00	6.64	1.23	14.1	2.18	0.344	194	0.87
CH_4	16.0	26.6	0.616	3.92	4.14	0.072	108	0.29
NH_3	17.0	28.2	0.597	3.42	4.43	0.051	97	0.27
H_2O vapor	18.0	29.9	0.582	3.18	4.60	0.055*	93	0.25
Ne	20.2	33.5	0.550	10.0	2.59	0.110	310	0.42
N_2	28.0	46.5	0.467	4.77	3.75	0.057	173	0.28
Air	28.7	47.6	0.459	4.86	3.72	0.057	180	0.27
O_2	32.0	53.1	0.437	5.15	3.61	0.057	200	0.28
HCl	36.5	60.6	0.409	3.38	4.46		140	0.21
A	39.9	66.2	0.391	5.06	3.64	0.039	220	0.25
CO_2	44.0	73.0	0.372	3.18	4.59	0.034	145	0.20
Hg	201	334	0.174		4.26			0.18
Electron	5.5×10^{-4}	9.1×10^{-4}	105					

*At 100°C.

M is taken from "Handbook of Chemistry and Physics," 29th ed., Chemical Rubber Publishing Co., Cleveland, Ohio, 1945, and is used by permission of the publisher.

m is computed, using $m = 1{,}660 \times 10^{-24}$ M.

$\bar{v}$ is from Kennard, "Kinetic Theory of Gases," p. 26, McGraw-Hill Book Company, Inc., New York, 1938. Data used by permission of the copyright holder, the National Academy of Sciences Washington, D.C.

λ is from Kennard, p. 149, the values there being reduced to 1 μ Hg here.

σ, κ, and η are from Kennard, p. 149, except κ for air, which is from "Handbook of Chemistry and Physics," 29th ed., Chemical Rubber Publishing Co., Cleveland, Ohio, 1945. Data used by permission of the publisher.

Relative diffusion computed from Eq. 14, Sec. 1.5.

Table 2 — Composition of Dry Air at Sea Level

Gas	Per cent by volume	Gas	Per cent by volume
N_2	78.03	H_2	0.01
O_2	20.99	N_3	0.0012
A	0.94	He	0.0004
CO_2	0.03		

Appendix E

MECHANICAL-PUMP OILS*

Brand of oil	Type of oil	Approx. price per gal, dollars	Viscosity, Saybolt units		Type of hydrocarbon	Resistance to (a) Cl_2, (b) HCl, (c) moisture clouding
			At 100°F	At 210°F		
Caloil Deturbo, medium	Turbine					
Gulf Crest B	Turbine	0.63	209	48	Paraffin	Good for a and b; poor for c
Gulf Crest C	Vacuum	0.65	311	55	Paraffin	Good for a and b; very poor for c
Gulf Mechanism E	Machine	0.48	205	45	Naphthalene	Good for a and b
Gulf Harmony E	Turbine	0.46	603	64	Paraffin	Fair for a and b
McMillan vacuum pump	Vacuum	0.68	350	50	Mixed	Poor for a and b
Shell Turbo 41	Turbine					
Socony Vacuum pump	Vacuum	0.71			Paraffin	
Socony D.T.E. light	Turbine	0.71	155	43	Paraffin	Poor for a and b
Texaco Regal B	Turbine	0.43	196	45	Paraffin	
Texaco Regal C	Turbine	0.45	325	49	Paraffin	
Texaco URSA P-10 (Navy Symbol 2110)	Turbine	0.32	165	45	Paraffin	Fair for a and b; good for c

*Data compiled by Tennessee Eastman Corporation.

Appendix F

DIFFUSION-PUMP OILS

Oil	Refined from	Ultimate vacuum at 25°C, mm Hg	Approx. list price per gallon, dollars	Resistance to oxidation
Apiezon A		10^{-5}		
Apiezon B	Petroleum	10^{-7}		Fair
Butyl phthalate		10^{-3}		
Butyl sebacate		10^{-5}		
Amdil	*n*-Amyl phthalate	7×10^{-6}	60	Poor
Amdil-X	*n*-Amyl sebacate	2×10^{-6}	95	Poor
Litton Molecular C	Petroleum	2×10^{-6}	40	Fair
Octoil	Diethylhexyl phthalate	2×10^{-7}	135	Poor
Octoil-S	Diethylhexyl sebacate	5×10^{-8}	160	Poor

Appendix G

Table 1—Cold-trap Data

Type	Temp., °C	Vapor pressure of water, μ Hg	Latent heat, calories/g	Specific gravity	Approx. cost
Solid CO_2	−78	0.6	45	1.56	3¢ per pound
Liquid O_2	−183	$\sim 10^{-18}$	3.3	1.14	
Liquid air	−187	$\sim 10^{-18}$			17½¢ per liter
Liquid N_2	−196	$\sim 10^{-18}$	6.1	0.81	

Table 2—Effectiveness of Drying Agents*

Drying agent	Formula	Residual water vapor in gas, mg/liter†
Phosphorus pentoxide	P_2O_5	2.0×10^{-5}
Magnesium perchlorate	$Mg(ClO_4)_2$	5.0×10^{-4}
Melted caustic potash	KOH	2.0×10^{-3}
Aluminum oxide	Al_2O_3	3.0×10^{-3}
Sulfuric acid	H_2SO_4	3.0×10^{-3}
Sulfuric acid, 95.1%	H_2SO_4, 95.1%	0.3
Calcium oxide	CaO	0.2
Calcium chloride (granular)	$CaCl_2$ (granular)	0.14−0.25
Calcium chloride (fused)	$CaCl_2$ (fused)	0.36
Copper sulfate	$CuSO_4$	1.4
Zinc chloride	$ZnCl_2$	0.8
Sodium hydroxide	NaOH (fused)	0.16

*"International Critical Tables," Vol. III, p. 385, McGraw-Hill Book Company, Inc., New York, 1928. Data used by permission of the copyright holder, the National Academy of Sciences, Washington, D.C.

†Dried at 25°C.

Appendix H

MISCELLANEOUS VACUUM MATERIALS

Table 1 — Vacuum Greases and Cements

Trade name	Supplier	Melting point, °C	Vapor pressure at 20°C, mm Hg	Solubility	General
Lubriseal	Arthur H. Thomas Co.	40	$<10^{-5}$		Grease
Vacuseal light	Central Scientific Co.	50	10^{-5}		Grease
Vacuseal heavy	Central Scientific Co.	60	10^{-5}		Grease
Celvacene light	Distillation Products, Inc.	90	10^{-6}		Grease
Celvacene medium	Distillation Products, Inc.	120	$<10^{-6}$		Grease
Celvacene heavy	Distillation Products, Inc.	130	$<10^{-6}$		Grease
Stopcock grease	Dow Corning Corp.	215	$<10^{-5}$		Grease
Apiezon L	James G. Biddle Co.	Probably <50	10^{-3} at 300°C (10^{-11} at 20°C)		Grease; should be kept free from contact with air when not in use
Apiezon M	James G. Biddle Co.	Probably <50	10^{-3} at 200°C (6×10^{-7} at 20°C)		Grease; more viscous than L; should be kept free from contact with air when not in use
Apiezon Q	James G. Biddle Co.		10^{-4}		Plasticinelike substance; graphite mixed with low-vapor-pressure residues of paraffin-oil distillation products
Apiezon W	James G. Biddle Co.	Softening point 60 – 70	$<10^{-8}$	Soluble in xylene	Hard substance. supplied in sticks
Picein	Central Scientific Co.	80, 105 (2 grades)	10^{-8} (3 – 10 at 50°C)	Inert to usual organic liquids and inorganic acids	Hard black wax

Table 1 —(Continued)

Trade name	Supplier	Melting point, °C	Vapor pressure at 20°C, mm Hg	Solubility	General
DeKhotinsky Cement	Central Scientific Co.	Softens at 50	$\sim 10^{-3}$	Comparatively insoluble in usual organic liquids and common acids	Mixture of shellac and pitch; useful for seals below 40°C
Dennison's sealing wax	James G. Biddle Co.	Softens at 60–80	$\sim 10^{-5}$	Soluble in alcohol	Hard wax
Shellac	Various			Soluble in alcohol and butyl phthalate	Usually used mixed with beeswax
Silver chloride	Various	455		Soluble in sodium thiosulfate	Applied at 450°C; useful sealing medium to stand high temperature
Beeswax	Various	60		Soluble in CCl_4 and alcohol	Mixture of beeswax and resin (melted together)
Bakelite cement		80		Soluble in methylated spirits	Widely used in radio-tube industry

Table 2—Solders, Brazing Alloy, and Fluxes

Material	Composition, per cent by weight	Melting point, °C
Soft and Intermediate Solders		
Wood's metal	Bi 50%, Cd 12.5%, Pb 25%, Sn 12.5%	61
Soft solder (high strength)	Pb 34%, Sn 66%	180
Half and half	Pb 50%, Sn 50%	205
Intermediate solder	Ag 20%, Cu 3%, Zn 2%, Sn 75%	400
Hard Solder and Brazing Alloy		
Silver solder	Ag 45%, Cu 30%, Zn 25%	720
Brazing compound	Cu 54%, Zn 46%	875
Fluxes for Soft and Intermediate Solders		
Liquid flux	$ZnCl_2$ 40%, NH_4Cl 20%, H_2O 40%	
Flux paste	Paste of petroleum 90%, NH_4Cl 10%	
Spirit of rosin	A solution of rosin in alcohol	
Fluxes for Hard Solders		
Borax–boric acid paste	A thin paste of 10 parts of powdered borax and 1 part of boric acid in water	
Borax	Dry borax	

Appendix I

PROPERTIES OF SOME SOLIDS AND LIQUIDS USED IN VACUUM PRACTICE

Table 1*

Liquid	Formula	Vapor pressure at 20°C, mm Hg
Acetone	C_3H_6O	184.8
Benzene	C_6H_6	74.65
Carbon disulfide	CS_2	298.0
Carbon tetrachloride	CCl_4	90.99
Chloroform	$CHCl_3$	159.6
Ethyl alcohol	C_2H_6O	43.9
Methyl alcohol	CH_4O	96.0
Ethyl ether	$C_4H_{10}O$	442.2
Ethyl bromide	C_2H_5Br	387.0
Turpentine	$C_{10}H_6$	4.4
Water	H_2O	17.535
Mercury	Hg	0.001201

*Taken from "Handbook of Chemistry and Physics," 30th ed., Chemical Rubber Publishing Co., Cleveland, Ohio, 1946, and used by permission of the publisher.

Table 2*

Substance	Composition	Melting point, °C	Specific gravity	Vapor pressure, mm Hg	Resistivity, μohm-cm	Remarks
Aluminum		658	2.70	10^{-8} at 680° C 10^{-2} at 1200°C	2.82	Used in aluminizing mirrors; in electrodes
Asbestos		1150 Hornblende 1550 Serpentine	2.5 – 3.5			Used as heat insulator, diffusion-pump lagging, etc.; thermal conductivity, cal/cm/sec/°C: fiber = 0.00019 (500°C), paper = 0.0006
Bakelite	Urea formaldehyde		1.44 – 1.55			Good electrical insulator; not used inside vacuum system (vapor pressure high above 30°C)
Barium		850	3.50	10^{-8} at 300°C 1.0 at 1000°C		Primarily used as a getter
Beryllium		1280	1.84	1.0 at 1550°C		Very hard; used for reflecting coatings, windows in X-ray tubes; Be-Cu used in vacuum gauges, etc. (springs)
Brass	Cu-Zn alloy	930–1030	8.5		6.4–8.4	Widely used in vacuum practice; easy to machine, solder
Bronze	Cu-Sn alloy	1000–1050	8.8		~18	Used for castings in vacuum apparatus; prone to air leaks
Cadmium		321	8.65	0.001 at 219°C 1.0 at 392°C	~7.5 at 18°C	Used in photocells, nuclear studies
Cesium		27	1.87	10^{-6} at 27°C 1.0 at 290°C	19.0 at 0°C	Oxidizes rapidly at 1 atm pressure; used for photosensitive surfaces
Carbon			2.22 (graph) 3.51 (diam)	10^{-8} at 2000°C 10^{-1} at 3000°C	2700 at 500°C 900 at 2500°C	Used for gas absorption, electrodes; difficult to outgas; aquadag is colloidal suspension of graphite in water; used as conductor
Copper		1083	8.89	10^{-8} at 800°C 10^{-1} at 1400°C	1.72	Good electrical and heat conductor; used widely in vacuum practice; can be sealed to glass; easily soldered
Gold		1063	19.3	0.001 at 1292°C 1.0 at 1768°C	1.42	Easily sputtered or evaporated in vacuum; used as conductor in instruments

Table 2* — (Continued)

Substance	Composition	Melting point, °C	Specific gravity	Vapor pressure, mm Hg	Resistivity, μohm-cm	Remarks
Iron (steels)	Steel — Fe + C alloyed with Cr, Ni, Cu, etc.	1530 (pure) 1400 – 1550 (steels)	7.80 (pure) 7.7 – 7.9 (steels)	10^{-8} at 750°C 0.3 at 1000°C	9.8 at 20°C 20 – 120 for common steels at 20°C	Constructional material for large vacuum systems; not attacked by Hg (mild steel commonly used); highly magnetic; special steels also used such as stainless, Duraloy, etc.
Lead		327	11.34	0.001 at 636°C 1.0 at 985°C	22 at 20°C	Used for gaskets in vacuum practice (elevated temperatures)
Mercury		−38.9	13.546 at 20°C	3×10^{-9} at − 78°C 3×10^{-2} at 60°C	94 at 0°C	Widely used in diffusion pumps, manometers, switches, protective devices; poisonous; forms amalgams with many metals
Mica	Na-Al-Si compound		2.7 – 3.0		Very large	Electrical insulator in vacuum practice; thin windows in Geiger-Mueller counters
Molybdenum		2470	10.1	0.001 at 2293°C	5.7 at 20°C	Seals to pyrex glass; spot-welds to Fe and Ni; readily absorbs O_2 at 1000°C; used for filaments
Nickel		1452	8.8	10^{-8} at 1100°C 10^{-2} at 1700°C	7.24 at 20°C	Used for electrodes; ferromagnetic alloys; nichrome (heaters), Invar (low coeff. of exp.)
Palladium		1555	12.2		11 at 20°C	Used as getter; absorbs H_2 strongly
Platinum		1773	21.45		10 at 20°C	Seals readily to glass; commonly used where minimum corrosion desirable; very ductile
Silica	Amorphous SiO_2		2.1 – 2.2		Very large	Chemically inert; used in insulators, to transmit ultraviolet light, where low coeff. of exp. is desired
Silver		960.5	10.5 – 10.6	0.001 at 837°C 1.0 at 1218°C	1.63 at 18°C	Easily sputtered and evaporated in vacuum; used as conductor, for reflecting coatings
Tantalum		2996	16.6		15.5 at 20°C	Used for filaments, electrodes; can be spot-welded to other metals
Tungsten		3370	18.6 – 19.1	8×10^{-9} at 2130°C 5×10^{-6} at 2530°C	5.51 at 20°C	Used for filaments, electrodes; seals to pyrex and Monax glasses readily

*Taken from "Handbook of Chemistry and Physics," 30th ed., Chemical Rubber Publishing Co., Cleveland, Ohio, 1946, and J. Yarwood, "High Vacuum Technique," Chapman & Hall, Ltd., London, and John Wiley & Sons, Inc., New York. Data used by permission of the publishers.

INDEX

R

S